THE COMMONWEALTH AND INTERNATIONAL LIBRARY
Joint Chairmen of the Honorary Editorial Advisory Board
SIR ROBERT ROBINSON, O.M., F.R.S., LONDON
DEAN ATHELSTAN SPILHAUS, MINNESOTA
Publisher: ROBERT MAXWELL, M.C., M.P.

INTERMEDIATE CHEMISTRY DIVISION
General Editor: J. E. SPICE

An Introduction to Polymer Chemistry

An Introduction to Polymer Chemistry

BY

D. MARGERISON, B. Sc., Ph. D.

*Lecturer in Inorganic, Physical and Industrial
Chemistry, University of Liverpool*

AND

G. C. EAST, B. Sc., Ph. D.

*Lecturer in High Polymer Chemistry, Department
of Textile Industries, University of Leeds*

PERGAMON PRESS

OXFORD · LONDON · EDINBURGH · NEW YORK
TORONTO · SYDNEY · PARIS · BRAUNSCHWEIG

Pergamon Press Ltd., Headington Hill Hall, Oxford
4 & 5 Fitzroy Square, London W.1

Pergamon Press (Scotland) Ltd., 2 & 3 Teviot Place, Edinburgh 1

Pergamon Press Inc., 44–01 21st Street, Long Island City, New York 11101

Pergamon of Canada Ltd., 6 Adelaide Street East, Toronto, Ontario

Pergamon Press (Aust.) Pty. Ltd., 20–22 Margaret Street, Sydney,
New South Wales

Pergamon Press S.A.R.L., 24 rue des Écoles, Paris 5e

Vieweg & Sohn GmbH, Burgplatz 1, Braunschweig

(2853/67)

CONTENTS

PREFACE

THIS book is concerned with the fundamental chemistry of synthetic organic polymers of high molecular weight. It is intended for those commencing the study of Polymer Chemistry for the first time and should be of interest not only to university and technical college students attending their first lecture course on the subject but also to more elementary students who wish to broaden their knowledge of chemistry. We have assumed that our readers possess no prior acquaintance with the concepts of polymer chemistry but possess a reasonable knowledge of elementary chemistry, physics and mathematics.

Since our object is to explain the basic principles of the subject, we have confined the major part of our discussion to the more important methods of molecular weight determination and to the simpler mechanisms of polymerization. Thus osmotic, light scattering and viscosity methods of molecular weight determination have been dealt with in some detail together with the kinetics of selected examples of condensation and free-radical addition polymerization. The main features of ionic polymerization have also received a reasonable amount of attention. Wherever possible, we have attempted to clarify our discussion with numerical examples. Several topics of considerable importance have been omitted; we have not dealt with the thermodynamics of polymer solutions or the methods of structure determination since these subjects require a knowledge of statistical thermodynamics and spectroscopic techniques. We hope that our discussion of what we have chosen to regard as the basic ideas of polymer chemistry will compensate for these omissions.

Like most authors, we owe a debt of gratitude to our teachers and colleagues who have so materially contributed to our understanding of the subject. In particular, we wish to thank Professor C. E. H. Bawn, F. R. S. for continued advice and encouragement. We also wish to thank Dr. T. B. Grimley for clarifying many aspects of the subject and Messrs. S. G. Canagaratna, P. McBride and R. G. M. Mirrlees for their comments on the manuscript. Any errors found in this book are, however, the responsibility of the authors. Our thanks are due to the Société français d'instruments de contrôle et d'analyse for the photograph of their light scattering instrument and for permission to use some of their experimental data. Finally, we wish to acknowledge the help given by our respective wives.

D. MARGERISON
G. C. EAST

LIST OF PRINCIPAL SYMBOLS

A	the pre-exponential factor in the Arrhenius equation; usually appears with subscript.
A_2 and A_3	the second and third virial coefficients in the π/c, c expansion.
A	a monomer molecule or a mer.
a	the total concentration of COOH groups at any time t.
a_0	the initial concentration of COOH groups.
B	the second virial coefficient in the π/c, c expansion.
B	a monomer molecule or a mer.
C	the third virial coefficient in the π/c, c expansion.
C	a mer.
$[C\cdot]$	the total concentration of polymer radicals at any time t.
$[C\cdot]_s$	the total concentration of polymer radicals at the steady state.
$[C^+]$	the total concentration of active centres in cationic polymerization at any time t.
$\mathcal{C}$	the transfer constant in radical polymerization; usually appears with subscript.
$\mathcal{C}+$	a positively charged ion or counter-ion.
$\mathcal{C}-$	a negatively charged ion or counter-ion.
c	the weight concentration of solute, i.e. the weight of solute per unit volume of solution.
$\mathbf{c}$	the velocity of light *in vacuo*.
'd'	one of the two alternative configurations of an asymmetric carbon atom.

E	the activation energy; usually appears with sub-script.
E	the strength of the electric field at any point in space.
E_0	the maximum strength of the electric field at any point in space.
H	the strength of the magnetic field at any point in space.
H_0	the maximum strength of the magnetic field at any point in space.
I_ϕ	the scattered intensity at an angle ϕ to the incident beam.
I_0	the incident intensity.
I_θ	the scattered intensity at an angle θ to the incident beam.
$\boldsymbol{I}_\theta$	the scattered intensity at an angle θ to the incident beam from unit volume of the scattering medium.
$\boldsymbol{I}_\theta'$	the contribution of concentration fluctuations to the scattered intensity at an angle θ to the incident beam from unit volume of the scattering medium.
I	an initiator molecule.
[I]	the concentration of the initiator at any time t.
$[I]_0$	the initial concentration of the initiator.
$\mathcal{I}_0$	the incident intensity of photochemically active radiation.
i	an integer.
J_ϕ	the energy scattered per unit solid angle per second at an angle ϕ to the incident beam.
j	an integer.
K	a constant appearing in the treatment of light scattering.
K	a constant of proportionality relating the limiting viscosity number to a power of the molecular weight.

K	the number of 'd' or 'l' sequences.
k	a rate constant—usually appears with subscript, the more important instances being listed below; also an integer or a proportionality constant.
k_i	the rate constant for initiation.
k_p	the rate constant for propagation.
k_t	the rate constant for termination.
k_{tr}	the rate constant for transfer.
k_{dp}	the rate constant for depropagation.
k_m	the rate constant for monomer transfer.
k_s	the rate constant for spontaneous decomposition.
k'	the Huggins' constant.
L	the number of A or B sequences.
'l'	one of the two alternative configurations of an asymmetric carbon atom.
M	a molecular weight—usually appears with subscript, the more important instances being listed below.
M_1	the molecular weight of the monomer or mer.
M_i	the molecular weight of the i-mer.
$\bar{M}_n$	the number average molecular weight.
$\bar{M}_w$	the weight average molecular weight.
$\bar{M}_v$	the viscosity average molecular weight.
M	a monomer molecule.
[M]	the concentration of monomer at any time t.
$[M]_0$	the initial concentration of the monomer.
M_i	a polymer molecule containing i-mers.
$[M_i]$	the concentration of the i-mer at any time t.
$M_i \cdot$	a radical containing i-mers.
$[M_i \cdot]$	the concentration of the radical containing i-mers at any time t.
N	the total number of molecules in an assembly.
N	the total number of molecules in unit volume—the number concentration.

N_i	the number of i-mers in an assembly.
$\mathbf{N}_i$	the number of i-mers in unit volume.
N_0	the Avogadro number.
n	the number average degree of polymerization, i.e. the average number of monomer units in a polymer molecule.
n	a number of moles.
n	the refractive index of a gas or solution.
n_0	the refractive index of the pure solvent.
$n_A(S)$	the number of sequences containing S A units.
$n_B(S)$	the number of sequences containing S B units.
P_0	the incident flux.
$P(\theta)$	the particle scattering factor for the angle θ.
[P]	the total concentration of polymer.
p	the magnitude of the induced dipole moment.
p	the extent of reaction.
p	the planar configuration of the carbon atom associated with the unpaired electron in a polymer radical.
p_{AA}	the probability that an A unit in a copolymer of A and B is followed by another A unit; p_{AB}, p_{BB}, p_{BA} are defined similarly.
R	the gas constant.
R_θ	the reduced intensity at an angle θ to the incident beam.
R_{90}	the reduced intensity at $90°$ to the incident beam; this is termed the Rayleigh ratio for a gas or a pure liquid.
R'_θ	the contribution of concentration fluctuations to the reduced intensity at an angle θ to the incident beam.
R·	a primary radical.
$(\overline{r^2})^{1/2}$	the root mean square end-to-end distance of the polymer chains.

r	the distance of a representative point in space from a scattering source.
r_1 and r_2	reactivity ratios in copolymerization.
S	the number of units in a sequence.
$\bar{S}_A$ and $\bar{S}_B$	the average number of A and B units in a sequence.
S	a solvating species.
T	the absolute temperature.
T_c	the ceiling temperature.
TH	a transfer agent.
t	time—occasionally appears with subscript.
W	the total weight of a mixture of polymer molecules of all sizes.
w_i	the total weight of i-mers in a mixture.
z	the dissymmetry coefficient.
α	the polarizability.
α	the exponent in the limiting viscosity number —molecular weight relation.
Γ_2 and Γ_3	the second and third virial coefficients in the π/c, c expansion.
η_1	the viscosity of the solvent.
η_2	the viscosity of a polymer solution.
$[\eta]$	the limiting viscosity number (formerly called the intrinsic viscosity).
θ	the Theta temperature.
θ	an angle.
λ	the wavelength of light *in vacuo*.
λ'	the wavelength of light in a medium of refractive index n.
π	the osmotic pressure of a solution.
ϱ	the density of a liquid; usually appears with subscript.
σ	the probability that a given asymmetric carbon atom is followed by another of the same configuration.

τ the turbidity of a pure liquid.

τ the average lifetime of a polymer radical at the steady state.

ϕ an angle.

ω a solid angle.

NOTE

1. Except in the case of the limiting viscosity number, the symbol [ ] indicates molar concentration, i.e. the number of moles of the species indicated per litre of solution.

2. The summation sign Σ has been used throughout the text to indicate a summation taken from one to infinity over the parameter in question unless otherwise stated.

CHAPTER 1

INTRODUCTION

THIS book is concerned with some of the simpler aspects of the chemistry and physics of high molecular weight compounds. The molecules of these substances are usually between 5000 and 2,000,000 times as heavy as a simple hydrogen atom and consequently are composed of many hundreds or thousands of atoms joined together. The arrangement of the atoms in such molecules is not, however, entirely random since their molecular formulae can always be represented as an integral multiple of simple atomic groupings. That is to say, molecules of the type under discussion contain a large number of simple *sub-units* joined together by covalent bonds. These sub-units or building blocks are termed *mers* and hence high molecular weight compounds are often referred to as *polymers* (many mers). Polymer molecules are usually derived from the compound or compounds containing only one mer—the monomer or monomers, as they are called; for this reason, we shall often use the terms, monomer unit or monomer residue, in place of the term, mer. Molecules which contain only a few of these sub-units joined together are termed *oligomers* (few mers); particular instances are the terms, dimer, trimer, etc., which are used for molecules containing two, three, etc., of the sub-units found in the polymer. It is generally more convenient, however, to use the single term, polymer, to describe all molecules containing more than one mer.

Before proceeding with further generalities, let us consider a simple case, poly(ω-hydroxy undecanoic acid). This polymer is formed from ω-hydroxy undecanoic acid, $HO(CH_2)_{10}COOH$, with the simple repeating structure

$$H{-}O(CH_2)_{10}\underset{\underset{O}{\|}}{C}{-}O(CH_2)_{10}\underset{\underset{O}{\|}}{C}{-}O(CH_2)_{10}\underset{\underset{O}{\|}}{C}{-} \ldots {-}O(CH_2)_{10}\underset{\underset{O}{\|}}{C}{-}OH$$

or more briefly

$$H\left\{O(CH_2)_{10}\underset{\underset{O}{\|}}{C}\right\}_i OH,$$

where i represents any integer from two upwards (the monomer is represented by $i = 1$). The mer in this case is clearly

$$-O(CH_2)_{10}\underset{\underset{O}{\|}}{C}-$$

TYPES OF POLYMER

The simplest types of polymer are those formed from a single mer as in the above example. The molecular formulae of such *homopolymers*, as they are called, are then always of the form

$$X\{A\}_iY,$$

where A represents the formula of the mer, and X and Y stand for the groups present at the beginning and end of a sequence of i sub-units to satisfy the valence requirements. These end groups which may or may not be identical will not be considered any further at this particular stage but will be discussed in the later chapters. Since all sub-units are identical by definition, only two types of homopolymer are possible. These are:

1. the *linear* homopolymers formed from *divalent* sub-units;
2. the *space network* homopolymers formed from sub-units with *valence greater than two*.

A good example of the first case is polymethylene

$$\sim\!\sim\!\sim CH_2-CH_2-CH_2-CH_2-CH_2-CH_2\sim\!\sim\!\sim$$

The wavy lines attached to the ends of the above formula represent the remainder of the polymethylene chain. (In general, a wavy line will be used to represent a portion of a polymer chain in those cases where the number and type of the component mers need not be specified.) One of the few homopolymers with a space network structure is diamond in which each

Fig. 1.1.

carbon atom is bonded to four other carbon atoms as shown in Fig. 1.1. It is perhaps worth mentioning at this stage that the typical properties of diamond, insolubility, infusibility and hardness are encountered in more complex polymers with space network structures.

Some of the most important polymers are built up from more than one sub-unit. These are termed *copolymers* to distinguish them from the simpler homopolymers. Just like the latter, their molecular formulae can always be represented in terms of the sub-units, thus

$$X\{A\}_i\{B\}_j\{C\}_k \ldots Y,$$

where A, B, C, etc., symbolize the formulae of the various mers incorporated into the copolymer, i, j, k, etc., stand for any integers and X and Y are end groups. As soon as more than one mer is involved, a wide diversity of polymer structure and type becomes possible. For example, even with only two mers A and B, there are several ways of forming a *linear* copolymer; these are:

1. the *alternating* copolymer   —A—B—A—B—A—B—A—B—A—B—A—

2. the *block* copolymer   —A—A—A—A—A—B—B—B—B—B—B—

3. the *random* copolymer   —B—A—A—B—A—B—A—B—A—B—B—

One example of each of these is shown below:

1. an alternating copolymer formed from styrene and maleic anhydride

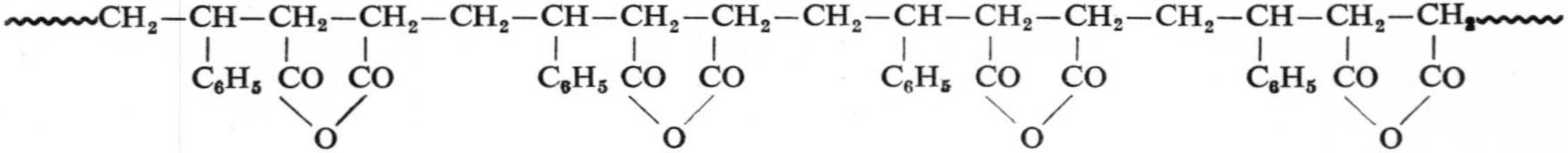

$$\sim CH_2-CH-CH_2-CH_2-CH-CH_2-CH_2-CH-CH_2-CH_2-CH-CH_2-CH_2\sim$$

with repeating C_6H_5, CO, CO, O groups

2. a block copolymer formed from styrene and isoprene

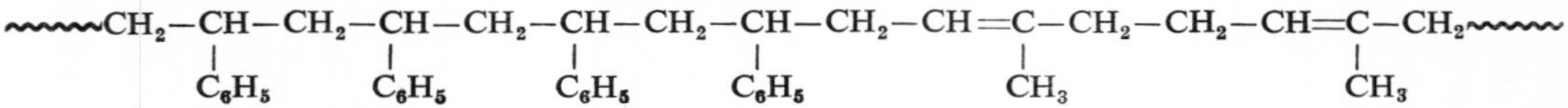

$$\sim CH_2-CH-CH_2-CH-CH_2-CH-CH_2-CH_2-CH=C-CH_2-CH_2-CH=C-CH_2\sim$$

with C_6H_5, C_6H_5, C_6H_5, CH_3, CH_3 groups

3. a random copolymer formed from styrene and methyl methacrylate

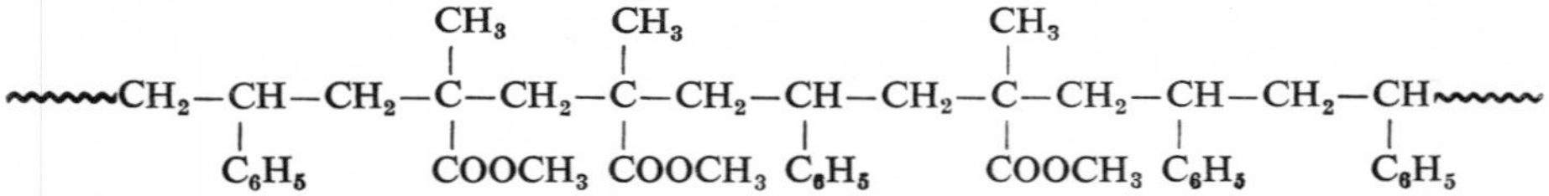

$$\sim CH_2-CH-CH_2-C-CH_2-C-CH_2-CH-CH_2-CH-CH_2-CH\sim$$

with C_6H_5, CH_3/$COOCH_3$, CH_3/$COOCH_3$, $COOCH_3$/C_6H_5, $COOCH_3$/C_6H_5, C_6H_5 groups

One small point, perhaps, ought to be mentioned; it is quite permissible to classify the perfectly alternating copolymer as a homopolymer, the mer being **AB**.

As in the case of homopolymers, *non-linear* structures may also be formed. Perhaps the simplest of the many possibilities are the *branched* copolymers which are composed predominantly of a single type of mer, thus:

In such structures, the longest linear sequence of mers is referred to as the "*polymer backbone*" and the trivalent subunits **B** as the *branch points*. For a given ratio of the numbers of **A** and **B**, a large number of different structures are possible according to the length of the branches and the way in which the branch points are distributed along the polymer backbone.

A simple example of a branched polymer of this type is the polyethylene formed at high temperatures and pressures, in which the majority[†] of the branches are short chains containing three or four carbon atoms. Its structure is:

$$\text{\raise2pt\sim\sim\sim} CH_2-CH_2-CH-CH_2-CH_2 \text{\sim\sim\sim} CH_2-CH_2-CH-CH_2 \text{\sim\sim\sim}$$

with branches $CH_2-CH_2-CH_2-CH_3$ and $CH_2-CH_2-CH_3$

[†] A few branches are much longer than those shown but since they occur at about one-tenth of the frequency of the short chain branches, they do not merit special consideration at this stage.

Under the usual conditions of preparation, these branches occur with frequencies ranging from one in twenty to one in a hundred backbone CH_2 units. It must be admitted that, where the number of branch points is a very small fraction of a large number of identical mers, there is a strong case for classifying these polymers as homopolymers. Indeed in the example chosen, few polymer chemists would regard high pressure polyethylene as a copolymer even though it can be regarded formally as built up from two mers CH_2 and CH; our purpose in imposing a rather rigid classification is simply to draw attention to the fact that the structure of the mer at the branch point is not identical with the structure of the main repeating unit.

These minor difficulties of definition disappear entirely if the branch is composed of different mers from those making up the backbone chain. Such polymers are termed *graft* copolymers, their structures being represented symbolically below:

The structure of the branch point is usually closely related to the structure of the mer making up the polymer backbone as in the case just discussed — in fact, B is most commonly formed by the loss of an atom or group from A during the formation of the branch. An example of a graft copolymer is that formed from methyl methacrylate and polystyrene.

$$\overset{\displaystyle C_6H_5}{\underset{|}{}} \quad \overset{\displaystyle C_6H_5}{\underset{|}{}} \quad \overset{\displaystyle C_6H_5}{\underset{|}{}} \quad \overset{\displaystyle C_6H_5}{\underset{|}{}} \quad \overset{\displaystyle C_6H_5}{\underset{|}{}}$$

$$\sim\sim\sim CH_2-CH-CH_2-CH-CH_2-C-CH_2-CH-CH_2-CH\sim\sim\sim$$

$$|$$
$$CH_2$$
$$|$$
$$CH_3-C-COOCH_3$$
$$|$$
$$CH_2$$
$$|$$
$$CH_3-C-COOCH_3$$
$$|$$
$$CH_2$$
$$|$$
$$CH_3-C-COOCH_3$$
$$\{$$

Two other types of non-linear polymer are the *cross-linked* and *space network* polymers. The structures described by these terms are represented in Figs. 1.2 and 1.3.

There is no essential difference between these two types of polymer — merely increasing the number of cross-links in what

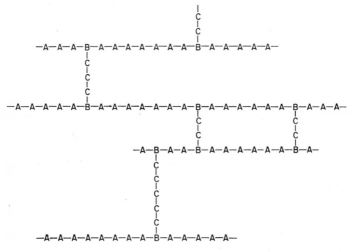

FIG. 1.2. A cross-linked polymer

we have termed the cross-linked polymer results in the formation of the space network. An example of the former type of
polymer is to be found in partially vulcanized rubber where a
limited number of short chains of sulphur atoms link together

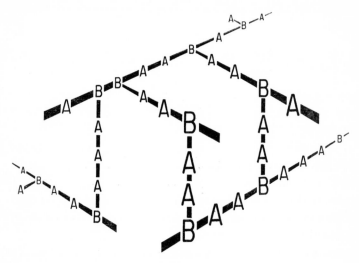

FIG. 1.3. A space network polymer

a large number of polyisoprene molecules; a specific structure
of this type is shown below.

$$\sim\sim\sim CH_2-\underset{\underset{\underset{\underset{\underset{\underset{\underset{\sim\sim\sim CH_2-\underset{\underset{CH_3}{|}}{C}-CH_2-CH_2-CH_2-\underset{\underset{CH_3}{|}}{C}=CH-CH_2\sim\sim\sim}{|}}{S}}{|}}{S}}{|}}{S}}{|}}{S}}{\overset{\overset{CH_3}{|}}{C}}-CH=CH-CH_2-\overset{\overset{CH_3}{|}}{C}=CH-CH_2\sim\sim\sim$$

The space network structures are exemplified by the urea-formaldehyde polymers, a portion of whose structure is given below.

$$
\begin{array}{c}
NH_2 \\
| \\
CO \\
| \\
\text{\scriptsize www}-N-CH_2-N-CH_2-N\text{\scriptsize www} \\
| \qquad\qquad\qquad | \\
CO \qquad\qquad\quad CO \\
| \qquad\qquad\qquad | \\
\text{\scriptsize www}CH_2-NH \qquad\quad NH \\
| \\
CH_2 \\
NH-CH_2-N-CH_2-N \\
| \qquad\quad | \qquad\quad | \\
CO \qquad CO \qquad CO \\
| \qquad\quad | \qquad\quad | \\
NH_2 \qquad NH-CH_2-N\text{\scriptsize www}
\end{array}
$$

Table 1.1 lists a few examples of the wide variety of polymeric materials known. It will be seen that many chemical types are represented from the purely organic polymers based on carbon and hydrogen to the purely inorganic formed from phosphorus, nitrogen and chlorine. Many of the organic polymers will be recognized as natural products of great biochemical or technological importance. Equally well represented are the synthetic polymers which are the mainstay of the new technologies of the "man-made" fibre, the plastics and the synthetic rubber industries.

TABLE 1.1

Cellulose	Rubber
Starch	Nylon
Chitin	Terylene
Pepsin	Polythene
Insulin	Polystyrene
Egg albumin	Perspex
Desoxyribose nucleic acid	Polyphosphorus chloronitride
Bakelite	Polysiloxane

In this book, we shall confine our attention almost entirely to *synthetic linear polymers based on carbon* whose structures are relatively simple. Table 1.2 shows a few of the polymers

TABLE 1.2

Monomer(s)	Formula(e)	Polymer	Mer
Ethylene glycol Terephthalic acid	$HO(CH_2)_2OH$ $HOOCC_6H_4COOH$	Polyethylene terephthalate (terylene)	$-O(CH_2)_2OOCC_6H_4CO-$
Hexamethylene diamine Adipic acid	$H_2N(CH_2)_6NH_2$ $HOOC(CH_2)_4COOH$	Polyhexamethylene adipamide (nylon 6.6)	$-HN(CH_2)_6NHCO(CH_2)_4CO-$
Ethylene	$CH_2{=}CH_2$	Polyethylene (polythene)	$-CH_2CH_2-$
Styrene	$CH_2{=}CH$ $\quad\ \ C_6H_5$	Polystyrene	$-CH_2CH-$ $\qquad C_6H_5$
Vinyl chloride	$CH_2{=}CH$ $\quad\ \ Cl$	Polyvinyl chloride (PVC)	$-CH_2CH-$ $\qquad Cl$
Vinyl acetate	$CH_2{=}CH$ $\quad\ \ OOCCH_3$	Polyvinyl acetate	$-CH_2CH-$ $\qquad OOCCH_3$

Monomer	Structure	Polymer	Structure
Methyl methacrylate	$CH_2{=}C(CH_3)(COOCH_3)$	Polymethyl methacrylate (perspex)	$-CH_2C(CH_3)(COOCH_3)-$
Isobutene	$CH_2{=}C(CH_3)(CH_3)$	Polyisobutene	$-CH_2C(CH_3)(CH_3)-$
Butadiene	$\underset{1}{CH_2}{=}\underset{2}{CH}{-}\underset{3}{CH}{=}\underset{4}{CH_2}$	Polybutadiene	$-CH_2-CH-$ with $CH{=}CH_2$ (1,2 structure); $-CH_2-CH{=}CH-CH_2-$ (1,4 structure)

Table 1.2 (continued)

Monomer	Formula	Polymer	Mer
Isoprene	$\begin{array}{c} CH_3 \\ | \\ CH_2{=}C{-}CH{=}CH_2 \\ 1 \quad 2 \quad 3 \quad 4 \end{array}$	Polyisoprene	$-CH_2-\underset{\underset{CH_3}{|}}{C}=CH-CH_2-$ (1,2 structure)
			$-CH_2-CH-$ $\underset{\underset{CH_2}{\parallel}}{C}-CH_3$ (3,4 structure)
			$\underset{-CH_2}{\overset{CH_3}{\diagdown}}C{=}C\underset{CH_2-}{\overset{H}{\diagup}}$ (*cis* 1,4 structure)
			$\underset{-CH_2}{\overset{CH_3}{\diagdown}}C{=}C\underset{H}{\overset{CH_2-}{\diagup}}$ (*trans* 1,4 structure)

with which we shall be most concerned and the monomers from which they are made.

MOLECULAR WEIGHTS AND DEGREE OF POLYMERIZATION

As we have already said, this book is concerned with linear molecules possessing very high molecular weights. Although it is undesirable to be too rigid in setting a lower limit to the molecular weight, the major part of our subsequent discussion will be confined to substances with molecular weights above 5000. Our somewhat arbitrary choice of subject matter similarly determines an upper limit of molecular weight of around 2,000,000. The determination of molecular weights between these limits is dealt with in detail in Chapter 2.

Molecules with molecular weights in this range are obviously composed of many mers. If we take a homopolymer molecule with a molecular weight of 100,000 for example, the mer molecular weight being 100, our molecule consists of 1000 mers. This latter quantity, the number of mers in the molecule, is termed the *degree of polymerization*. In the case of a copolymer molecule, this term is perhaps less informative and certainly a little more difficult to calculate. Suppose we take a particular copolymer molecule of the same molecular weight as above containing 25% by weight of a mer A (molecular weight 100) and 75% by weight of a mer B (molecular weight 150). Then if we have n_A mers of A and n_B mers of B in this molecule,

$$n_A \times 100 = \frac{25}{100} \times 100,000,$$

$$n_B \times 150 = \frac{75}{100} \times 100,000,$$

so that there are 250 A mers and 500 B mers; the total number of mers in the molecule or its degree of polymerization is thus

750. It will be noticed that no attempt has been made in these calculations to correct for the contribution of the end groups to the molecular weight. This could be done, of course, if the number and type of the end groups are known; such corrections are unimportant, however, when the polymer molecular weight is very high. What is important is the conception that polymer molecules are composed of many mers joined together in long chains.

THE CONFIGURATION OF POLYMERIC MOLECULES AND ASSOCIATED PROPERTIES

Polymeric substances can be divided into two groups according to whether their molecules are *rigid* or *flexible;* there will be some polymers whose molecules do not fit neatly into either category or which pass from the first classification to the second as the temperature is raised. Such difficulties do not, however, lessen the utility of this classification.

Perhaps the best examples of rigid structures are to be found in the proteins. The presence of extensive intramolecular hydrogen bonding in these molecules is largely responsible for their inflexibility and, in consequence, their definite *shape.* As a rule, these shapes can be quite adequately represented by simple geometrical shapes such as spheres, ellipsoids, rods or discs. The dimensions of the molecules, therefore, present no conceptual difficulties; the experimental determination of the shape and characteristic dimensions of such molecules is, however, by no means an easy matter.

Because of our own experience and interests, this book is concerned mainly with synthetic linear polymers whose molecules possess a great deal of flexibility. This flexibility arises as a result of the *freedom of rotation* which exists about each mer–mer bond. In consequence molecules of this type in the solid and liquid states and in solution tend to coil up and assume a more compact configuration than that shown by the extended structures given previously. To this extent, the previous formulations of the structures of linear homopolymers and copolymers are misleading for they show only the most orderly possible arrangement of the component mers. What actually happens is that the configuration of a particular molecule fluctuates with time about some average. We shall understand the problems involved better if we commence with a comparatively simple situation.

1. Flexible linear molecules in dilute solution

To simplify the problem for a typical polymer based on carbon, let us take a long chain of carbon atoms in which free rotation about each C—C bond is possible subject to the C—C—C bond angle being fixed at 109°, the C—C internuclear distance being 1·54 Å. We wish to know the possible relative positions of the nuclei of the carbon atoms making up the chain. Relative to the first two carbon nuclei C_1 and C_2, the third carbon nucleus can be placed anywhere on a circle swept out by rotating the C_2—C_3 bond at a constant angle of 109° to the C_1—C_2 bond, as shown in Fig. 1.4. Similarly, the

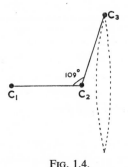

Fig. 1.4.

fourth carbon nucleus can be placed anywhere on an equivalent
circle drawn relative to the C_2—C_3 bond and so there are a
large number of positions of the four carbons relative to some
fixed axes in space; the four configurations which happen to

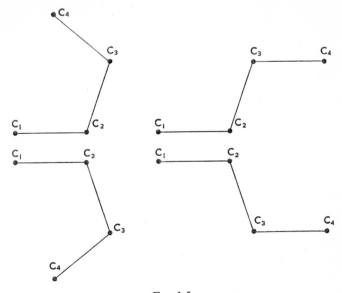

FIG. 1.5.

lie in the plane of the paper are shown in Fig. 1.5. It is most
important to realize that these structures are interconvertible
by appropriate rotation about C—C bonds. If, for the moment, we forget that the carbon atoms have a finite volume so
that more than one atom can occupy the same volume element
of space, it is possible to construct analogous diagrams for the
many-atom chain. We can see immediately that the number
of possible configurations increases rapidly as the number of
atoms increases.

However, in the case of a real polymer chain, the finite size
of the backbone carbon atoms and the substituents cannot be

neglected, for clearly the overlap of two different portions of the polymer chain is prohibited. This restriction means that certain configurations open to the "volumeless" chain are not available to the real polymer chain. In addition the rotation about each C—C bond is hindered by repulsive forces between the substituents on adjacent carbon atoms (this effect is particularly important with bulky substituents such as phenyl or methyl

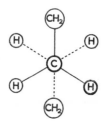

FIG. 1.6.

groups). Taking a portion of a polymethylene chain as the simplest case, the configuration shown in Fig. 1.6 in which the CH_2 groups on adjacent carbon atoms are staggered relative to one another is more frequently assumed by the chain than any other. The dotted lines in Fig. 1.6 represent projections on a plane below and parallel to the plane of the paper; the line joining the two central carbon atoms in each plane is the C—C bond about which rotation is envisaged to take place. Despite these two complications, the fact remains that a long polymer chain can take up an immense number of different configurations.

Our picture of an isolated polymer molecule is, thus, as follows. Because of the continuous rotation about C—C bonds, there is *no* one fixed configuration of the chain. Instead the chain adopts a succession of different poses; a series of instantaneous "photographs" of the chain would in fact reveal its internal motions to be highly complex. Figure 1.7 shows three of the many possible configurations of a short chain polymer projected on a plane. Over a sufficiently long period of time, all accessible configurations are taken up by the molecule, those configurations in which repulsive forces between groups are low being the most frequently assumed. On this basis, we can

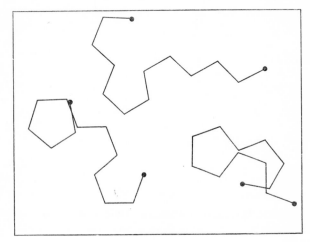

FIG. 1.7.

characterize the dimensions of the molecule by taking the time-average of the distance separating the two ends of the chain. Because of the increased occupation of the less-hindered expanded arrangements, *this averaged end-to-end distance* of an actual polymer molecule will be rather *greater* than the corresponding quantity for the "volumeless" chain where no steric hindrance need be considered.

With this picture of the behaviour of an isolated single polymer molecule, it is now possible to describe the state of affairs in dilute solution. If the solution is sufficiently dilute, the polymer molecules are separated from one another by a region of solvent so that each can execute its complex internal motion independently of every other molecule. Consequently, the same considerations apply to the configuration of the molecules in solution as apply to the single isolated molecule. An instantaneous "photograph" of the solution would show molecules in every possible configuration; some molecules would be tightly coiled up, others would be highly expanded while countless numbers would be in intermediate states.

To digress for a moment, it might be thought that the most heavily populated state would be the highly extended configuration, the zig-zag chain shown in Fig. 1.8 in which steric hindrance is at a minimum :†

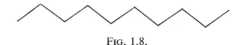

FIG. 1.8.

Without going deeply into the detailed arguments, a situation in which the majority of the polymer molecules were in these highly extended states is very unlikely because of the high degree of order which would be created in the solution.

Returning to our consideration of the instantaneous "photograph" of a large number of polymer molecules in solution it is clear that we can calculate an average distance between the two ends by simply measuring the end-to-end distance of each separate molecule. If we found, for example, that we had n_1 molecules with distance r_1 between the ends, n_2 molecules with distance r_2, ..., n_i molecules with distance r_i, and so on, then the average end-to-end distance $\bar{r}$ is

$$\bar{r} = \frac{n_1 r_1 + n_2 r_2 + \ldots + n_i r_i + \ldots}{n_1 + n_2 + \ldots + n_i + \ldots} = \frac{\sum n_i r_i}{\sum n_i}.$$

† The diagram is possibly misleading for like the others it represents a situation occurring in three dimensions on a plane surface. With bulky substituents, the backbone chain in the position of minimum steric hindrance is likely to have a twist in it to relieve overcrowding — hence the generation of helical configurations.

It so happens that the experimental parameters which are related to the end-to-end distance yield the average square of the distance between the ends. Consequently, we usually calculate the *root mean square end-to-end* distance rather than the simple average defined above. That is,

$$(\overline{r^2})^{1/2} = \left\{ \frac{n_1 r_1^2 + n_2 r_2^2 + \ldots + n_i r_i^2 + \ldots}{n_1 + n_2 + \ldots + n_i + \ldots} \right\}^{1/2}$$

$$= \left\{ \frac{\sum n_i r_i^2}{\sum n_i} \right\}^{1/2}.$$

These averages are identical to those which would be obtained on a time averaged basis for the reason that a single "shot" of an assembly of N molecules would contain precisely the same distribution of configurations as N "shots" of a single molecule.

Although these quantities are truly equilibrium properties —the distribution of configurations being constant in time— they are characteristic of the polymer–solvent system and the temperature and not just of the polymer alone because of the interaction between the polymer and the solvent. Thus the same polymer dissolved in two different types of solvent at the same temperature can have quite different values of the root mean square end-to-end distance. This problem will be discussed in Chapter 2.

2. Flexible linear molecules in more concentrated solution

The previous picture of a solution of a polymer is only useful for very dilute solutions (usually less than 1 % by weight of polymer—see Chapter 2). Because of the large dimensions of polymer molecules with high molecular weights, increasing the concentration of polymer from these low values quickly results in entanglement of the polymer chains. That is, the solution changes from that shown in Fig. 1.9 to that shown in Fig. 1.10 on adding more polymer.

In concentrated solutions the chains still possess a high degree of flexibility but now the segmental motion of one chain is not independent of that of another chain. It is clear

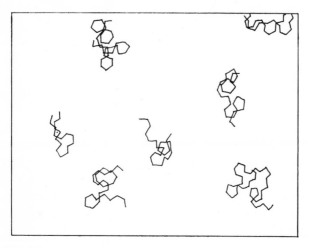

FIG. 1.9. An instantaneous "photograph" of a dilute polymer solution

that the flow properties of these solutions will be very different from those containing simple solutes.

One other consequence of the molecular entanglement should be noted. For reasonably concentrated solutions where the polymer molecules occupy a significant fraction of the total volume of the solution, the polymer chains are so completely intertwined that there is no point in thinking of a particular mer as belonging to a particular chain; it is best to regard the solution as made up of a large number of volume elements in each of which the number of mers fluctuates with time about some average value.

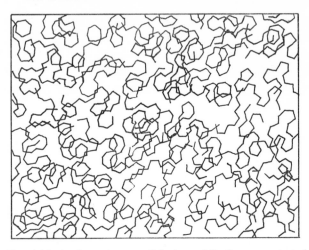

FIG. 1.10. An instantaneous "photograph" of a concentrated
polymer solution

3. *Flexible linear molecules in the pure liquid and solid states*

Polymer molecules in the pure liquid state can easily be pictured in the terms used to describe concentrated solutions. If we consider the effect of removal of solvent from solutions of polymer at temperatures above the polymer melting point, it is clear that the polymer molecules become more and more entangled as the amount of solvent in the solution decreases. The pure liquid state in which the molecular entanglement is at a maximum thus represents the limiting case of the very concentrated solution.

These ideas are fairly straightforward provided that the polymer is in the liquid state where the molecules not only possess complex internal motions but also are free to move throughout the body of the liquid albeit with great difficulty. The situation becomes considerably more complicated, however, when the temperature is lowered and this translational

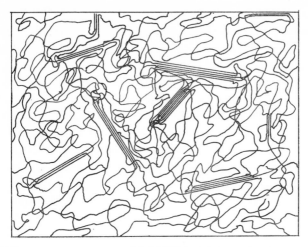

Fig. 1.11.

freedom is lost. With familiar low molecular weight liquids, this loss of translational freedom occurs at a definite temperature known as the freezing point—the random structure of the liquid being replaced by the ordered arrangement of the crystalline solid. For the liquid polymer, the analogous process in which all the chains disentangle themselves and line up to form an ordered array is obviously highly unlikely—in other words *perfectly crystalline* polymers cannot be obtained by simply cooling the melt. All that happens is that occasionally portions of a number of polymer chains line up in a regular fashion in the solid to form *crystalline regions* or *crystallites*. These crystalline regions are surrounded by disordered regions where the polymer chains are more or less arranged in the same disorganized fashion as in the pure liquid state—these regions are termed *amorphous*. That this is a correct description of the solid state of polymers is shown by their characteristic X-ray diffraction pattern; this shows features analogous to those observed from both simple liquids and crystalline solids.

Figure 1.11 shows schematically in two dimensions the arrangement of polymer chains in the usual semi-crystalline polymer. The crystallites are of varying size but since their linear dimensions are always considerably less than the length of a polymer molecule, any one polymer molecule will usually pass through several crystalline and amorphous regions.

As would be expected from this account, the percentage of the polymer present in crystalline regions depends to some extent on its thermal history; for example, whether it was cooled slowly or rapidly from the liquid state. In that some of the physical properties of the solid such as its density and melting point are dependent on its crystallinity,† this fact gives rise to a certain indeterminacy in these quantities for a given polymer.

Some polymers show a much greater tendency to solidify with high degrees of crystallinity than do others. For example, if a polymer has a geometrically regular structure, then the segments of different polymer chains are assisted in packing together closely enough for the attractive forces between them to "lock" large portions of the chains together in an ordered fashion. Linear polyethylene and the stereoregular vinyl polymers (see Chapter 4) are cases in point. The branched polyethylenes, on the other hand, cannot pack as economically together because of the random spacing and length of the branches; consequently, branched polyethylene is largely amorphous and possesses a lower density than its linear counterpart. Of course, if there are specially strong attractive forces between segments of different chains, the tendency to produce largely crystalline solids is greatly enhanced. Particularly important in this context is the hydrogen bonding which occurs in the polyamides and polyesters (see Chapter 3).

---

† Since the density of a polymer usually increases as the degree of crystallinity increases, measurements of density may be used to measure the percentage crystallinity in a solid polymer.

The point of mentioning these ideas in some detail is that the degree of disorder in the solid, that is, whether it is largely amorphous or predominantly crystalline, determines very much the type of use to which it can be put. The highly disordered solids often show *rubber-like* properties if the temperature is high enough for a large amount of segmental motion to exist; once this motion is suppressed by reducing the temperature, the material changes to a brittle, *glass-like* solid with no elastomeric properties—the temperature at which this occurs is called the *glass-transition temperature*. The usual *plastics* at room temperature (they are not plastic at all!) such as polystyrene or polymethyl methacrylate are examples of highly disordered materials below their glass-transition temperatures; natural rubber under the same conditions exemplifies a highly amorphous solid well above its glass-transition temperature. Just as natural rubber can be changed into a brittle material by cooling so polystyrene can be induced to possess some elastomeric properties if the temperature is raised to a sufficiently high value.[†] The highly ordered solids, on the other hand, are usually ideal for the production of *fibres*—the rigidity of the crystalline regions confers strength on the fibre while the amorphous regions permit the necessary flexibility.

GENERAL PHYSICAL PROPERTIES

All high molecular weight polymers are solids at room temperature. Those possessing linear or branched structures melt on raising the temperature to give a liquid of extremely high viscosity. The heavily cross-linked and space network polymers, on the other hand, are usually quite infusible; these structures break up giving low molecular weight material

[†] Strictly speaking, unless the molecular weight is very high, a small proportion of cross-links between the chains is also necessary for typical rubber-like behaviour.

instead of melting. This same process, known as *degradation*, effectively prevents all known polymers from being vaporized.

Once a certain value of the molecular weight is reached (around, say, 10,000) the physical properties of a polymer such as density or melting point show no detectable variation with molecular weight. At lower values, these properties vary systematically with increasing molecular weight tending asymptotically to the value characteristic of high molecular weight material.

Most linear and branched polymers can usually be dissolved in some solvent to form quite concentrated solutions, the general rule of "like dissolves like" being equally applicable to these systems as to simpler systems. Polystyrene, for example, with the repeating unit

$$CH_2CH$$
$$|$$
$$C_6H_5$$

is miscible in all proportions with ethyl benzene

$$CH_3CH_2$$
$$|$$
$$C_6H_5$$

In general the process of solution is quite slow, two distinct stages being observable—a polymer absorbs the solvent to give a gel which then slowly disperses to give a solution.

With some liquids the process stops at the swelling stage, the polymer never going completely into solution. With other liquids, there is not even this partial solubility—these liquids are termed non-solvents and are often used to precipitate the polymer from solution. The system cyclohexane–polystyrene at 25°C illustrates the limited solubility behaviour extremely well; in that the highly disordered solid polymer is not so dissimilar from a liquid, the phenomenon may be discussed in the usual terms employed to describe the partial miscibility of two liquids. That is, we have two liquid phases both of which contain the two components; they differ simply in the proportions of polymer, one being relatively rich in this component (the gel phase) and the other containing very little (the solvent-rich phase). As the temperature is raised, the compositions of the two liquid phases become more and more similar until a temperature is reached—the critical solution temperature—above which complete miscibility always occurs. In other words, there is no essential difference between solvents of this type and those which completely dissolve the polymer—it is simply a matter of the value of the critical solution temperature. These ideas present no special difficulty if we are dealing with a polymer containing molecules all of the same molecular weight. The critical solution temperature is a function of the molecular weight just like any of the other physical properties. However, most polymers contain molecules with a range of molecular weights, a fact which we shall discuss in some detail in Chapter 2. Consequently discussions of limited solubility behaviour must be conducted in the terms used for multi-component systems; since, in general, the lower molecular weight species are the more soluble, it follows that, where limited miscibility exists in a polymer-solvent system, there is an enrichment in low molecular weight species in the solvent-rich phase and a corresponding enhancement in the concentration of high molecular weight species in the gel phase. This process which we shall discuss in Chapter 2 is termed *fractionation*.

The criteria which determine whether or not a given polymer is soluble in a given solvent are best discussed in *thermodynamic* terms. We start with the general statement that every physico-chemical system at equilibrium has a definite value of an energy parameter G (the Gibbs Free Energy) in just the same way as it has a definite volume V. The actual value taken by G (like V) depends on the temperature and pressure of the system as well as on the number of moles present. The importance of G is simply this: if we mix two systems with G

values G_1 and G_2 in a thermostat to keep the temperature constant and under constant pressure, then only those changes occur, be they physical or chemical, which result in the value of G for the mixture being less than $G_1 + G_2$. If a change does occur, the new equilibrium position corresponds to the lowest value of G accessible to the particular system. Putting this a slightly different way, the change in G, ΔG, given by

$$\Delta G = G_{final} - G_{initial}$$

is always negative for a spontaneous change.

Now, in our case, the change in G which occurs on mixing polymer and solvent is by definition

$$\Delta G_{mix} = G_{solution} - (G_{polymer} + G_{solvent}).$$

The value it takes depends on three factors:

1. the heat released on mixing polymer and solvent, Q_{mix};
2. the temperature T;
3. a parameter measuring the increase in disorder resulting from mixing polymer and solvent, ΔS_{mix}.

At constant temperature and pressure, it can be shown that

$$\Delta G_{mix} = -Q_{mix} - T\Delta S_{mix}.\dagger$$

Without going into too much detail, we can usually say that the process of solution is accompanied by an increase in disorder so that ΔS_{mix} is positive. At a given temperature, therefore, ΔG_{mix} will be negative—the necessary condition for solution to actually take place—if

(a) Q_{mix} is +ve; i.e. heat is given up to the thermostat on polymer dissolving in the solvent;

(b) Q_{mix} is 0; i.e. heat is neither required for nor obtained from the dissolution of polymer in the solvent;

(c) Q_{mix} is −ve but small; i.e. some heat is absorbed from the thermostat but insufficient to offset the product $T\Delta S_{mix}$.

† This equation is usually written $\Delta G_{mix} = \Delta H_{mix} - T\Delta S_{mix}$ but, since the enthalpy change, ΔH_{mix}, is identical with $-Q_{mix}$ for a process occurring a constant pressure, we have used the more familiar term.

The polymer will not dissolve to any appreciable extent if a large amount of heat has to be supplied from the thermostat for then $-Q_{mix}$ is sufficiently positive to exceed $T\Delta S_{mix}$ at ordinary temperatures.

In many polymer-solvent systems Q_{mix} is positive or zero over the whole range of composition and so complete miscibility is observed. In many other cases, however, Q_{mix} is always negative and this leads to incomplete miscibility below a certain temperature—the critical solution temperature. Without considering the detailed arguments in which the composition and temperature dependence of Q_{mix} and ΔS_{mix} are taken into account, we can see that the greater the value of $-Q_{mix}$ the higher will be the value of the critical solution temperature. For example, high values of $-Q_{mix}$ are usually observed with semi-crystalline polymers since substantial amounts of heat are necessary to break up the crystalline regions. As a general rule, therefore, higher temperatures are required to produce extensive miscibility in semi-crystalline polymer-solvent systems than in mixtures containing amorphous polymers.

The fact that linear and branched polymers can usually be obtained in solution if the solvent and temperature are chosen correctly is of paramount importance. Without this property, the determination of their molecular weights and root mean square end-to-end distances would be extremely difficult. This will be quite clear at the conclusion of Chapter 2 which deals mainly with these problems. Apart from these considerations, the information which we have on the mechanism of polymerization has been largely obtained from kinetic studies of homogeneous systems—in those systems where polymer precipitates in the reaction, complications are almost always found.

Finally, we must emphasize that polymer solutions show great deviations from ideal behaviour. One example will suffice for the present: the solvent vapour pressure above a solution of polymer is much lower than that predicted from Raoult's law on the basis of the number of molecules present. This aspect of polymer solutions will be considered in a little more detail in Chapter 2.

GENERAL CHEMICAL PROPERTIES

The chemical properties of a polymer depend, of course, on its structure; as a general rule, a polymer shows the same reactivity towards a given reagent as a low molecular weight compound with a similar structure to the repeating unit of the chain. For example, polyethylene is similar to n-hexane in that both are unaffected by strong acids and alkalies at room temperature. The reaction of polystyrene with bromine is similar to that of toluene:

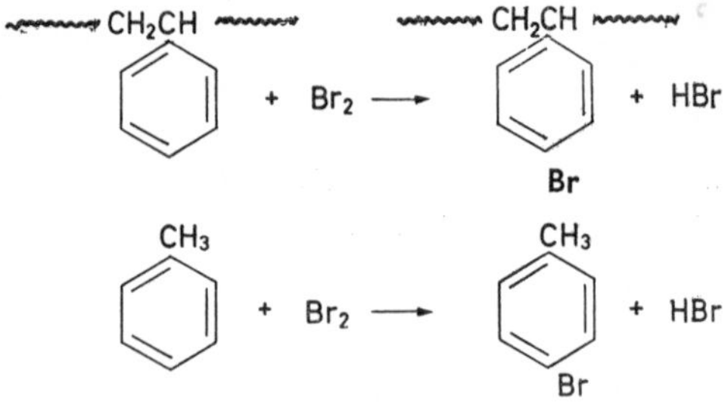

Just like any other ester, polyvinyl acetate hydrolyses when treated with dilute acids or alkalies:

$$\sim\sim CH_2\underset{\displaystyle OOCCH_3}{\underset{|}{CH}}\sim\sim + NaOH \rightarrow \sim\sim CH_2\underset{\displaystyle OH}{\underset{|}{CH}}\sim\sim$$
$$+CH_3COONa$$

If the polymer is unsaturated, it can be hydrogenated or brominated under similar conditions to those used for simple olefins. A particularly interesting application of hydrogenation is the demonstration that the two naturally occurring polyisoprenes, natural rubber and gutta percha, are geometrical isomers; both give the same product on hydrogenation.

The effect of heating high molecular weight organic polymers to reasonably high temperatures should also be mentioned. In the presence of oxygen, the usual products of combustion, carbon dioxide, water and so on, are formed so enabling an elemental analysis to be made. In the absence of oxygen, a polymer usually breaks up into low molecular weight products, mainly monomer. These degradation products enable the arrangement of the various mers in the polymer chains to be deduced. We shall not, however, devote any attention to the mechanism of the degradation process, the main portion of this book being concerned with the opposite reaction—polymerization.

KINETICS AND MECHANISMS OF POLYMERIZATION

In Chapters 3, 4 and 5 we shall discuss in some detail the reactions by which synthetic polymers are made. We shall see that these polymerization reactions fall into two general types according to whether the *essential* overall stoichiometry is

$$nM \rightarrow M'_n + (n-1)A$$

$$\text{or} \quad nM \rightarrow M_n.$$

In the first type of reaction, n monomer molecules represented by the symbol M which may or may not be identical are converted into a polymer molecule containing n mers, M_n', *with the elimination* of $(n-1)$ simple molecules represented by the symbol A. This reaction is termed *condensation polymerization*. From the fact that a large number of simple molecules are formed at the same time as the polymer, it follows that the mers in a condensation polymer do not contain the same number of atoms as the monomers from which they derived; we have used the primed symbol M_n' for the polymer to emphasize his point. One specific example of a condensation polymerization reaction will suffice at this stage.

$$n \ HO(CH_2)_{10}COOH \rightarrow H\{O(CH_2)_{10}CO\}_n \ OH + (n-1)H_2O$$

The second reaction is termed *addition polymerization* since the polymer is formed by n monomer molecules (which again may or may not be identical) joining together; in this case, the number of atoms in the mers is the same as in the corresponding monomers. Two examples of addition polymerization reactions are given below:

$$n \ CH_2=CH \xrightarrow{HClO_4} CH_3CH \left\{ CH_2CH \right\}_{n-2} CH=CH$$
$$\underset{C_6H_5}{|} \qquad \underset{C_6H_5}{|} \quad \underset{C_6H_5}{|} \quad \underset{C_6H_5}{|}$$

$$^1/_2 C_6H_5COOOOCC_6H_5 + n \ CH_2=\underset{\underset{COOCH_3}{|}}{\overset{\overset{CH_3}{|}}{C}} \rightarrow$$

$$C_6H_5COO \left\{ CH_2\underset{\underset{COOCH_3}{|}}{\overset{\overset{CH_3}{|}}{C}} \right\}_{n-1} CH=\underset{\underset{COOCH_3}{|}}{\overset{\overset{CH_3}{|}}{C}}$$

In each of the examples, the polymer chains possess two end groups to satisfy the valence requirements of the terminal mers. The first example illustrates the perchloric acid *catalysed* polymerization of styrene; perchloric acid added to styrene causes the polymerization to proceed at a finite rate and at the end of the reaction can be recovered. The second example illustrates the polymerization of methyl methacrylate *initiated* by benzoyl peroxide; as the reaction proceeds, this material disappears from the system, fragments of it appearing as end groups of the polymer. Substances which act in this way are termed *initiators* to distinguish them from *catalysts* which are recoverable unchanged at the end of a polymerization.

These stoichiometric equations, whether they refer to condensation or addition polymerization, tell us *nothing* about the mechanisms of the reactions. The information we have concerning the mechanisms of polymerization is, in fact, largely derived from the study of the rates of these processes. Unfortunately, a great deal of confusion exists at an elementary level concerning the basic ideas of chemical kinetics. The strange thing is that these ideas are very much simpler than many of those in other branches of chemistry, a fact which we shall attempt to demonstrate.

Let us take the *experimental* side of the subject first. Assuming that we are dealing with a reaction proceeding at finite speed, our first object is the determination of the concentrations of the reactants, products and intermediates† as a function of time at constant temperature. The experimental difficulties thus reduce to the determination of the various concentrations; if there are no intermediates or if these are in very low concentration and if the stoichiometry of the reaction is known, the concentration of the products can be deduced from that of the reactants. Having obtained the concentration-time data for as many species as possible for a series of different initial concentrations, it is usually possible to represent the rates of disappearance of each species in terms of the concentrations of the reactants (and occasionally in terms of the

† Very often, the concentration of the intermediates cannot be measured.

concentrations of the products and intermediates). For example, a study of the benzoyl peroxide (ROOR) initiated polymerization of methyl methacrylate (M) carried out in this way would yield the two expressions:

$$\frac{-d[\text{ROOR}]}{dt} = k_0'[\text{ROOR}],$$

$$-\frac{d[\text{M}]}{dt} = k_0[\text{ROOR}]^{1/2}[\text{M}],$$

where k_0 and k_0' are numerical constants. The differential forms of the rate expressions indicate that these equations refer to a particular instant of time when the concentrations of the two reactants are [ROOR] and [M], the negative signs signifying that the two species are decreasing in concentration. We summarize these expressions by the term *order;* we say that the rate of disappearance of the initiator is first order with respect to the initiator (that is, directly proportional to the concentration of initiator) and zero order with respect to the monomer (that is, independent of the monomer concentration); likewise, the rate of the monomer disappearance is half-order with respect to the initiator, and first order with respect to the monomer. Note that these orders *cannot be deduced* from the stoichiometric equation—they must be determined experimentally.

To obtain the mechanism of the reaction, we make use of a number of theoretical ideas. The most important is the conception that a complex reaction such as polymerization is made up of a series of *elementary* reactions in which only *one, two* or *three* molecules take part. If we represent the possible elementary reactions symbolically as follows

Case 1   A → products

Case 2   A+B → products

Case 3   A+B+C → products

then all theories of reaction rates suggest that

$$\frac{-d[A]}{dt} = k_1[A] \qquad \text{for case 1}$$

$$\frac{-d[A]}{dt} = k_2[A][B] \qquad \text{for case 2}$$

$$\frac{-d[A]}{dt} = k_3[A][B][C] \quad \text{for case 3}$$

where k_1, k_2 and k_3 are constants termed the unimolecular, bimolecular and termolecular rate constants. We shall make extensive use of the first two results in this book. A possible mechanism for a reaction is the set of elementary reactions which when analysed kinetically according to the above rules produces the same expression for the rate of disappearance of the reactant as observed experimentally. In a particularly simple case, the decomposition of HI in the gas phase to $H_2 + I_2$, the experimental rate expression is

$$\frac{-d[HI]}{dt} = k[HI]^2$$

so that we need look no further for the mechanism than the single step

$$HI + HI \rightarrow H_2 + I_2$$

In the case of polymerization, a moment's reflection will make it quite clear that there is no possibility of its being so simple—the fact of our having a large number of monomer molecules reacting together to give a single polymer molecule automatically means that we must have a large number of elementary reactions involved. It is our intention in the chapters that follow to demonstrate that a large set of reactions can be devised and analysed kinetically—with appropriate approximations—to yield rate equations identical with the experimental. A note of caution, however, must be sounded; it does not follow that a particular reaction sequence *is* the correct mechanism simply because its kinetic consequences match the experimental observations—the agreement simply means that the mechanism is a possibility. Generally, other types of experiment have to be performed before any kinetically acceptable mechanism can be regarded as correct.

Before leaving this short introduction to chemical kinetics, we ought to explain in just a little more detail the basic reasons underlying the form of the rate expressions for unimolecular and bimolecular reactions (we shall not need to consider termolecular reactions in this book).

Taking unimolecular reactions first, we consider that, before a molecule can decompose, it must possess energy in excess of a certain amount. The concentration of these *activated* molecules $[A^*]$ determines the rate at which the product is formed— doubling the concentration of activated molecules doubles the rate of formation of product. These activated molecules are simply those which have gained a large amount of internal rotational and vibrational energy by a series of fortuitous collisions with other molecules. Decomposition occurs when a chance coupling of the internal motions concentrates more energy in the weakest bond than it can accommodate. At constant temperature, the proportion of activated molecules is a constant fraction of the total number of molecules of the type in question and so

the rate of product formation $\quad \infty \; [A^*]$
$$\infty \; [A]$$
$$= k_1[A].$$

In the case of bimolecular reactions the primary condition for reaction is that the two reactant molecules collide. Not all collisions, however, are fruitful since the molecules of the colliding pair must possess a certain critical energy between them and be correctly oriented before reaction can take place. Since, at constant temperature, the fraction of the total number of bimolecular collisions which meet these criteria is constant, the rate of formation of product is proportional to the number of collisions between reactant molecules in unit time. If we consider the reaction $A + B \rightarrow$ products, the total number of collisions which take place between A and B molecules in unit time z_{AB} is proportional to the number of ways of selecting AB pairs from a mixture of the two. Taking one litre of reaction mixture, this latter quantity is

$$N_0[A] \times N_0[B],$$

since any A molecule can be taken with any B, N_0 being the Avogadro number.

Thus $$z_{AB} \infty N_0^2[A][B]$$

and as the rate of product formation is proportional to z_{AB}, we obtain

rate of product formation ∞ [A][B]

$$= k_2[A][B].$$

Both proportionality constants or rate constants as we shall term them depend exponentially on temperature, thus

$$k = A \exp(-E/RT),$$

where A is called the pre-exponential factor and E is the activation energy. For the purposes of this book, these two quantities must be taken simply as characteristics of the reaction, the theories which have been put forward to account for the magnitudes of these quantities being outside the scope of this book.

UNITS

In Chapters 2, 3 and 4 which deal with well-established phenomena we have attempted to clarify our discussion by numerical data wherever possible. In general to avoid confusion, we have adopted the following conventions in dealing with quantities possessing units:

(1) no units are attached to symbols;

(2) all arithmetical quantities which possess units are written explicitly with the units;

(3) units where they appear in an expression are treated exactly as algebraical symbols.

Let us see how these rules work in an actual case. A convenient example is Poiseuille's expression for the volume rate of flow of a liquid through a tube (see Chapter 2 for the full details of the conditions under which this is applicable).

This equation is

$$v = \frac{\pi P r^4}{8 \eta l},$$

where v is the volume rate of flow, P is the pressure head maintaining the flow, r is the radius of the tube, η is the viscosity of the liquid, and l is the length of the tube.

In the first place, note that we do *not* say "where v is the volume rate of flow in ccs per second, and P is the pressure head maintaining the flow in dynes per sq. cm", etc. Now suppose we actually wish to calculate v given a set of numerical values for P, r, η and l; if

$$P = 10^4 \text{ dyne cm}^{-2},$$
$$r = 0 \cdot 02 \text{ cm},$$
$$\eta = 6 \times 10^{-3} \text{ poise},$$
$$l = 12 \text{ cm},$$

we write

$$v = \frac{\pi \times 10^4 \times (2 \times 10^{-2})^4}{8 \times 6 \times 10^{-3} \times 12} \frac{\text{dyne cm}^{-2} \text{ cm}^4}{\text{poise cm}}$$

$$= 8 \cdot 72 \times 10^{-3} \frac{\text{dyne cm}}{\text{poise}}.$$

Since   1 dyne $= 1$ g cm sec^{-2}
and   1 poise $= 1$ g cm^{-1} sec^{-1},

$$v = 8 \cdot 72 \times 10^{-3} \frac{\text{g cm sec}^{-2} \text{ cm}}{\text{g cm}^{-1} \text{ sec}^{-1}}$$

$$= 8 \cdot 72 \times 10^{-3} \text{ cm}^3 \text{ sec}^{-1}.$$

The units of the final answer result naturally from this derivation.

If we had wished to leave the equation in a form suitable for calculating the volume rate of flow through the same tube for a liquid of any viscosity under the same pressure head, we would write

$$v = \frac{\pi \times 10^4 \times (2 \times 10^{-2})^4}{8 \times \eta \times 12} \, \frac{\text{dyne cm}^{-2} \text{ cm}^4}{\text{cm}}$$

$$= \frac{5 \cdot 23 \times 10^{-5}}{\eta} \text{ g cm}^2 \text{ sec}^{-2}.$$

On substituting the numerical value of η *and* its units into this equation, we obtain the volume rate of flow in the usual units of cm^3 sec^{-1}.

In addition to these rules, we adopt the convention that any numerical quantity referring to a molecular property is *not* qualified by the symbol, molecule. For example, we write the Avogadro number as $6 \cdot 023 \times 10^{23}$ mole^{-1} and the root mean square end-to-end distance of a particular polymer molecule as 1000 Å rather than $6 \cdot 023 \times 10^{23}$ molecule mole^{-1} and 1000 Å molecule^{-1}. To achieve complete consistency, we write all molecular weights which appear in equations with the units g mole^{-1}. One final example will suffice; suppose we wish to calculate the weight of a molecule of a particular substance given its molecular weight M and the Avogadro number N_0. By definition, a weight M of the substance contains N_0 molecules and hence the weight of each molecule m is given by

$$m = \frac{M}{N_0}.$$

Given that $M = 100$ g mole^{-1}, we write

$$m = \frac{100}{N_0} \text{ g mole}^{-1}$$

$$= \frac{100}{6 \cdot 023 \times 10^{23}} \, \frac{\text{g mole}^{-1}}{\text{mole}^{-1}}$$

$$= 1 \cdot 66 \times 10^{-22} \text{ g}.$$

CHAPTER 2

DETERMINATION OF MOLECULAR WEIGHT

THE determination of the molecular weights of polymeric materials presents, in general, two problems not normally encountered with low molecular weight substances. The first problem arises because polymer samples usually contain molecules with a range of molecular weights. The second problem is encountered whenever the physical properties of polymer solutions are studied—the concentration dependence of these properties is usually so much more pronounced than in the case where low molecular weight solutes are used that the well-established methods for molecular weight determination cannot be employed without considerable modification.

We shall discuss first the problems raised by the presence of a distribution of molecular weights in a polymer sample.

MOLECULAR WEIGHT DISTRIBUTION

The majority of samples of synthetic polymers contain molecules with a wide range of molecular weights. As a result, any measurement of molecular weight on such a sample necessarily yields an average value. It so happens that not all the practical methods which are used involve the same averaging procedure and consequently two measurements of the molecular weight of the same polymer may give quite different results.

To illustrate the two types of average which are commonly measured, let us consider a numerical example. We shall suppose that in a particular sample the number of polymer molecules which contain i mers depends on the value of i according to the simple equation

$$N_i = N(1-p)p^{i-1}. \qquad (2.1)$$

In this equation, N_i is the number in question, N the total number of molecules present, and p a quantity less than 1 whose physical significance will become clearer later on. It is sufficient at this stage to appreciate that this equation does represent the distribution of chain lengths in certain practical cases.

We shall now use this equation to calculate (a) the number and (b) the weight of polymer molecules containing 1, 2, 3, etc., mers (note that the number of monomer molecules is automatically calculated by putting $i = 1$); for this purpose, we shall take the molecular weight of the monomer and the mer to be identical and equal to 100. The weight of each mer is, therefore,

$$\frac{100}{N_0} \text{ g mole}^{-1},$$

where N_0 is the Avogadro number, $6 \cdot 023 \times 10^{23}$ mole^{-1}. Hence the weight of each mer is

$$\frac{100}{6 \cdot 023 \times 10^{23}} \frac{\text{g mole}^{-1}}{\text{mole}^{-1}} = 1 \cdot 66 \times 10^{-22} \text{ g.}$$

We must of course decide on the number of molecules in the sample and the value of p in eqn. (2.1). It will be arithmetically convenient and at the same time realistic if we consider that our sample contains 10^{21} molecules and that p is $0 \cdot 90$. Substituting these values in eqn. (2.1) enables the quantities shown in Table 2.1 to be calculated, the symbol M_i standing for the molecular weight of the i-mer.

Note that we have only accounted for 880×10^{18} molecules out of the 10^{21} which we took in our example so that there are

TABLE 2.1

NUMBER DISTRIBUTION OF MOLECULAR WEIGHT

i	M_i	$N_i \times 10^{-18}$	i	M_i	$N_i \times 10^{-18}$
1	100	100	11	1100	35
2	200	90	12	1200	31
3	300	81	13	1300	2
4	400	73	14	1400	25
5	500	66	15	1500	23
6	600	59	16	1600	21
7	700	53	17	1700	19
8	800	48	18	1800	17
9	900	43	19	1900	15
10	1000	39	20	2000	14

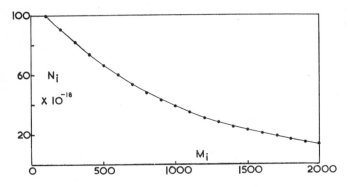

FIG. 2.1. A typical number distribution of molecular weight

120×10^{18} molecules containing more than 20 monomer units. A graph of this number distribution is shown in Fig. 2.1.

We can now calculate the weight of each species in the sample. For example, we have 81×10^{18} molecules each containing 3 monomer units in the chain. Since each monomer unit weighs $1 \cdot 66 \times 10^{-22}$ g, the total weight of the 300 molecular weight material in the sample is

$$81 \times 10^{18} \times 3 \times 1 \cdot 66 \times 10^{-22} \text{ g} = 0 \cdot 0403 \text{ g}.$$

A similar calculation for each of the other polymeric species produces the values w_i shown in Table 2.2, w_i being the *total* weight of the ith species.

TABLE 2.2. WEIGHT DISTRIBUTION OF MOLECULAR WEIGHT

i	M_i	w_i g	i	M_i	w_i g
1	100	0·0166	11	1100	0·0636
2	200	0·0299	12	1200	0·0624
3	300	0·0403	13	1300	0·0609
4	400	0·0485	14	1400	0·0591
5	500	0·0544	15	1500	0·0571
6	600	0·0588	16	1600	0·0548
7	700	0·0618	17	1700	0·0523
8	800	0·0634	18	1800	0·0500
9	900	0·0642	19	1900	0·0473
10	1000	0·0642	20	2000	0·0448

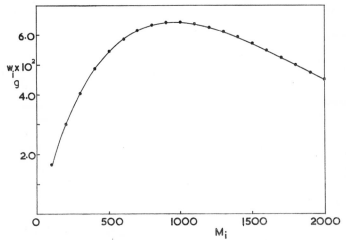

FIG. 2.2. A typical weight distribution of molecular weight

The weight distribution curve is shown in Fig. 2.2. Starting at the low molecular weight end of the distribution and moving towards the higher molecular weights, the weight of each species increases proportionately more than the number decreases and hence the total weight of each rises with increasing molecular weight. After a certain molecular weight is reached, the increasing weight of the molecules is not sufficient to counterbalance their decreasing number and so the total weights of the various species decrease continuously as the molecular weights increase.

Now the total number of monomer units whether as monomer or polymer segments is

$$
\begin{aligned}
1 \times 100 + 2 &\times 90 + 3 \times 81 + \ldots \\
&= \sum i N_i \\
&= N(1-p)(1+2p+3p^2+\ldots) \\
&= \frac{N}{1-p} \\
&= 10^{22}
\end{aligned}
$$

and consequently our sample size must be 1·66 g. Thus from Table 2.2, it can be seen that 0·61 g of this sample consists of polymeric molecules with molecular weights greater than 2000.

So far we have concentrated our attention on the number and total weight of each polymeric species in a given sample characterized by the particular distribution equation (2.1). Each of these quantities can be used to average the molecular weight. If we decide to average the molecular weight according to the number of molecules of each type, we obtain the *number average molecular weight* $\overline{M}_n$. This is defined in such a way that the total number of polymeric molecules of all types multiplied by $\overline{M}_n$ gives the sum of the products of M_i and N_i; i.e.

$$N\overline{M}_n = \sum N_i M_i$$

or
$$\overline{M}_n = \frac{\sum N_i M_i}{N} = \frac{\sum N_i M_i}{\sum N_i}. \tag{2.2}$$

In our particular example, $\overline{M}_n$ could be calculated by the laborious operation implied by the summation sign:

$$\overline{M}_n = \frac{100 \times 100 + 90 \times 200 + 81 \times 300 + \ldots}{100 + 90 + 81 + \ldots}$$

or more directly by the algebraical operations below:

$$\overline{M}_n = \frac{\sum N_i M_i}{N} = \frac{\sum N(1-p)p^{i-1}iM_1}{N},$$

where M_1 is the molecular weight of the monomer and the mer.

Therefore
$$\overline{M}_n = M_1(1-p)(1+2p+3p^2+\ldots)$$
$$= \frac{M_1}{1-p}$$
$$= 1000 \quad \text{(since } p = 0\cdot90 \text{ and } M_1 = 100\text{)}.$$

On the other hand if we decide to average the molecular weight according to the weight of molecules of each type, we obtain the *weight average molecular weight* $\overline{M}_w$. This is defined in an analogous way to the number average molecular weight such that the total weight of the polymeric molecules of all types W multiplied by $\overline{M}_w$ gives the sum of the products of M_i and w_i; i.e.

$$W\overline{M}_w = \sum w_i M_i$$

or
$$\overline{M}_w = \frac{\sum w_i M_i}{W} = \frac{\sum w_i M_i}{\sum w_i}. \tag{2.3}$$

Thus using our previous calculations on our $1\cdot66$ g of polymer the arithmetical method of calculating $\overline{M}_w$ is simply that implied by the equation, i.e.

$$\overline{M}_w = \frac{0\cdot0166 \times 100 + 0\cdot0299 \times 200 + 0\cdot0403 \times 300 + \ldots}{0\cdot0166 + 0\cdot0299 + 0\cdot0403 + \ldots}.$$

Since we know the number of molecules of each type in the sample from eqn. (2.1), it is an easy matter to substitute for w_i in terms of i and hence perform the above summation algebraically. From the definition of the Avogadro number N_0, we know that N_0 molecules of the ith type weigh M_i and hence in our sample where we have N_i molecules of this type, their total weight w_i is given by

$$w_i = \frac{N_i M_i}{N_0}.$$

Hence the quantity $\bar{M}_w$ becomes

$$\frac{\sum (N_i M_i/N_0) M_i}{\sum (N_i M_i/N_0)} = \frac{\sum N_i M_i^2}{\sum N_i M_i}$$

$$= \frac{\sum N(1-p)p^{i-1} \cdot (iM_1)^2}{\sum N(1-p)p^{i-1} \cdot iM_1},$$

where, as before, M_1 is the molecular weight of the monomer and the mer.

Therefore

$$\bar{M}_w = M_1 \cdot \frac{\sum i^2 p^{i-1}}{\sum i p^{i-1}}$$

$$= M_1 \cdot \frac{(1+4p+9p^2+16p^3+\ldots)}{(1+2p+3p^2+4p^3+\ldots)}$$

$$= \frac{1+p}{(1-p)^3} \cdot (1-p)^2 \cdot M_1$$

$$= \frac{1+p}{1-p} \cdot M_1$$

$$= 1900 \text{ (in our example)}$$

cf. $$\bar{M}_n = 1000.$$

The most important thing to notice is the large difference between the two types of average. In fact, for this distribution, the ratio of $\bar{M}_w/\bar{M}_n$ approaches *two* as the parameter p approaches one so that a molecular weight measurement which depends on a weight averaging procedure gives nearly *twice* the value of a measurement based on a number averaging procedure. Consequently, in stating the molecular weight of a polymer, the type of average must also be given.

Of course, it is possible in principle to obtain a polymer in which all the molecules are of the same molecular weight; such polymers are termed *monodisperse*. The summations which define the two averages $\overline{M}_n$ and $\overline{M}_w$ then become

$$\overline{M}_n = \frac{N_k M_k}{N_k} = M_k$$

and
$$\overline{M}_w = \frac{N_k M_k^2}{N_k M_k} = M_k,$$

N_k and M_k being the number and molecular weight of the particular type k making up the polymer sample. In this special case, therefore, the two averages become identical as would be expected and so the ratio $\overline{M}_w/\overline{M}_n$ becomes unity. The value of the parameter $\overline{M}_w/\overline{M}_n$ in a practical case thus gives a measure of the range of molecular weights in the sample: a value close to unity indicates that the molecular weights of the majority of the polymer molecules are closely similar whereas a value of two or greater indicates considerable *polydispersity;* that is, the weights of the various molecular weight species are of the same order. Hence in characterizing a polymer, not only is a measurement of molecular weight desirable but also some indication of the molecular weight distribution. This latter object may be achieved by measuring more than one of the molecular weight averages or by deliberately separating the sample into a series of fractions each containing a narrow band of molecular weights. The weights and molecular weights of these fractions are then measured, giving the weight distribution curve directly.

FRACTIONATION

The separation of a polymer into fractions of different molecular weights is a laborious and difficult process. Most of the methods commonly used depend on the fact that, as the molecular weight of a polymer increases, its solubility in a particular solvent decreases. Two rather different types of procedure are employed.

In the first method of *precipitation fractionation*, the polymer sample is dissolved in some suitable solvent to give a solution containing about 1% by weight of polymer. To this dilute solution, a non-solvent is added dropwise with vigorous stirring at constant temperature to cause the separation of the mixture into two liquids called the precipitated and supernatant phases. The precipitated phase consists mainly of solvent, some non-solvent, and no more than 10–20% of the original polymer if the precipitation conditions have been chosen correctly; the volume of this phase is considerably smaller than that of the supernatant phase and hence the polymer concentration greater. Each polymer species is distributed between the two phases but the distribution is such that the precipitated phase contains a greater proportion of the high molecular weight material. The temperature of the system is then raised until the two-phase system becomes one; on allowing the temperature to fall slowly to its original value, a polymer-rich phase again separates. The object of this refinement is simply to ensure that precipitation occurs at a slow rate without the complications caused by local excesses of precipitant which are bound to occur on dropwise addition. After decanting off the supernatant phase, the first fraction of polymer is recovered from the precipitated phase, weighed, and its molecular weight measured by one of the methods to be described. Further polymer fractions of decreasing molecular weight are similarly obtained by further additions of precipitant to the supernatant phase.

In the second method of fractionation called *elution fractionation*, the lowest molecular weight material is extracted into solution from the solid polymer. To ensure that true equilibration takes place between the solvent and the solid phase, the polymer is precipitated on to an inert support of high specific surface area, usually glass beads of 0·1–0·3 mm diameter. In this way, there results a thin skin of polymer on each bead— for example, the reader might check that 10 g of polymer uniformly coated on 1 kg of glass beads of diameter 0·1 mm forms a layer 4000 Å thick if the densities of the polymer and glass are 1·00 g cm^{-3} and 2·40 g cm^{-3} respectively. The coated beads are normally packed into a column and a solvent–precipitant mixture, whose composition is adjusted so that only the lowest molecular weight polymers dissolve, slowly dripped through. If the rate of flow is sufficiently low and the thickness of the polymer layer small enough, equilibration between the solid and liquid phases is reached quickly and consequently the effluent from the bottom of the column contains the particular molecular weights appropriate to the chosen solvent–precipitant mixture. Clearly, this fraction can be obtained by evaporation of the solvent–precipitant mixture, weighed and its molecular weight measured. Other fractions can then be obtained by increasing the proportion of solvent in the solvent–precipitant mixture, so extracting higher molecular weights. In practice, the procedure is considerably simplified over that described above by making the solvent–precipitant composition continuously variable and the collection of the various fractions automatic. The schematic diagram of Fig. 2.3 illustrates these arrangements.

Finally in this section, mention must be made of a third method of fractionation which is essentially a combination of the precipitation and extraction methods. A temperature gradient is arranged along the length of the column and the coated beads confined to a layer at the top and hottest part of the column. As a result, the initial fractionation due to extraction is improved by the precipitation of the high molecular weight "tails" at lower and cooler parts of the column. It would be expected that this method would give the best results combining as it does the two basic techniques of fractionation while retaining the great practical advantages of automation and continuous operation. Unfortunately, however, few direct comparisons of the three methods have been undertaken because of the tremendous expenditure of time required and consequently the choice of method in a particular instance is largely conditioned by personal considerations.

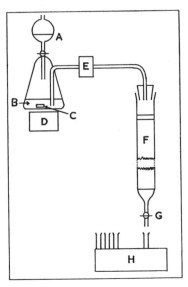

FIG. 2.3. A schematic diagram of an apparatus suitable for elution fractionation; A, solvent; B, solvent–precipitant mixture; C, magnetic stirrer; D, rotating magnet; E, metering pump for controlled delivery to column; F, glass beads coated with polymer; G, tap to equalize inflow and outflow thus maintaining a constant head of liquid; H, fraction collector

Before concluding this section, we must emphasize that the molecular weight fractions obtained by these methods are in no sense monodisperse. They contain a distribution of molecular weights just as the original polymer, the difference being that the distribution is rather narrower; for most fractions, a typical value of the ratio $\overline{M}_w/\overline{M}_n$ is about 1·2.

MEASUREMENT OF THE NUMBER
AVERAGE MOLECULAR WEIGHT

Let us suppose that we have a weight of polymer W containing exactly the Avogadro number of molecules N_0, in which there are N_1 molecules of molecular weight M_1, N_2 molecules of molecular weight M_2, and so on. Then the total weight W is given by

$$W = \frac{N_1 M_1}{N_0} + \frac{N_2 M_2}{N_0} + \cdots$$

or $\qquad N_0 W = \sum N_i M_i,$

and clearly W, the weight containing the Avogadro number of molecules, is identical with the number average molecular weight. Consequently, in order to evaluate this latter quantity, it is only necessary to count the total number of molecules in a known weight of polymer whence the number average molecular weight follows by simple proportion. Thus, if we were to find that $6 \cdot 023 \times 10^{18}$ molecules were present in 1 g of polymer, the Avogadro number of molecules would be present in 100,000 g of polymer and hence, as we have explained, the number average molecular weight is 100,000.

End-group analysis

This method of counting the number of polymer molecules present in a known weight of polymer is available when the polymer molecules possess a known number of detectable end groups per molecule. These end groups are estimated by standard physical or chemical methods and hence the number of polymer molecules calculated directly.

For example, suppose we take 1 g of a polystyrene sample in which each molecule possesses one COOH group. This is dissolved in sufficient methanol–methyl ethyl ketone to give a homogeneous solution and titrated against methanolic potassium hydroxide of known concentration to the phenolphthalein end point. If 12 cm^3 of 0·01 M KOH were required for neutralization, the number average molecular weight is calculated as follows:

Number of moles KOH added $= \dfrac{12}{1000} \times 0.01.$

Therefore number of moles COOH groups present $= \dfrac{12}{1000} \times 0.01.$

Therefore number of moles polymer present $= \dfrac{12}{1000} \times 0.01.$

Hence $\dfrac{12}{1000} \times 0.01$ moles are present in 1 g polymer.

Therefore 1 mole is present in $\dfrac{1000 \times 1}{12 \times 0.01}$ g polymer $= 8333$ g.

The molecular weight of the polymer is thus 8300 expressed to the correct order of precision. It should be noted that we have slightly simplified the calculation by working in terms of moles, one mole, of course, being the weight of material containing the Avogadro number of molecules.

If we examine this calculation, it can be seen that the method becomes rather inaccurate with molecular weights an order of magnitude greater if reasonable amounts of polymer are to be handled. It is not a limitation peculiar to COOH groups or acid-base titrations—the difficulty arises simply because 1 g of a polymer of molecular weight 100,000 is only 10^{-5} moles and this means that the analytical methods employed must be capable of detecting at least 10^{-6} moles of end groups for 10% accuracy in the final molecular weight. In fact with the standard analytical procedures available, this requirement cannot usually be met and so there is an upper limit of around 20,000 in the number average molecular weight which can be measured by end-group analysis. Only by using radio-chemical labelling techniques can the end-group detection be pushed to lower limits but a discussion of these procedures is out of place in this book.

METHODS BASED ON COLLIGATIVE PROPERTIES OF SOLUTIONS

The physical properties of a solution are, in general, different from those of the pure solvent, the difference being a function of the concentration of the solute. It is usually possible to represent the concentration dependence of a particular physical property Q by a power series in the concentration of the solute; the most convenient concentration unit for many purposes is the number of molecules of solute present in unit volume of the solution, a quantity which we shall represent by the symbol N. In terms of this unit,

$$Q = Q_0 + K_1 N + K_2 N^2 + K_3 N^3 + \ldots \quad (2.4)$$

Q_0 being the corresponding physical property of the pure solvent and K_1, K_2 and K_3 being constants. This type of expression is called a *virial equation* and the constants K_1, K_2, K_3, etc., the *virial coefficients* in the Q, N expansion.

Of particular importance in molecular weight determination are those properties for which K_1 is independent of the chemical nature of the solute and calculable from other data. Examples of these properties are:

1. the partial pressure of the solvent vapour in equilibrium with the solution;
2. the freezing point of the solution;
3. the boiling point of the solution;
4. the pressure on the solution in osmotic equilibrium with the pure solvent.

In all these properties, the solvent in the solution is in equilibrium with pure solvent either across a membrane or in another phase. If we rewrite eqn. (2.4) so that the difference between the property of the solution and that of the pure solvent appears on the left-hand side, we obtain the following expressions for the four colligative properties, Δp_1, ΔT_f, ΔT_b and π.

$$\left.\begin{aligned}
\Delta p_1 &= \frac{p_1^0 V_1^0}{N_0} \cdot N + K_2' N^2 + K_3' N^3 + \dots \\[2mm]
\Delta T_f &= \frac{RT_f^2 V_1^0}{L_f N_0} \cdot N + K_2'' N^2 + K_3'' N^3 + \dots \\[2mm]
\Delta T_b &= \frac{RT_b^2 V_1^0}{L_v N_0} \cdot N + K_2''' N^2 + K_3''' N^3 + \dots \\[2mm]
\pi &= \frac{RT}{N_0} \cdot N + K_2'''' N^2 + K_3'''' N^3 + \dots
\end{aligned}\right\} \quad (2.5)$$

In each case, the appropriate value of K_1 has been written out explicitly, the symbols having the following meanings:

V_1^0 is the molar volume of the solvent at the various temperatures at which the values Δp_1, ΔT_f, and ΔT_b are measured;

N_0 is the Avogadro number;

Δp_1 is the difference between the partial pressure of the solvent vapour above the solution and the vapour pressure of the pure solvent p_1^0 at the same temperature;

ΔT_f is the difference between the freezing point of the solution and that of the pure solvent T_f, whose latent heat of fusion is L_f;

ΔT_b is the difference between the boiling point of the solution and that of the pure solvent T_b, whose latent heat of vaporization is L_v;

π is the osmotic pressure of the solution at a temperature T.

For low molecular weight solutes, it is usually possible to make the terms in N^2, N^3, etc., quite negligible in comparison with the first by

1. working in dilute solution, usually less than 5 per cent by weight;

2. choosing a solvent whose molecules are not dissimilar in size from the solute molecules and which has no tendency to form loose compounds with the solute.

Under such conditions, the various quantities Δp_1, ΔT_f, ΔT_b, and π become directly proportional to the number of solute molecules per unit volume of solution N—in these circumstances, the solutions are described as "ideal". Consequently, a determination of any one of these four quantities for a given solution enables N to be calculated since the proportionality constants are known in each case; if the weight concentration of the same solution is also known, the molecular weight M follows at once from the equation

$$N = \frac{N_0 c}{M}.$$

In this and all subsequent expressions in this chapter, c stands for the weight concentration of the solute, that is, the weight of solute per unit volume of solution.

On the other hand, for high molecular weight solutes, conditions cannot usually be arranged so as to enable the terms in N^2, N^3, etc., to be neglected without at the same time making the four quantities so small as to be immeasurable. The best that can be done is to make the third and subsequent terms so small as to be unimportant. This is achieved by (1) working at low weight concentrations of polymer, usually less than 1% by weight—at the outside, less than 5%; and where possible, (2) choosing a suitable solvent and temperature (this latter choice is not available, of course, if ΔT_f or ΔT_b is to be measured).

Under such conditions, our difference property ΔQ, i.e. $Q - Q_0$, is related to the solute concentration by the equation

$$\Delta Q = K_1 N + K_2 N^2. \tag{2.6}$$

Although, as we have said, K_1 is known, K_2 is not, and so there is no question of our calculating N for a particular solution by measuring ΔQ and solving the quadratic. Instead we substitute for N in the expression in terms of c using the following argument. Consider unit volume of the solution; in this volume, we have N solute molecules with a range of molecular weights $M_1, M_2, \ldots, M_i, \ldots$, etc., of total weight c. By definition

$$N\overline{M}_n = \sum N_i M_i$$

while

$$c = \frac{\sum N_i M_i}{N_0},$$

N_i representing the number of molecules of the ith type present in unit volume. From these two expressions

$$N = \frac{N_0 c}{\overline{M}_n}, \tag{2.7}$$

which is exactly analogous to the previous equation which applied to simple solutes. From eqns. (2.6) and (2.7), we obtain

$$\Delta Q = \frac{K_1 N_0}{\overline{M}_n} c + K_2 \left(\frac{N_0}{\overline{M}_n}\right)^2 c^2. \tag{2.8}$$

Therefore

$$\frac{\Delta Q}{c} = \frac{K_1 N_0}{\overline{M}_n} + K_2 \left(\frac{N_0}{\overline{M}_n}\right)^2 c. \tag{2.9}$$

This equation is the basis of the method used to measure $\overline{M}_n$. The procedure is as follows. We prepare a series of polymer solutions of different concentrations not exceeding, say 2×10^{-2} g cm^{-3}. We measure the quantity ΔQ for each solution and then plot $\Delta Q/c$ against c to obtain a graph of the general form shown in Fig. 2.4.

The graph is curved tending towards linearity at low values of c where the neglect of the higher terms of the expansion becomes increasingly justifiable. From eqn. (2.9), the intercept of the linear portion on the $\Delta Q/c$ axis at $c = 0$ is

$$\frac{K_1 N_0}{\bar{M}_n}.$$

Since K_1 is known, $\bar{M}_n$ follows directly.

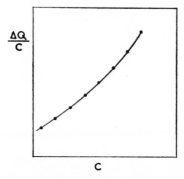

FIG. 2.4. The general concentration dependence of $\Delta Q/c$.

In Table 2.3 we have calculated the magnitudes of the first terms in the equations generalized by eqn. (2.8) for the four colligative properties previously considered for two solutions of polymer in benzene. These "ideal" contributions as they might be called, are:

$$(\Delta p_1)_{\text{ideal}} = \frac{p_1^0 V_1^0}{\bar{M}_n} c,$$

$$(\Delta T_f)_{\text{ideal}} = \frac{RT_f^2 V_1^0}{L_f \bar{M}_n} c,$$

$$(\Delta T_b)_{\text{ideal}} = \frac{RT_b^2 V_1^0}{L_v \bar{M}_n} c,$$

$$(\pi)_{\text{ideal}} = \frac{RT}{\bar{M}_n} c.$$

In calculating the results shown in Table 2.3, we have used the following numerical data:

$$p_1^0 = 99 \cdot 5 \text{ mm Hg at } 25°C.$$

$$V_1^0 = 89 \cdot 4 \text{ cm}^3 \text{ mole}^{-1} \text{ at } 25°C.$$

$$\frac{RT_f^2}{L_f} = 65 \cdot 2°K \text{ at } 1 \text{ atmos.}$$

$$\frac{RT_b^2}{L_v} = 34 \cdot 6°K \text{ at } 1 \text{ atmos.}$$

$$RT = 2 \cdot 48 \times 10^{10} \text{ erg mole}^{-1} \text{ at } 25°C.$$

TABLE 2.3. CONTRIBUTION OF THE FIRST TERMS OF EQNS.
(2.5) TO THE VARIOUS QUANTITIES Δp_1, ΔT_f, ΔT_b and π

ΔQ	$\bar{M}_n = 10,000$ $c = 2 \times 10^{-2} \text{ g cm}^{-3}$	$\bar{M}_n = 1,000,000$ $c = 2 \times 10^{-2} \text{ g cm}^{-3}$
Lowering of vapour pressure at 25°C	0·0178 mm Hg	0·000178 mm Hg
Depression of freezing point at 1 atmos	0·0116°K	0·000116°K
Elevation of boiling point at 1 atmos	0·0062°K	0·000062°K
Osmotic pressure at 25°C	$4 \cdot 96 \times 10^4$ dyne cm^{-2}	$4 \cdot 96 \times 10^2$ dyne cm^{-2}

In these calculations, no account has been taken of the variation of V_1^0 with temperature since this is a small effect.

Of course, the actual values of these quantities will be rather greater than those listed because of the contributions of the higher terms of eqns. (2.5). Nevertheless the order of magnitude of the various quantities is at the most only one greater in a practical case than that calculated by considering the first term only. Consequently, 10,000 represents an approximate upper limit of the molecular weight which may be determined using the first three properties. On the other hand the measurement of an osmotic pressure of 5×10^2 dyne cm^{-2} is quite practicable since it corresponds to a hydrostatic head of just under 6 mm benzene—a quantity easily determined. Hence molecular weights of the order of 1,000,000 may be determined experimentally using the osmotic method. With suitable semi-permeable membranes, the osmotic pressure method may be used for the determination of number average molecular weights as low as 5,000 and hence it is of wide applicability. For this reason, we shall not consider the other methods any further.

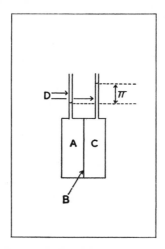

FIG. 2.5. A schematic diagram of an osmometer; A, solvent; B, a membrane permeable to solvent but not to polymer; C, polymer solution; D, measuring capillaries; π, the osmotic pressure

In Table 2.4 we give an example of some actual experimental data obtained at 25°C for a sample of polystyrene dissolved in toluene. The actual measurements were made using an apparatus illustrated schematically in Fig. 2.5. The solvent, toluene in this case, passes from the solvent compartment into the solution until a hydrostatic head is set up just sufficient to prevent any further solvent flow—this pressure being termed the osmotic pressure. It is measured in the first place as a height difference h and then converted into an actual pressure by the usual formula $h \varrho g$, where ϱ is the solution density and g is the acceleration due to gravity—in practice the density of the solution can be replaced by the density of the pure solvent without serious error.

TABLE 2.4. OSMOTIC PRESSURES OF A SERIES OF POLYSTYRENE SOLUTIONS IN TOLUENE AT 25°C[1]

$$\varrho_{toluene} = 0 \cdot 8618 \text{ g cm}^{-3}$$
$$g = 981 \text{ cm sec}^{-2}$$

c g cm$^{-3} \times 10^3$	2·56	3·80	5·38	7·80	8·68
π cm toluene	0·325	0·545	0·893	1·578	1·856
π dyne cm$^{-2} \times 10^{-3}$	0·275	0·461	0·755	1·334	1·569
π/c cm^2 sec$^{-2} \times 10^{-5}$	1·07	1·21	1·40	1·71	1·81

For convenience, we shall write eqns. (2.8) and (2.9) in a form appropriate for osmotic pressure work by replacing K_1 by RT/N_0 and $K_2(N_0/\bar{M}_n)^2$ by B.

Thus
$$\pi = \frac{RT}{\bar{M}_n} \cdot c + Bc^2 \qquad (2.10)$$

and
$$\frac{\pi}{c} = \frac{RT}{\bar{M}_n} + Bc. \qquad (2.11)$$

Hence the limiting value of π/c at $c = 0$ is

$$\frac{RT}{\bar{M}_n}.$$

In Fig. 2.6 π/c is plotted against c from which it can be seen

dyne = g cm sec^{-2}.

that

$$\left(\frac{\pi}{c}\right)_{c=0} = 0{\cdot}77 \times 10^5 \text{ cm}^2 \text{ sec}^{-2}.$$

Therefore
$$\overline{M}_n = \frac{RT}{0{\cdot}77 \times 10^5 \text{ cm}^2 \text{ sec}^{-2}}$$

$$= \frac{8{\cdot}314 \times 10^7 \times 298{\cdot}2}{0{\cdot}77 \times 10^5} \; \frac{\text{erg mole}^{-1} \; {}^{\circ}\text{K}^{-1} \; {}^{\circ}\text{K}}{\text{cm}^2 \text{ sec}^{-2}}$$

$$= 3{\cdot}22 \times 10^5 \text{ g mole}^{-1}.$$

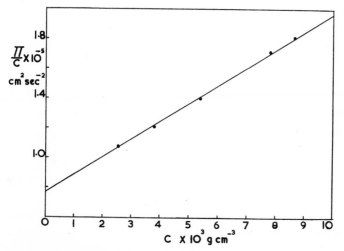

FIG. 2.6. A graph of π/c against c for a sample of polystyrene in toluene at 25°C

In other words the number average molecular weight of this particular polystyrene is 322,000. The value of the second virial coefficient B in the expansion of π/c against c (note the terminology) is derived directly from the slope of the line. In this case

$$B = 1{\cdot}20 \times 10^7 \text{ cm}^5 \text{ sec}^{-2} \text{ g}^{-1}$$

from which the separate contributions of the two terms of eqn. (2.10) to the osmotic pressure can be calculated at any concentration. Taking the highest concentration of Table 2.4 as an example, the results of this calculation are as follows:

Contribution of 1st term to $\pi = 668$ dyne cm^{-2}
(0·790 cm toluene).
Contribution of 2nd term to $\pi = 901$ dyne cm^{-2}
(1·066 cm toluene).

Note that, at this concentration (about 1 %), the term describing the deviation from ideality accounts for over half the value of the observed property even though by ordinary standards the solution is extremely dilute; in fact only three in every million molecules are polymer.

We ought to point out that we have somewhat oversimplified the treatment of osmotic pressure data by choosing to neglect the terms in N^3 and beyond in the virial expansion (2.5). In practice this is not always possible and, therefore, a procedure has to be devised to make allowance for their contribution to the measured property. How this is done is outside the scope of this book; it is sufficient to say that, provided low concentrations are used, the procedure described here gives substantially correct values for the molecular weights of polymers. That this procedure is not completely valid is obvious if the reader remembers that the ratio of the osmotic pressure to concentration is strictly a power series in concentration in which the number of terms which need be considered is determined by the value of the concentration. The power series or virial expansion is written in three forms

$$
\left.
\begin{aligned}
\frac{\pi}{c} &= \frac{RT}{\overline{M}_n} + Bc + Cc^2 + \ldots \\[2mm]
\frac{\pi}{c} &= RT\left(\frac{1}{\overline{M}_n} + A_2 c + A_3 c^2 + \ldots\right) \\[2mm]
\frac{\pi}{c} &= \left(\frac{\pi}{c}\right)_{c=0} \{1 + \Gamma_2 c + \Gamma_3 c^2 + \ldots\}
\end{aligned}
\right\}
\qquad (2.12)
$$

of which eqn. (2.11) is a special case. It will be obvious that the numerical values and dimensions of the various coefficients differ from one equation to the next.

Summarizing the position now reached, it should be clear that the number average molecular weights of most soluble polymers can be obtained from osmotic pressure measurements if the data is processed in the manner described to correct for the non-ideal behaviour of the solutions. Furthermore some idea of the deviations from ideality in these dilute solutions can be obtained by evaluation of the second virial coefficients. This latter quantity depends on a large number of factors:

1. the particular polymer–solvent system;

2. the molecular weight and molecular weight distribution of the polymer;

3. the temperature;

4. the tacticity of the chain (see Chapter 4).

Most of these points are illustrated in Table 2.5.

TABLE 2.5

1. Dependence of second virial coefficient on the polymer–solvent system: data for polymethyl methacrylate ($\bar{M}_n = 1 \cdot 28 \times 10^5$) at 27°C[2]

Solvent	$B \times 10^{-7}$ cm^5 sec^{-2} g^{-1}
Chloroform	1·41
Toluene	0·82
Acetone	0·57
Diethyl ketone	0·24
m-Xylene	0·02

Table 2.5 (contd.)

2. Dependence of second virial coefficient on the molecular weight: data for poly α-methyl styrene in toluene at 30°C[3]

$\overline{M}_w$	$B \times 10^{-7}$ cm^5 sec^{-2} g^{-1}
20,600	1·35
39,500	1·19
80,500	1·14
130,000	0·99
350,000	0·77

3. Dependence of second virial coefficient on temperature:[4]
   (a) data for polystyrene ($\overline{M}_w = 1,610,000$) in cyclohexane (a "poor" solvent)

Temperature °C	$B \times 10^{-7}$ cm^5 sec^{-2} g^{-1}
27·0	—0·092
31·0	—0·026
35·0	0
39·0	+0·016
41·5	+0·068

   (b) data for polystyrene ($\overline{M}_w = 1,610,000$) in toluene (a "good" solvent)

Temperature °C	$B \times 10^{-7}$ cm^5 sec^{-2} g^{-1}
22·0	0·77
67·0	0·70

Table 2.5 (contd.)

4. Dependence of second virial coefficient on the tacticity of the chain: data for polystyrene ($\overline{M}_n = 100{,}000$) in toluene at 30°C[5]

Configuration	$B \times 10^{-7}$ $cm^5 \, sec^{-2} \, g^{-1}$
Predominantly isotactic	1·18
Predominantly atactic	0·99

The fact that this coefficient depends on so many variables explains why it has not been possible to predict its value from fundamental molecular parameters.

However, we should not leave this section without drawing attention to the very similar behaviour of real gases. The significant parameters in studying such systems are the pressure, volume, temperature and number of moles. As in the case of polymer solutions, it is possible to represent the experimental data by a virial expansion:

$$PV = nRT + \frac{n^2\beta'}{V} + \frac{n^3\gamma'}{V^2} + \dots$$

which rearranges to

$$\frac{P}{c} = \frac{RT}{M} + \beta c + \gamma c^2 + \dots$$

where c represents the weight concentration (which in the case of a single gas is the same thing as the gas density). The marked similarity of this equation to eqn. (2.12) is obvious. Attention should be drawn to the temperature dependence of the second virial coefficient β. At high temperatures β is positive but decreases as the temperature is lowered to become zero at one particular temperature known as the Boyle temperature.

Below the Boyle temperature, the value of β becomes increasingly negative as the temperature is lowered until aggregation of the molecules sets in and liquefaction of the gas results.

This behaviour is exactly paralleled by the second virial coefficient of the polymer–solvent system. At high temperatures B is positive, decreases to zero as the temperature is reduced to a particular temperature known as the Theta temperature[†] and finally becomes negative as the temperature is lowered further. At temperatures lower than the Theta temperature, aggregation of the polymer molecules sets in with precipitation of the polymer. At the Theta temperature, the polymer solution behaves ideally over a range of concentration just as at the Boyle temperature a gas is ideal over a range of pressure.[‡]

The dependence of the second virial coefficient on temperature and solvent in the case of polymer solutions is intimately connected with the variation of the average dimensions of the polymer molecules with these factors. The polymer chains assume a configuration in solution such that the attractive and repulsive forces on each segment due to other segments and solvent molecules are exactly counterbalanced. When the combined effect of these forces causes the polymer to take up the same configuration as that calculated assuming free rotation about the bonds between segments and no segment–segment interaction—the *unperturbed configuration* as it is called—the solvent in the solution behaves ideally and the osmotic pressure is given by

$$\pi = \frac{RT}{\overline{M}_n} \cdot c.$$

[†] Since the second virial coefficient is a function of the molecular weight, the Theta temperature as defined here will be molecular weight dependent.

[‡] For this reason, it is clearly advantageous to work close to the Theta temperature of a particular polymer–solvent system in the determination of molecular weight.

This is the situation at the Theta temperature. At temperatures considerably above the Theta temperature, the polymer molecules in solution are expanded compared to the unperturbed configuration and the second virial coefficient is large and positive. When this occurs, the solvent is described as a "good" solvent. A "poor" solvent, on the other hand, is one in which the polymer dimensions approach those of the unperturbed configuration so that the second virial coefficient is close to zero.

In Table 2.6 we give a few values of Theta temperatures for various polymer–solvent systems extrapolated to infinite molecular weight polymer.

TABLE 2.6. THETA TEMPERATURES FOR VARIOUS
POLYMER–SOLVENT SYSTEMS FOR POLYMER OF INFINITE
MOLECULAR WEIGHT

Polymer	Solvent	θ °C
Polystyrene	Cyclohexane	34·4
Polystyrene	Toluene	~ -100
Poly α-methyl styrene	Cyclohexane	38·0
Polyisobutylene	Benzene	24·0
Polymethyl methacrylate	50 : 50 Methyl ethyl ketone: isopropanol	25·0
Poly n-butyl methacrylate	Isopropanol	21·5
cis 1,4 Polybutadiene	Isobutyl acetate	20·5
cis 1,4 Polyisoprene	Methyl n-propyl ketone	14·5
trans 1,4 Polyisoprene	n-Propyl acetate	~ 60
Polyvinyl acetate	Ethyl n-butyl ketone	29·0
Polyvinyl chloride	Benzyl alcohol	155·4
Polydimethyl siloxane	Methyl ethyl ketone	20·0

MEASUREMENT OF THE WEIGHT
AVERAGE MOLECULAR WEIGHT

It will be recalled that the weight average molecular weight is defined in the following way:

$$\overline{M}_w = \frac{\sum w_i M_i}{\sum w_i},$$

where w_i is the total weight of the ith species. In terms of the number of molecules of the ith species N_i, the above equation defining $\overline{M}_w$ becomes

$$\overline{M}_w = \frac{\sum N_i M_i^2}{\sum N_i M_i}.$$

It must not be thought that weight averaging processes are restricted to polymer chemistry. If we measure the specific volume of a mixture of two substances of different density, we necessarily obtain a weight average value as we shall now show. Suppose we mix a weight w_A of a substance A with a weight w_B of a substance B. If there is no volume change on mixing, the specific volume of the mixture, $\bar{v}_{AB}$, namely

$$\frac{\text{the total volume of the mixture}}{\text{the total weight of the mixture}}$$

can be written in terms of the specific volumes of the pure components A and B, v_A and v_B, thus

$$\bar{v}_{AB} = \frac{w_A v_A + w_B v_B}{w_A + w_B}$$

This equation is exactly analogous to that defining weight average molecular weight and the result is, therefore, a weight average specific volume. It arises simply and naturally since the volume of 1 g of the mixture (the measured property in this case) is the sum of the products of the weights and specific volumes of the component parts of the mixture.

The method of light scattering

The basic phenomenon which is used in this method is made familiar to us in everyday life when we enter a somewhat dusty room illuminated by a single shaft of sunlight. Our experience tells us that the beam appears well defined even though we may be standing at right angles to the direction in which the light is travelling. The cause of the deviation of the light from its straight line path is the presence of minute particles of dust suspended in the air. The deviation of the incident light through all angles to the direction of travel is termed *scattering* (note the distinction between scattering and reflection; in reflection the incident light is deviated through one particular angle such that the angles of incidence and reflection are equal). In exactly similar experiments using dust-free gases, pure liquids or solutions, we find that some of the incident energy is scattered in three dimensions at all angles to the incident beam but that due to the much smaller size of the scattering centres, the fraction of the incident energy dissipated per second by scattering is much smaller than in the case of a dusty room. In the case of polymer solutions, the energy scattered per second, the scattered *flux* as it is termed, is related to the weight average molecular weight of the polymer sample and to a characteristic dimension of the molecules themselves —in the case of random coil polymers, for example, to the root mean square end-to-end distance. Our prime object in this section is to explain the reasons why these quantities are involved in fixing the magnitude of the scattered light from a polymer solution; once this is done, we shall show how they can be obtained numerically from experimental data. We shall discuss two simpler situations first: scattering from gases and scattering from pure liquids.

Scattering from gases

In the first place, we shall take a single molecule in a vacuum and examine its interaction with plane polarized monochromatic light. We shall suppose that the molecule is spherical so that no problems of orientation relative to the plane of polarization arise and that its diameter is small compared to the wavelength of light λ. The situation is shown in Fig. 2.7, the

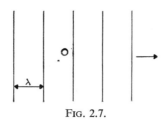

FIG. 2.7.

arrow indicating the direction in which the light wave moves. Now we know that what we term light is the effect produced when oscillating electric and magnetic fields mutually at right angles interact one with the other. When a beam of light travels through space, these two fields move from point to point with velocity c —the velocity of light—the direction of propagation of these disturbances being at right angles to the plane in which the field strengths fluctuate. So our previous diagram becomes a little more complex as shown in Fig. 2.8. As drawn, the light wave moves in the direction of increasing X and is polarized in the XZ-plane. At the point O the electric field strength changes continuously with time as shown in Fig. 2.9. The lengths of the arrows give the magnitude of the electric field and their direction indicates the direction in which a free unit charge would be accelerated. Simultaneously, the magnetic field strength is varying in an analogous fashion along the Y-axis as in Fig. 2.10. Again the height of these arrows gives the magnitude of the magnetic field at the point

O and their direction, the direction in which a free unit pole would be accelerated. The representation of the strength and

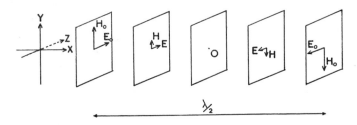

FIG. 2.8. A vectorial representation of the electric and magnetic fields E and H at a series of points in space at a particular instant of time for a polarized beam of monochromatic light moving in the direction of increasing X. At this instant, both fields are zero at the point O, the position of the molecule; at a time $\lambda/4c$ later, the field strengths at this point will have risen to their maximum values E_0 and H_0

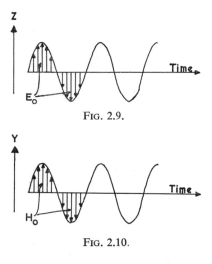

FIG. 2.9.

FIG. 2.10.

direction of the electric and magnetic fields by arrows is of course a familiar vectorial representation. Now, as the electric field oscillates in the region of the molecule, the motion of the extranuclear electrons belonging to its component atoms is thereby perturbed with the result that an induced oscillatory dipole moment is set up. The magnitude of this moment p at any time t is proportional to the electric field strength E, the constant of proportionality α being termed the *polarizability* of the molecule.

$$p = \alpha E,$$

where
$$E = E_0 \cos\left(\frac{2\pi ct}{\lambda}\right).$$

p itself is a vector and is directed along the Z-axis. This non-uniform variation of p with time taking place in a varying magnetic field results in the propagation of a secondary electro-magnetic disturbance throughout space centred on O. This is precisely what we mean by scattering for energy is found in all directions relative to the exciting incident radiation. The next stage is clearly the calculation of the energy passing through 1 cm² per second—that is, the light intensity—at various

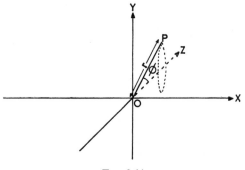

Fig. 2.11.

angles to the direction OZ. Let us consider a point P in space distance r from O such that OP is inclined at an angle ϕ to OZ. This is shown in Fig. 2.11. The result obtained for the intensity of scattered light at the point P, I_ϕ, involves the square of the amplitude of the oscillating electric field at P and is given by

$$I_\phi = \frac{16\pi^4\alpha^2 E_0^2}{\lambda^4 r^2} \sin^2 \phi$$

or

$$I_\phi = \frac{16\pi^4\alpha^2 I_0}{\lambda^4 r^2} \sin^2 \phi, \tag{2.13}$$

where I_0 is the incident intensity. An alternative way of expressing the scattered energy at the angle ϕ is the energy radiated per second per unit solid angle J_ϕ. With such a unit,

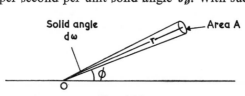

FIG. 2.12.

the purely geometrical factor r does not enter the calculation for clearly the energy radiated per unit solid angle is not influenced by the distance of P from O. In terms of the symbols of Fig. 2.12, the energy radiated per second is equal to

$$J_\phi \, d\omega = I_\phi A = I_\phi r^2 \, d\omega.$$

Therefore

$$J_\phi = I_\phi r^2.$$

So eqn. (2.13) simply shows that the energy radiated in a given direction per second per unit solid angle is a constant fraction of the incident energy input and is symmetrical about the line OZ. The intensity decreases inversely as the distance squared in the usual fashion. The distribution of scattered intensity with angle at a series of points in space, P_1, P_2, P_3, etc., *equidistant from O*, is thus found by rotating Fig. 2.13 about the Z-axis, where each length OP_1, OP_2, OP_3, etc., is proportional to the intensity of scattered light in that particular direction. The resulting three-dimensional figure, called the scattering envelope, is rather similar to a doughnut with an infinitesimal centre hole. There are four points which should be noted at this stage. Firstly, the scattered light resulting from plane polarized incident light is itself plane polarized in the

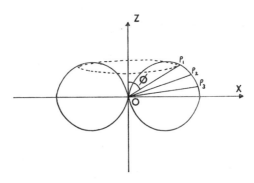

FIG. 2.13.

plane defined by the three points P, O and Z. Secondly, the intensity of the scattered light at 90° to the incident beam is zero. Thirdly, the forward and backward scattered intensities at equivalent angles to the incident beam are identical—that is,

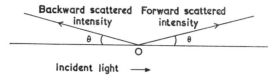

FIG. 2.14.

the intensities in the two directions θ and $\pi - \theta$ to the incident beam are equal. This is illustrated in Fig. 2.14. We describe this situation by saying that the scattering envelope has a dissymmetry coefficient z of unity at all angles where

$$z = \frac{I_\theta}{I_{\pi-\theta}},$$

the two intensities referring to the same distance r from the scattering source. Fourthly, the scattered intensity in any particular direction and at a given distance from the source depends on the reciprocal of the fourth power of the wavelength of the incident radiation. Putting it another way, if we use the 4358 Å line from a mercury arc rather than the 5461 Å line[†] of equal intensity, we obtain an enhanced scatter of $(5461/4358)^4$—that is, 2·47 times as much energy is dissipated by scattering from the lower wavelength incident light.

If we use unpolarized incident light instead of the plane polarized radiation we have considered for simplicity, the scattering envelope becomes a little different. To derive the spatial distribution of scattered intensity, we regard the unpolarized light as consisting of two equal intensity beams polarized in planes mutually at right angles to one another, each one-half the intensity of the incident unpolarized beam. Consequently, the scattering envelope becomes the superimposition of two separate envelopes—one corresponding to the rotation of a figure of eight about the Z-axis (incident beam polarized in the XZ-plane) and the other corresponding to the rotation of a similar figure about the Y-axis (incident beam polarized in the XY-plane). The result corresponds to the rotation of Fig. 2.15 about the X-axis. The important points to notice are that the forward and backward scatter is symmetrical and that only the light scattered at 90° is plane polarized (since it results from only one of the constituent polarized beams). In quantitative terms, the intensity at a point P situated such that the line OP makes an angle θ with OX is

$$I_\theta = \frac{8\pi^4\alpha^2 I_0(1+\cos^2\theta)}{\lambda^4 r^2}. \tag{2.14}$$

[†] These two wavelengths are the ones most often used in light-scattering work.

From this equation, it can be seen that the scattered intensity at 90° is just one-half of that scattered at 0° or 180°.

So far we have said little about the quantity α which measures the magnitude of the perturbation induced in the electron clouds of the molecule by an imposed electric field. To proceed further we shall have to relate it either to some other measur-

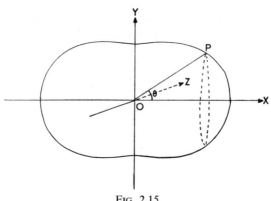

Fig. 2.15.

able property of the single molecule or alternatively to a measurable property of a molecular assembly. In practice, we do both and find that α is dependent on the weight of a single molecule and on the rate of change of refractive index of the assembly with concentration dn/dc. Provided this latter quantity is small, α is given by

$$\alpha = \frac{1}{2\pi} \left(\frac{dn}{dc} \right) \cdot \frac{M}{N_0},$$

where M/N_0, the molecular weight divided by the Avogadro number, is the weight of each molecule.

From equn. (2.14), it is readily possible to calculate the scattering resulting from ideal gases by assuming that a system containing N *molecules per unit volume* will produce per *unit volume* exactly N times the scatter from a single molecule.

For unpolarized incident light, the scattered intensity at P *from unit volume* of the system I_θ is

$$I_\theta = 2\pi^2 \left(\frac{dn}{dc}\right)^2 \cdot \frac{I_0}{\lambda^4 r^2} \cdot (1 + \cos^2 \theta) \cdot \frac{NM^2}{N_0^2} \qquad (2.15)$$

$$= 2\pi^2 \left(\frac{dn}{dc}\right)^2 \cdot \frac{I_0}{\lambda^4 r^2} \cdot (1 + \cos^2 \theta) \cdot \frac{cM}{N_0}, \qquad (2.16)$$

since c, the weight concentration, is equal to NM/N_0. The appearance of the product NM^2 in eqn. (2.15) should be noted.

These equations are usually rearranged to give the *reduced intensity* R_θ. This quantity is defined by the equation

$$R_\theta = \frac{I_\theta r^2}{I_0},$$

it being emphasized that I_θ refers to *unit volume* of the scattering medium. For example, eqn. (2.15) becomes

$$R_\theta = 2\pi^2 \left(\frac{dn}{dc}\right)^2 \cdot \frac{1}{\lambda^4} \cdot (1 + \cos^2 \theta) \frac{NM^2}{N_0^2}.$$

From its definition, R_θ is the energy scattered in a direction θ to the incident beam per unit solid angle per second from unit volume of the scattering medium for unit incident intensity. An alternative interpretation of the reduced intensity is obtained as follows. Suppose the flux incident on a volume element of scattering medium of cross-section A is P_0. Then the total energy scattered per second (the scattered flux) over a solid angle $d\omega$ in a direction θ to the incident beam, $J_\theta d\omega$, is related to the length l of the medium from which the scattering takes place by the expression

$$J_\theta d\omega = I_\theta (Al) r^2 \, d\omega = R_\theta P_0 l d\omega.$$

This shows that R_θ is the scattered flux in a direction θ to the incident beam per unit solid angle per unit incident flux *per unit path length* of scattering medium. In the normal c.g.s. units, therefore, R_θ has the units cm^{-1}.

Scattering from pure liquids

When we consider scattering from pure liquids, the above arguments might lead one to suppose that such an effect would be non-existent. Viewed simply, one would say that dn/dc would be zero since simply adding more solvent molecules would not cause any increase in the refractive index (compare the situation in a gas where addition of more molecules undoubtedly results in an increased refractive index). Yet by experiment, there is no doubt that light is scattered from a pure liquid. The apparent contradiction can be resolved by regarding the problem more fundamentally and asking ourselves why dn/dc entered the calculation. In essence it arose because the response of the volume element of space in the region of the molecule to the electric field of the light wave differed from the surrounding volume elements—in fact we had to introduce the term α to characterize this special volume element and this in turn led to the introduction of the quantity dn/dc. Putting it another way, the scattering of the incident light arises primarily from the existence of discontinuities in optical properties in the medium through which the light passes. In a gas these discontinuities are the molecules themselves, whereas in a pure liquid they correspond to volume elements of differing density arising from microscopic fluctuations in molecular concentration. Such fluctuations arise as the result of the random thermal motion of the molecules creating and destroying holes in the liquid and increase as the absolute temperature increases. Examination of this problem shows that for small spherical molecules the scattered intensity at an angle θ to the incident beam *per unit volume of liquid* I_θ is given by

$$I_\theta = \frac{2\pi^2 RT\beta I_0}{\lambda^4 N_0 r^2} \cdot \frac{n_0^2(\partial n_0/\partial T)^2}{\gamma^2} \cdot (1+\cos^2\theta), \qquad (2.17)$$

where β is the coefficient of isothermal compressibility, γ is the coefficient of cubical expansion, and n_0 is the refractive index of the liquid. There are two ways of utilizing this equation to calculate the magnitude of the effect with which we are dealing. In the first place we calculate the quantity

$$R_\theta = \frac{I_\theta r^2}{I_0}$$

for $\theta = 90°$; that is, we calculate the energy scattered per unit solid angle per second at 90° to an incident beam of unit intensity *from unit volume* of the liquid. This quantity R_{90} is termed the *Rayleigh ratio* and is clearly given by

$$R_{90} = \frac{2\pi^2 RT\beta}{\lambda^4 N_0} \cdot \frac{n_0^2(\partial n_0/\partial T)^2}{\gamma^2}. \tag{2.18}$$

The alternative method is to calculate the fraction of the incident flux which is scattered in all directions as a result of traversing 1 cm path in the liquid—a quantity termed the turbidity τ. For this problem, we simply sum the products $R_\theta \, d\omega$ over the solid angle 4π. We obviously need to know how R_θ depends on θ; that is, we need to know the shape of the scattering envelope. In the particular case of small spherical molecules, we can use eqn. (2.17) from which we find

$$\tau = \frac{16\pi}{3} R_{90}. \tag{2.19}$$

As a specific example of the magnitude of the effect for incident radiation of wavelength 5461 Å, we shall consider carbon tetrachloride at 23° C since the molecules of this liquid are effectively spherical. The various quantities in the equation for R_{90} are as follows:[6]

$$R = 8{\cdot}314 \times 10^7 \text{ erg mole}^{-1} \text{ °K}^{-1},$$
$$T = 296{\cdot}2°\text{K},$$
$$\beta = 106 \times 10^{-12} \text{ cm}^2 \text{ dyne}^{-1},$$
$$n_0 = 1{\cdot}460,$$
$$\partial n_0/\partial T = 58{\cdot}5 \times 10^{-5} \text{ °K}^{-1},$$

$$\lambda = 5 \cdot 461 \times 10^{-5} \text{ cm,}$$
$$N_0 = 6 \cdot 023 \times 10^{23} \text{ mole}^{-1},$$
$$\gamma = 1 \cdot 21 \times 10^{-3} \text{ °K}^{-1},$$

giving $R_{90} = 4 \cdot 81 \times 10^{-6}$ cm^{-1} compared with an experimental value of $5 \cdot 38 \times 10^{-6}$ cm^{-1}. The calculated value of R_{90} corresponds to a turbidity of $8 \cdot 06 \times 10^{-5}$ cm^{-1}. In other words, if we pass 1 erg sec^{-1} through 1 cm of carbon tetrachloride at 23°C in the form of unpolarized monochromatic light of wavelength 5461 Å, $8 \cdot 06 \times 10^{-5}$ erg sec^{-1} are dissipated by scattering. Obviously, the attenuation of the primary beam will be almost negligible so that the scattering must be observed directly rather than deduced from the difference between the incident and transmitted flux. The scattering envelope for carbon tetrachloride based on eqn. (2.18) is illustrated in the scale diagram, Fig. 2.16.

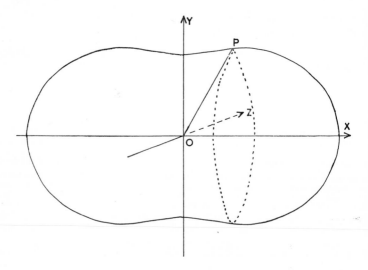

FIG. 2.16. The scattering envelope for carbon tetrachloride at 23°C — scale 1 cm = $2 \cdot 5 \times 10^{-6}$ cm^{-1}

Finally, in connection with this problem of scattering from pure liquids, it must be realized that an additional complication arises when the molecules are *anisotropic*. By this, we mean that the optical properties of the molecules differ according to their orientation with respect to some fixed axes in space—a property which is associated with a lack of symmetry in the molecules themselves. A very good example of such a molecule is benzene which we know to be an almost flat hexagonal ring. In such instances, the expression for R_{90} has to be corrected to allow for the degree of depolarization of the 90° scatter and no simple relation for the turbidity can be given since the scattering envelope no longer depends on θ according to $(1 + \cos^2 \theta)$.

Scattering from solutions

In the case of solutions, the cause of the scattering of light is essentially the same as in the case of pure liquids; that is, the mass and polarizability of a particular volume element in the liquid fluctuate with time. A solution differs from a pure liquid simply because, superimposed on the fluctuation in the number of voids in a volume element, fluctuations in the solute concentration occur. This latter effect is the significant one as far as the calculation of the properties of the solute molecules is concerned. If the total scattered flux from the solution is no greater than, say, five times the scattered flux from the solvent, it is permissible to regard these two effects as occurring independently so that the contribution of concentration fluctuations to the scattered intensity at an angle θ is simply the difference between the value observed for the solution and that for the pure solvent at the same temperature. Using the symbols defined previously, we write

$$I'_{\theta_{\text{Concentration fluctuations}}} = I_{\theta_{\text{Solution}}} - I_{\theta_{\text{Solvent}}},$$

where for preciseness each of these quantities refers to *unit volume*. For simplicity, we shall drop the subscript "concentration fluctuations" and retain the superscript prime to indicate the above difference.

For the case where all the solute molecules have the same molecular weight, M, I'_θ is given by

$$I'_\theta = 2\pi^2 n_0^2 \left(\frac{dn}{dc}\right)^2 \cdot \frac{I_0}{\lambda^4 r^2} (1+\cos^2 \theta) \frac{NM}{N_0^2} \cdot \frac{RT}{(\partial\pi/\partial c)_T} \quad (2.20)$$

provided that the solute molecules are no larger than $\lambda'/20$, λ' being the wavelength of the incident light in the solution which, for the dilute solutions to which all these arguments apply, is the same as that in the pure solvent. In this equation n_0 is the refractive index of the pure solvent, dn/dc is the rate of change of refractive index of the solution with increasing solute concentration, $(\partial\pi/\partial c)_T$ is the rate of change of the osmotic pressure of the solution with increasing solute concentration at constant temperature, and the other symbols are as previously defined. Writing the osmotic pressure as a virial expansion in c in the form

$$\pi = \frac{RT}{M} (c+\Gamma_2 c^2+\ldots),$$

$$\left(\frac{\partial\pi}{\partial c}\right)_T = \frac{RT}{M} (1+2\Gamma_2 c+\ldots).$$

Hence eqn. (2.20) becomes

$$I'_\theta = 2\pi^2 n_0^2 \left(\frac{dn}{dc}\right)^2 \cdot \frac{I_0}{\lambda^4 r^2} (1+\cos^2 \theta) \frac{NM^2}{N_0^2} \cdot \frac{1}{(1+2\Gamma_2 c+\ldots)} \cdot \quad (2.21)$$

If, on the other hand, the polymer contains a range of molecular weights, the total value of the scattered intensity at an angle θ produced from unit volume of solution is the sum of the separate contributions of each species. For this case, eqn.

(2.21) becomes

$$I'_\theta = 2\pi^2 n_0^2 \left(\frac{dn}{dc}\right)^2 \cdot \frac{I_0}{\lambda^4 r^2}(1+\cos^2\theta) \cdot \frac{\sum N_i M_i^2}{N_0^2} \cdot \frac{1}{(1+2\Gamma_2 c + \ldots)}$$

(2.22)

Γ_2 being now an averaged quantity of a type which need not concern us. To simplify this equation, we write:

1. $$\sum N_i M_i^2 = \bar{M}_w \sum N_i M_i = \bar{M}_w c N_0.$$

2. $$R'_\theta = \frac{I'_\theta r^2}{I_0}.$$

3. $$K = \frac{2\pi^2 n_0^2 (dn/dc)^2}{\lambda^4 N_0}.$$

(2.23)

Equation (2.22) then becomes

$$R'_\theta = K(1+\cos^2\theta) \cdot \frac{\bar{M}_w c}{(1+2\Gamma_2 c + \ldots)}.$$

(2.24)

Figures 2.17 and 2.18 show the dependence of R'_θ on the

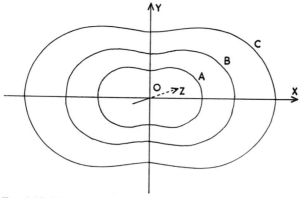

Fig. 2.17. The dependence of the excess scattering envelope on the concentration for polystyrene in benzene at 25°C; no interference effects have been considered. Scale 1 cm $= 2\cdot5 \times 10^{-5}$ cm $^{-1}$. The molecular weight of the polystyrene $\bar{M}_w = 50,000$ and $\Gamma_2 = 30$ cm^3 g^{-1}. The three curves A, B and C correspond to the three concentrations $0\cdot5 \times 10^{-2}$, $1\cdot0 \times 10^{-2}$ and $2\cdot0 \times \times 10^{-2}$ g cm^{-3}

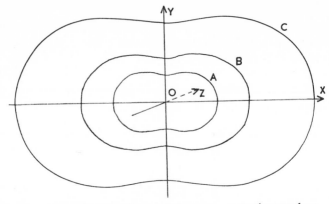

FIG. 2.18. The dependence of the excess scattering envelope on molecular weight for polystyrene in benzene at 25°C; no interference effects have been considered. Scale 1 cm = $2 \cdot 5 \times 10^{-5}$ cm^{-1}. The concentration of the polymer is 1×10^{-2} g cm^{-3}. The following values have been assumed for curves A, B and C; (A) $\overline{M}_w = 25{,}000$, $\Gamma_2 = 15$ cm^3 g^{-1}; (B) $\overline{M}_w = 50{,}000$, $\Gamma_2 = 30$ cm^3 g^{-1}; (C) $\overline{M}_w = 100{,}000$, $\Gamma_2 = 40$ cm^3 g^{-1}

concentration and molecular weight respectively. These diagrams have been calculated for the case of polystyrene in benzene at 25°C using the values

$$n_0 = 1 \cdot 5014,$$
$$dn/dc = 0 \cdot 106 \text{ cm}^3 \text{ g}^{-1},$$
$$\lambda = 5 \cdot 461 \times 10^{-5} \text{ cm},$$
$$N_0 = 6 \cdot 023 \times 10^{23} \text{ mole}^{-1}.$$

It should be noted that dn/dc is independent of the concentration and molecular weight of the polymer so that K is a genuine constant for a particular polymer–solvent system. Of great importance practically is the fact that the measured quantity R'_θ (or I'_θ) increases as the weight average molecular weight increases; by way of contrast the opposite tendency is observed in the case of osmotic pressure, for here the measured quantity (the hydrostatic head preventing the net flow of solvent) decreases with increasing number average molecular weight.

In order to obtain $\overline{M}_w$ from the experimental measurements of R'_θ, eqn. (2.24) is rearranged to give

$$\frac{K(1+\cos^2\theta)c}{R'_\theta} = \frac{1}{\overline{M}_w}(1+2\Gamma_2 c + \ldots) \qquad (2.25)$$

The procedure, therefore, is as follows. We take a series of polymer solutions (dust free) of differing concentration. We choose a particular angle to the incident beam (usually 90°) and determine R'_θ for each solution. Having previously calculated K, we evaluate $K(1+\cos^2\theta)c/R'_\theta$ for each concentration and plot this against c. Extrapolation of the linear portion to zero concentration eliminates the effects due to polymer–solvent interaction and the intercept on the $K(1+\cos^2\theta)c/R'_\theta$ axis

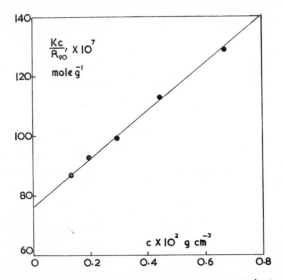

FIG. 2.19. The concentration dependence of Kc/R'_{90} for a solution of polystyrene in benzene at 22°C for which no interference effects were observed

gives $1/\overline{M}_w$ directly. The data of Table 2.7 plotted in Fig. 2.19 illustrate this procedure, K being calculated using

$$n_0 = 1.5130,$$
$$dn/dc = 0.111 \text{ cm}^3 \text{ g}^{-1},$$
$$\lambda = 4.358 \times 10^{-5} \text{ cm},$$

whence $\qquad K = 2.564 \times 10^{-7} \text{ cm}^2 \text{ g}^{-2} \text{ mole}.$

TABLE 2.7. EXCESS SCATTERING FROM A SOLUTION
OF POLYSTYRENE IN BENZENE AT 22°C[7]

$c \times 10^3$ g cm^{-3}	1·32	1·97	2·96	4·45	6·67
$R'_{90} \times 10^5$ cm^{-1}	3·88	5·44	7·63	10·1	13·3
$Kc/R'_{90} \times 10^7$ mole g^{-1}	87·1	92·7	99·4	113	129

From the graph

$$\frac{1}{\overline{M}_w} = 76.4 \times 10^{-7} \text{ mole g}^{-1}.$$

Therefore $\qquad \overline{M}_w = 1.31 \times 10^5 \text{ g mole}^{-1}.$

From the slope of the graph, we can also find the value of the second virial coefficient for this particular polymer–solvent system, thus:

$$\frac{2\Gamma_2}{\overline{M}_w} = 80.1 \times 10^{-5} \text{ mole g}^{-2} \text{ cm}^3.$$

Therefore $\qquad \Gamma_2 = 52 \text{ cm}^3 \text{ g}^{-1}.$

All these arguments apply to the case where the characteristic dimension of the polymer molecules is less than $\lambda'/20$. Using light of wavelength 5461 Å and benzene as solvent (refractive index 1·5014), this condition sets an upper limit on the root mean square end-to-end distance of a polymer coil of 182 Å if its molecular weight is to be calculated correctly from a series of measurements at a single angle. (If the molecules were spherical or rod-like, 182 Å would represent the critical value of the diameter or length.) At dimensions greater than $\lambda'/20$, the molecule can no longer be regarded as a point source and we have to consider that the light scattered from different points along the molecule will not necessarily be in phase. Consequently, interference effects arise which result firstly in a general reduction in the total scattered flux and secondly in the appearance of an unsymmetrical scattering envelope. Both of these effects are illustrated in Fig. 2.20.

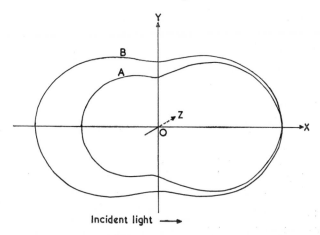

FIG. 2.20. A scale diagram showing the effect of interference. Scale 1 cm $= 2 \cdot 5 \times 10^{-5}$ cm^{-1}. Curve A shows the scattering envelope from a solution of polystyrene in benzene with $\overline{M}_w = 730{,}000$, $\Gamma_2 = 320$ cm^3 g^{-1}, at a concentration of 1×10^{-3} g cm^{-3}. Curve B shows the scattering envelope which would have resulted from the same solution in the absence of interference

The reader should note that (a) the forward scatter exceeds the backward scatter, i.e. the dissymmetry coefficient z, $R'_\theta/R'_{\pi-\theta}$, exceeds 1, and (b) the forward scatter at zero angle is the same whether interference effects are present or not. Experimentally, therefore, it is very easy to decide whether interference effects must be considered or not; if the two quantities R'_θ and $R'_{\pi-\theta}$ differ significantly from one another, interference effects are present. To take these effects into account, the following modifications to our previous treatment are required.

Firstly, we define a parameter $P(\theta)$ which we term the particle scattering factor by the ratios

$$P(\theta) = \frac{R'_\theta}{(R'_\theta)_{\text{No interference}}} = \frac{I'_\theta}{(I'_\theta)_{\text{No interference}}}.$$

R'_θ and I'_θ are the actual values observed experimentally and $(R'_\theta)_{\text{No interference}}$ and $(I'_\theta)_{\text{No interference}}$ are the values which would have been observed in the absence of these interference effects. Secondly, our previous equations which have been written in terms of these latter quantities are rearranged in terms of the observed quantities and the particle scattering factor, thus

$$\frac{K(1+\cos^2\theta)c}{R'_\theta} = \frac{1}{\overline{M}_w \cdot P(\theta)}(1+2\Gamma_2 c + \ldots). \qquad (2.26)$$

The best method of utilizing this equation makes use of the fact that $P(0)$, the particle scattering factor at $\theta = 0$, is unity. In other words the scattered intensity at zero angle to the incident beam is not attenuated by interference and so the above equation becomes

$$\frac{2Kc}{R'_0} = \frac{1}{\overline{M}_w}(1+2\Gamma_2 c + \ldots)$$

for this particular value of $\theta = 0$. The snag is that the scattered intensity at zero angle to the incident beam is quite inaccessible experimentally since it is superimposed on a transmitted intensity approximately 10,000 times greater. The value of R'_0 for a particular concentration has to be obtained by appropriate extrapolation of finite angle values to $\theta = 0$ and the results then extrapolated to zero concentration to obtain $\overline{M}_w$. The extrapolation to zero angle in the case of random coil polymers depends on the fact that

$$P(\theta) = 1 - \frac{8\pi^2 \overline{r^2}}{9\lambda'^2} \cdot \sin^2 \theta/2 + \ldots$$

where $\overline{r^2}$ is the mean square end-to-end distance of the polymer molecules. Since the second term is small and higher terms even smaller, $P(\theta)^{-1}$ can be obtained by binomial expansion and our basic equation becomes

$$\frac{K(1+\cos^2 \theta)c}{R'_\theta} = \frac{1}{\overline{M}_w} (1 + 2\Gamma_2 c + \ldots) \left(1 + \frac{8\pi^2 \overline{r^2}}{9\lambda'^2} \sin^2 \theta/2 + \ldots \right).$$
(2.27)

This shows that a plot of $K(1+\cos^2 \theta)c/R'_\theta$ against $\sin^2 \theta/2$ at constant c should give a reasonably good straight line which can be extrapolated to $\theta = 0$ (see Fig. 2.21). The intercepts at $\sin^2 \theta/2 = 0$, which correspond to zero angle, clearly give the value of the quantity $2Kc/R'_0$ at the series of concentrations, while the slopes of the lines give the ratio of the root mean square end-to-end distance of the polymer molecules to the wavelength of light in the medium. Having obtained the quantities $2Kc/R'_0$, it is an easy matter to extrapolate these to zero concentration and so obtain the molecular weight for we know from our previous equation that these are linearly dependent on c (see Fig. 2.22). The slope of this line gives the second virial coefficient Γ_2.

In practice, these two extrapolations are usually performed on the same graph by a method devised by Zimm. In Zimm's procedure, the quantity $K(1+\cos^2 \theta)c/R'_\theta$ is plotted against $\sin^2 \theta/2 + kc$, where k is an arbitrary constant (usually 100 or 1000) chosen to separate the lines corresponding to various values of c. Two sets of lines result, one corresponding to a constant value of θ but various values of c while the other set corresponds to a constant value of c but varying θ. In this way,

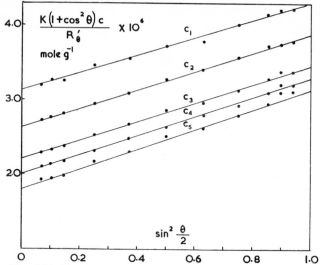

FIG. 2.21. The dependence of the quantity $K(1+\cos^2\theta)c/R_\theta'$ on $\sin^2 \theta/2$ for a series of solutions of polystyrene in benzene of differing concentrations at 25°C; c_1, c_2, c_3, c_4 and c_5 are $2\cdot0\times10^{-3}$, $1\cdot5\times10^{-3}$, $1\cdot0\times10^{-3}$, $0\cdot75\times10^{-3}$ and $0\cdot5\times10^{-3}$ g cm^{-3} respectively

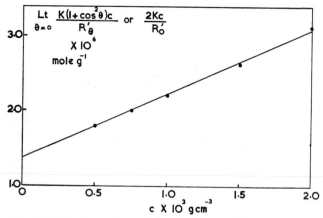

FIG. 2.22. The dependence of the quantity $2Kc/R_0'$ on concentration for the same sample of polystyrene in benzene as used in Fig. 2.21

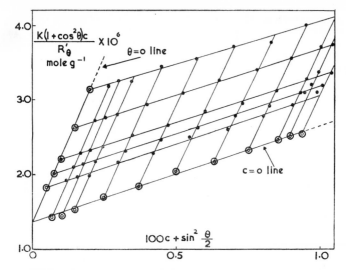

FIG. 2.23. A plot of both the angular and concentration dependence of the quantity $K(1+\cos^2\theta)c/R'_\theta$ for the polystyrene sample of Figs. 2.21 and 2.22; the Zimm plot. The concentration units employed are g cm^{-3}. The symbols ◎ represent extrapolated points

we obtain the grid-type graph shown in Fig. 2.23. The data for Fig. 2.23 and Figs. 2.21 and 2.22 are tabulated in Tables 2.8, 2.9 and 2.10.

From Fig. 2.23, three quantities are calculable.

1. The weight average molecular weight is found from the intercept of the two limiting lines on the $K(1+\cos^2\theta)c/R'_\theta$ axis since

$$\mathop{\mathrm{Lt.}}_{\substack{c=0 \\ \theta=0}} \frac{K(1+\cos^2\theta)c}{R'_\theta} = \frac{1}{\overline{M}_w}.$$

In our case, the value of the intercept is 1.37×10^{-6}

TABLE 2.8

Scattering from pure benzene and a series of polystyrene solutions in the same solvent: the "raw" data.[8] The galvanometer readings G_θ were obtained with a photomultiplier situated at the various angles shown to an incident beam of unpolarized, monochromatic light of wavelength 5461 Å in vacuo.

c g cm^{-3} \ θ	30°	37·5°	45°	60°	75°	90°	105°	120°	135°	142·5°	150°
2·00 ×10^{-3}	1542	1153	917	607	461	408	440	540	755	936	1235
1·50 ×10^{-3}	1383	1045	820	550	413	363	384	475	660	820	1080
1·00 ×10^{-3}	1158	872	682	455	343	301	319	392	540	660	880
0·75 ×10^{-3}	998	750	590	396	297	263	275	339	464	565	755
0·50 ×10^{-3}	803	607	477	319	241	214	224	275	376	454	607
Pure benzene	282	213	170	128	105	100	105	127	170	207	285

TABLE 2.9

The values of $R'_\theta \times 10^6$ in cm^{-1} for the series of polystyrene solutions in benzene calculated from the simple equation $R'_\theta = 16·3 \times 10^{-8} G'_\theta \sin \theta$ cm^{-1}.

c g cm^{-3} \ θ	30°	37·5°	45°	60°	75°	90°	105°	120°	135°	142·5°	150°
2·00 ×10^{-3}	102·7	93·3	86·1	67·6	56·0	50·2	52·7	58·3	67·4	72·3	77·4
1·50 ×10^{-3}	89·7	82·6	74·9	59·6	48·5	42·9	43·9	49·1	56·5	60·8	64·8
1·00 ×10^{-3}	71·4	65·4	59·0	46·2	37·5	32·8	33·7	37·4	42·6	45·0	48·5
0·75 ×10^{-3}	58·4	53·3	48·4	37·8	30·2	26·6	26·8	29·9	33·9	35·5	38·3
0·50 ×10^{-3}	42·5	39·1	35·4	27·0	21·4	18·6	18·7	20·9	23·7	24·5	26·2

The factor converting the $G'_\theta \sin \theta$ values to R'_θ was obtained from the known Rayleigh ratio of benzene of $16·3 \times 10^{-6}$ cm^{-1}. We can easily show that $R_\theta = k G_\theta \sin \theta$ and $R'_\theta = k G'_\theta \sin \theta$ so that knowing G_{90} for pure benzene (100) gives k, the proportionality constant.

TABLE 2.10

The values of $K(1+\cos^2\theta)c/R'_\theta \times 10^6$ in mole g^{-1} for the series of polystyrene solutions in benzene calculated using $K = 9.34 \times 10^{-8}$ cm^2 g^{-2} mole.

c g cm^{-3}	30°	37.5°	45°	60°	75°	90°	105°	120°	135°	142.5°	150°
2.00 $\times 10^{-3}$	3.18	3.26	3.25	3.45	3.56	3.72	3.78	4.01	4.16	4.21	4.22
1.50 $\times 10^{-3}$	2.73	2.76	2.81	2.94	3.08	3.27	3.40	3.57	3.72	3.75	3.78
1.00 $\times 10^{-3}$	2.29	2.33	2.37	2.53	2.66	2.85	2.96	3.12	3.29	3.38	3.37
0.75 $\times 10^{-3}$	2.10	2.14	2.17	2.32	2.47	2.64	2.79	2.93	3.10	3.21	3.20
0.50 $\times 10^{-3}$	1.92	1.95	1.98	2.16	2.33	2.51	2.66	2.79	2.96	3.11	3.12

The quantity $K = 2\pi^2 n_0^2 (dn/dc)^2 / \lambda^4 N_0$ was calculated using

$n_0 = 1.5014$ $\qquad\qquad$ $\lambda = 5.461 \times 10^{-5}$ cm,

$dn/dc = 0.106$ cm^3 g^{-1}, $\qquad$ $N_0 = 6.023 \times 10^{23}$ mole^{-1}.

mole g^{-1} and hence

$$\overline{M}_w = \frac{1}{1.37 \times 10^{-6}} \text{ g mole}^{-1} = 730,000 \text{ g mole}^{-1}.$$

2. The value of the second virial coefficient of the π/c versus c expansion is found from the limiting slope of the $\theta = 0$ line. The relation is

limiting slope of the $\theta = 0$ line $= \dfrac{2\Gamma_2}{\overline{M}_w}$

and hence, in our case, where the slope is 8.76×10^{-4} mole g^{-2} cm^3

$$\Gamma_2 = \frac{8.76 \times 10^{-4} \times 730,000}{2} \text{ cm}^3 \text{ g}^{-1} = 3.20 \times 10^2 \text{ cm}^3 \text{ g}^{-1}.$$

3. The root mean square end-to-end distance of the polymer chains is found from the limiting slope of the $c = 0$ line. The equation is

$$\text{limiting slope of the } c = 0 \text{ line} = \frac{8\pi^2 \overline{r^2}}{9\overline{M}_w \lambda'^2}$$

and consequently, in the case under discussion, where this slope is 1.29×10^{-6} mole g^{-1}

$$\overline{r^2} = \frac{9 \times 1.29 \times 10^{-6} \times 730,000}{8\pi^2} \cdot \left(\frac{5461}{1.5014}\right)^2 \text{ Å}^2.$$

Therefore $(\overline{r^2})^{1/2} = 1190$ Å.

The data of Table 2.8 were obtained using solutions of polystyrene in benzene illuminated by light of 5461 Å and thermostatted at 25°C. The scattered light was measured using a photomultiplier which could be set at various angles to the incident beam; consequently the "raw" experimental data consist of a series of galvanometer readings, each proportional to the output current of the photomultiplier which, in turn, is proportional to the light flux scattered from the "viewed" volume of the solution at the particular angle θ. A schematic diagram of the experimental arrangements is shown in Fig. 2.24 and a photograph of a modern instrument in Fig. 2.25. Note that G_θ must be multiplied by $\sin \theta$ to correct for the unavoidable variation of effective scattering volume as θ is varied; multiplication by $\sin \theta$ computes the value the galvanometer would have read, had the "viewed" volume remained constant. This is made clear in Fig. 2.26.

An alternative method of utilizing eqn. (2.26) is to obtain the value of $P(\theta)$ for a particular angle—usually 90°—from measurements of the dissymmetry of the scattered envelope. This procedure is called the *dissymmetry method* and, though less reliable than the double extrapolation already described, has the great merit of simplicity and rapidity. As before a series of dust-free polymer solutions of varying concentration

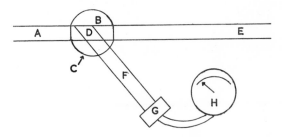

FIG. 2.24. A schematic diagram of a light scattering photometer; A, incident light beam; B, polymer solution, or solvent; C, scattering cell; D, effective scattering volume; E, light trap; F, scattered light beam; G, photomultiplier; H, galvanometer

are prepared. For each solution, the values of R_{45}, R_{90} and R_{135} are obtained from which are subtracted the corresponding solvent values to give the excess quantities R'_{45}, R'_{90} and R'_{135}. At each concentration two quantities are calculated:

1. the dissymmetry coefficient $z = R'_{45}/R'_{135}$;
2. Kc/R'_{90} (the value of $1+\cos^2 90 = 1$).

The limiting value of the dissymmetry coefficient at zero concentration enables the particle scattering factor $P(\theta)$ to be found from tables for any given value of θ and for certain shapes of the polymer molecules. Since from eqn. (2.26) the limiting value of $K(1+\cos^2 \theta)c/R'_\theta$ at zero concentration is $1/\overline{M}_w P(\theta)$, the molecular weight can clearly be found.

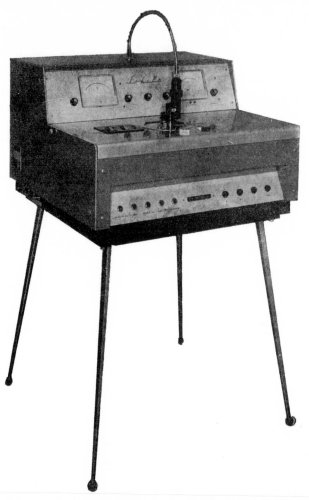

Fig. 2.25. A photograph of a modern light scattering instrument. (By courtesy of the Société française d'instruments de contrôle et d'analyse.)

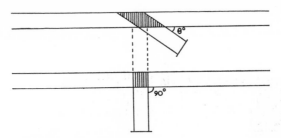

Fig. 2.26. The variation of the effective scattering volume with angle

As an illustration of this method, let us take the data of Table 2.9. The various values of z at the five different concentrations are then as shown below in Table 2.11.

TABLE 2.11. THE VARIATION OF THE DISSYMMETRY COEFFICIENT WITH CONCENTRATION FOR THE POLYSTYRENE SAMPLE USED IN THE PREVIOUS EXAMPLE

$c \times 10^3$ g cm^{-3}	2·00	1·50	1·00	0·75	0·50
z	1·277	1·326	1·385	1·428	1·494

To obtain the value of z at zero concentration, we extrapolate a graph of $1/(z-1)$ against c to $c = 0$. Thus $z_{c=0} = 1\cdot641$. (The graph of $1/(z-1)$ against c is usually linear and hence suitable for extrapolation; the more direct plot of z against c is usually curved and so is less suitable. Both these graphs are shown in Fig. 2.27.) If we assume that this sample of polystyrene contains a distribution of molecular weights and that the polystyrene molecules are random coils, then corresponding to the value of $z_{c=0}$ of $1\cdot641$, we find from tables (a) the particle scattering factor for 90° scatter $P(90)$ and (b) the ratio

$(\overline{r^2})^{1/2}/\lambda'$. The results are

$$P(90) = 0.663,$$

$$\frac{(\overline{r^2})^{1/2}}{\lambda'} = 0.291.$$

The values of Kc/R'_{90} at the five concentrations are shown in Table 2.12.

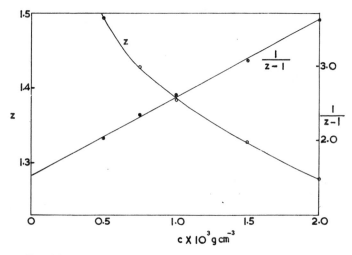

Fig. 2.27. Two plots which may be made to obtain the limiting value of the dissymmetry coefficient at zero concentration; data from Table 2.11.

TABLE 2.12. THE VARIATION OF Kc/R'_{90} WITH CONCENTRATION FOR THE POLYSTYRENE SAMPLE USED IN PREVIOUS EXAMPLES

$c \times 10^3$ g cm^{-3}	2·00	1·50	1·00	0·75	0·50
$\dfrac{Kc}{R'_{90}} \times 10^6$ mole g^{-1}	3·72	3·27	2·85	2·64	2·51

A plot of the values of Kc/R'_{90} against c gives a good straight line as shown in Fig. 2.28 which on extrapolation to $c = 0$ gives

$$\frac{1}{\overline{M}_w P(90)} = 2 \cdot 04 \times 10^{-6} \text{ mole g}^{-1},$$

which combined with the above value of $P(90)$ gives

$$\overline{M}_w = 739{,}000 \text{ g mole}^{-1}.$$

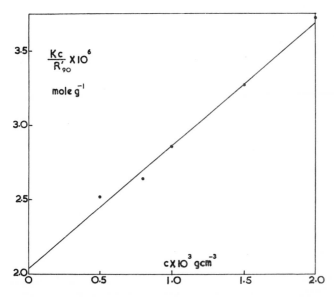

FIG. 2.28. The concentration dependence of the quantity Kc/R'_{90} for the sample of polystyrene of Figs. 2.21 and 2.22

Since λ' is 3637 Å, $(5461/1 \cdot 5014)$ Å, the root mean square end-to-end distance follows directly from the tabulated value of $(\overline{r^2})^{1/2}/\lambda'$ for random coils, $0 \cdot 291$:

$$(\overline{r^2})^{1/2} = 0 \cdot 291 \times 3637 \text{ Å},$$
$$(\overline{r^2})^{1/2} = 1060 \text{ Å}.$$

The agreement between this method and the Zimm method is quite satisfactory.

To conclude this section, we must recognize that the previously described theory of light-scattering as applied to polymer solutions depends on two essential conditions being satisfied. These are:

1. that the polymer molecules are isotropic;
2. that a finite but not too large difference exists between the refractive indices of the solutions and the solvent.

The first of these provisos is usually fulfilled for random coil polymers. For other shapes such as rods and discs, corrections have to be made to the formulae describing the excess scattering envelope based on the magnitude of the depolarization induced in the 90° scatter. Such corrections are outside the scope of this book.

The second of these conditions sets practical limits on the solvents which may be used for a particular polymer. The relevant parameter is the refractive index increment, dn/dc, for, as the various equations indicate, the measured quantity R'_θ is proportional to its square. Thus in the special case where dn/dc happened to be zero—polymer and solvent having the same refractive index—there would be no excess scatter to measure! On the other hand excessive refractive index increments, say above $0\cdot2$ cm³ g⁻¹, give rise to scattering no longer simply proportional to $(dn/dc)^2$ and so the equations which we have summarized are no longer valid. What is required is a value between these limits which can be measured accurately since a 2% error in this quantity introduces a 4% error in the derived molecular weights. That this is no easy task can be illustrated by reference to the polystyrene–benzene system already used in our examples. In this case

$$dn/dc = 0\cdot106 \text{ cm}^3 \text{ g}^{-1}$$

so that for a solution containing 1 g polystyrene per 100 cm³, Δn, the difference between the refractive index of this solution and that of the pure solvent, is

$$\Delta n = 0\cdot106 \times 0\cdot01 \text{ cm}^3 \text{ g}^{-1} \text{ g cm}^{-3}$$
$$= 0\cdot00106.$$

In other words with polymer concentrations of the same order as those used in scattering determinations, we have to be able to measure refractive index differences to $\pm0\cdot00002$ to ensure 4% accuracy in the derived molecular weights. Obviously, specialized apparatus is necessary for such determinations which requires a separate discussion. At this stage, we merely wish to emphasize the importance of accurate determinations of the refractive index increment.

Finally, the problem of clarification of the solutions and solvent from dust must be mentioned. Generally speaking, centrifuging and/or filtering the liquids through fine sintered glass discs has proved successful but it cannot be stressed too highly that great care has to be taken if large errors due to the presence of dust are to be avoided.

DETERMINATION OF MOLECULAR
WEIGHT BY VISCOSITY MEASUREMENTS

A particularly noticeable feature of polymer solutions is their increased viscosity compared with the pure solvent. This increase is obvious for most polymers even at weight concentrations as low as $0\cdot5$–1 % and depends on:

(1) the nature of the solvent;
(2) the type of polymer;
(3) the molecular weight of the polymer;
(4) the concentration of polymer;
(5) the temperature.

Particularly advantageous from the point of view of molecular weight measurement is the experimental fact that, other things being equal, an increase in molecular weight is paralleled by an increased viscosity. This fact is illustrated in the data of Table 2.13 where the viscosities of solutions of polystyrene in toluene at 30 °C are given, each solution containing a different molecular weight polymer.

TABLE 2.13. VISCOSITIES OF SOLUTIONS
OF POLYSTYRENE IN TOLUENE AT 30 °C
AT A CONCENTRATION
2×10^{-3} g cm^{-3} [5]

$\overline{M}_n$	Viscosity $\times 10^2$ poise
850,000	0·790
556,000	0·717
440,000	0·674
336,000	0·645
163,000	0·602
135,000	0·591
76,000	0·567
Toluene	0·526

On the other hand, the use of this phenomenon suffers from the great disadvantage that it has not been found possible to relate the observed viscosity difference between solution and solvent to the polymer molecular weight without introducing parameters which are experimentally inaccessible. As a result, the viscosity method has been developed into a *secondary* method of molecular weight determination; that is, by taking a series of polymer fractions of known molecular weight ($\overline{M}_w$ or $\overline{M}_n$) and determining the viscosities of their solutions in a common solvent at a fixed temperature, an empirical relation between molecular weight and some function of the solution viscosity is found. Consequently, a determination of the solution viscosity of a fraction of unknown molecular weight but having the same distribution as those employed in the calibration experiments permits the calculation of its molecular weight. Lest it be thought that this procedure is of limited use since it relies on one of the fundamental methods already discussed, we must emphasize that the determination of the viscosity of a polymer solution can be carried out quickly, accurately and with comparatively simple apparatus in contrast to the methods already discussed. In other words the viscosity method has the outstanding merit of experimental simplicity as we shall now see.

The usual method employed to measure the solution and solvent viscosities utilizes an Ostwald viscometer or a modified version due to Ubbelohde. Both of these viscometers are shown in Fig. 2.29. In these viscometers the time taken for the level of solvent or solution to pass between two fixed marks is determined and this is related to the viscosity by Poiseuille's equation as follows:

$$v = \frac{\pi P r^4}{8 \eta l}, \qquad (2.28)$$

where v is the volume rate of flow, P is the pressure difference maintaining the flow, r is the radius of the capillary, η is the viscosity of the liquid, and l is the length of the capillary. This equation is valid as long as the flow is Newtonian and streamlined, and provided that the potential energy of the liquid over and above that which it possesses when the two liquid levels become stationary is solely used up in work against the internal viscous forces and not in imparting kinetic energy to the liquid. In streamline flow every volume element of liquid moves parallel to the walls of the tube in contrast to turbulent flow where the motion is much more complex. If the flow is Newtonian so that the viscous force between two liquid layers is directly proportional to the velocity gradient existing between them, then the flow pattern of the liquid is characterized by a parabolic velocity distribution with the maximum velocity at the centre of the tube as shown in Fig. 2.30.

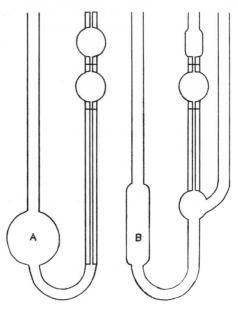

FIG. 2.29. The Ostwald (A) and Ubbelohde suspended level (B) viscometers

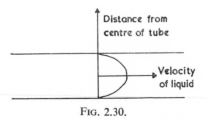

FIG. 2.30.

The condition requiring that the liquid acquires zero kinetic energy is obviously incompatible with the requirement of a finite rate of flow. To avoid, therefore, introducing into eqn. (2.28) a term to correct for the kinetic energy imparted to the liquid, the dimensions of the capillary are chosen so as to make the linear velocity of the liquid at the centre of the tube small; when this is so, the flow is streamlined and usually Newtonian. For polymer solution work, suitable capillary dimensions are 12 cm in length and 0·4 mm in diameter giving flow times of around 150 sec for 2 cm³ of the common organic solvents.

We can now recast eqn. (2·28) into a suitable form for the calculation of the *viscosity ratio*, defined by

$$\frac{\eta_{\text{solution}}}{\eta_{\text{solvent}}} = \frac{\eta_2}{\eta_1} \quad \text{for brevity,}$$

it being understood that both measurements refer to the same temperature. Suppose the volume of liquid contained between the two fixed marks is V and that the flow times for solvent and solution are t_1 and t_2. We can clearly write

$$\frac{V}{t_1} = \frac{\pi P_1 r^4}{8\eta_1 l},$$

$$\frac{V}{t_2} = \frac{\pi P_2 r^4}{8\eta_2 l},$$

so that

$$\frac{\eta_2}{\eta_1} = \frac{t_2 P_2}{t_1 P_1}.$$

Our only remaining problem is the calculation of the ratio of the pressure heads P_1 and P_2. This is straightforward if the same average height of liquid $\bar{h}$ is present in each case† so that the two pressures are in the ratio of the densities of solution and solvent ϱ_2 and ϱ_1.

$$\frac{\eta_2}{\eta_1} = \frac{t_2 \bar{h} \varrho_2 g}{t_1 \bar{h} \varrho_1 g} = \frac{t_2 \varrho_2}{t_1 \varrho_1}.$$

† This condition is fulfilled in the Ubbelohde suspended level viscometer shown in Fig. 2.29; it is only true in the case of the Ostwald viscometer when the same volumes of solvent and solution are compared.

For dilute solutions ϱ_2 and ϱ_1 are practically identical and hence without serious error

$$\frac{\eta_2}{\eta_1} = \frac{t_2}{t_1}.$$

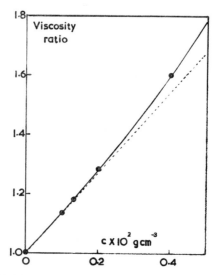

Fig. 2.31. The concentration dependence of the viscosity ratio; data for a sample of polystyrene in toluene at 30°C

The variation of the viscosity ratio with concentration of dissolved polymer can be expressed as a power series in concentration as follows:

$$\frac{\eta_2}{\eta_1} = 1+[\eta]c+kc^2+\ldots, \qquad (2.29)$$

where $[\eta]$ and k are both constants. This equation simply shows that at zero concentration the viscosity ratio is unity and that at higher concentrations this quantity increases in an approximately parabolic fashion with increasing c (the fourth term in the expansion does not become important until high values of

c are reached). This is shown in Fig. 2.31. If we confine our attention to fairly dilute polymer solutions so that only the first three terms in the above expansion need be considered, eqn. (2.29) can be rearranged to the following form:

$$\frac{\eta_2 - \eta_1}{\eta_1 c} = [\eta] + kc.$$

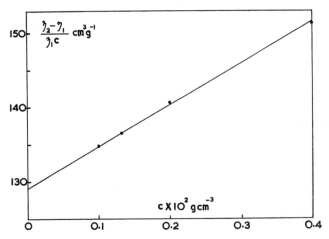

FIG. 2.32. The concentration dependence of the viscosity number at low concentrations; the same data as used in Fig. 2.31

This shows that a plot of the quantity on the left-hand side of the equation against c is a straight line of slope k and intercept at $c = 0$ of $[\eta]$. The data of Fig. 2.31 are plotted in this way in Fig. 2.32 and yield

$$[\eta] = 129 \cdot 2 \text{ cm}^3 \text{ g}^{-1},$$
$$k = 5 \cdot 65 \times 10^3 \text{ cm}^6 \text{ g}^{-2}.$$

The quantity $(\eta_2 - \eta_1)/\eta_1 c$ is termed the viscosity number and hence the quantity $[\eta]$, the *limiting viscosity number*. (In older texts this latter quantity is called the *intrinsic viscosity*.)

For a given polymer–solvent system at a fixed temperature, both $[\eta]$ and k depend on molecular weight. The results shown in Table 2.14 for the typical system polystyrene–toluene at 30°C show that both $[\eta]$ and k increase as the molecular weight increases, the latter of these quantities showing the stronger dependence.

TABLE 2.14. VALUES OF THE TWO CONSTANTS $[\eta]$
AND k FOR A SERIES OF POLYSTYRENE SAMPLES OF
DIFFERING NUMBER AVERAGE MOLECULAR WEIGHT
DISSOLVED IN TOLUENE AT 30°C.[5]

$\overline{M}_n$	$[\eta]$ $cm^3\ g^{-1}$	$k \times 10^{-3}$ $cm^6\ g^{-2}$
76,000	38·2	0·45
135,000	59·2	1·17
163,000	69·6	1·58
336,000	105·4	3·90
440,000	129·2	5·65
556,000	165·0	8·40
850,000	221·0	15·0

Detailed examination of the relationship between these three quantities shows that

$$[\eta] = KM^{\alpha}$$

or

$$\log_{10} [\eta] = \log_{10} K + \alpha \log_{10} M$$

and

$$k = k'[\eta]^2,$$

where M can be either the number or weight average molecular weight. In these equations K, α and k' are independent of molecular weight; the exponent α usually lies between 0·5 and 0·8 and the constant k' (known as the Huggins' constant) between 0·3 and 0·4. Each of these equations is illustrated by the data of Table 2.14 plotted in Figs. 2.33 and 2.34. Clearly, if tables of K and α are available for a variety of polymer–

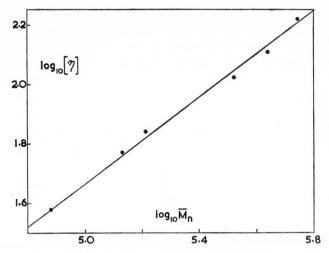

FIG. 2.33. A log–log plot of the limiting viscosity number against molecular weight; data for polystyrene in toluene at 30°C

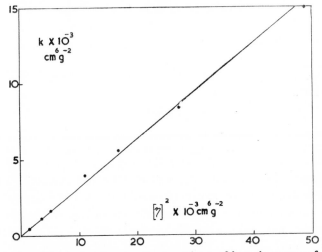

FIG. 2.34. A plot showing the dependence of k on the square of the limiting viscosity number; data for polystyrene in toluene at 30°C

solvent systems, then measurement of $[\eta]$ in a particular case enables M to be computed directly.

The measurement of $[\eta]$, it will be recalled, involves the determination of the viscosity ratio η_2/η_1 at a series of concentrations of polymer. The most obvious method involves the preparation of a series of solutions of differing concentration and the separate determination of the corresponding flow-times in the simple Ostwald viscometer shown in Fig. 2.29. In practice it is more convenient to prepare a single solution of the highest concentration to be used, say 1 or 2%, and carry out the dilution in the viscometer itself. For this purpose, the Ubbelohde modification is particularly convenient since the effective pressure head maintaining the flow is independent of the amount of liquid in the large bulb and hence of the dilution. With this device and with proper attention to accurate dilution, mixing, temperature control and exclusion of dust, viscosity ratios at five separate concentrations can be obtained within a couple of hours and hence a molecular weight rapidly calculated.

In Table 2.15 a few examples of K and α are given for several polymer–solvent systems.

In particular, the values for the system polystyrene–toluene at 30°C are

$$K = 1.05 \times 10^{-2} \text{ cm}^3 \text{ g}^{-1},$$
$$\alpha = 0.73.$$

Hence the value of $[\eta]$ obtained from Fig. 2.32, 129·2 cm³ g⁻¹, corresponds to a molecular weight of 440,000. Assuming that the distribution of molecular weights within this sample is the same as that used in the calibration experiments, the above molecular weight is a number average molecular weight. If the molecular weight distribution is markedly different, then the molecular weight so obtained is neither a weight nor a number average value but a viscosity average defined by the

TABLE 2.15. VALUES OF K AND α FOR VARIOUS
POLYMER–SOLVENT SYSTEMS

Polymer	Solvent	t °C	$K \times 10^2$ cm³ g^{-1}	α	Calibration method
Polyisobutylene	Benzene	24	8·30	0·50	Osmotic pressure
Polyisobutylene	Benzene	60	2·60	0·66	Osmotic pressure
cis 1,4 Polyiso-prene	Toluene	25	5·00	0·67	Osmotic pressure
Poly α-methyl styrene	Toluene	30	1·08	0·71	Light scattering
Polystyrene	Toluene	30	1·05	0·73	Osmotic pressure
Polystyrene	Benzene	25	1·03	0·74	Osmotic pressure
Polymethyl methacrylate	Benzene	25	0·57	0·76	Light scattering

equation

$$\overline{M}_v = \left(\frac{\sum N_i M_i^{1+\alpha}}{\sum N_i M_i} \right)^{1/\alpha}.$$

In the special case when $\alpha = 1$, $\overline{M}_v$ becomes identical with $\overline{M}_w$. However, since α usually lies between 0·5 and 0·8, the viscosity average molecular weight is normally less than $\overline{M}_w$ but rather greater than $\overline{M}_n$.

So far we have not considered the changes produced when a different solvent type is used for a particular polymer or when the temperature at which the measurements are made is altered. In principle we can study the effects produced by such changes in one of two ways; either we can choose a particular concentration, say 1%, and compare the viscosity ratio in different solvents and at different temperatures or we can evaluate the parameters $[\eta]$ and k' and study the variation in these quantities. The latter procedure has proved to be the more rewarding for, as we shall see shortly, some physical interpretation can be put on the limiting viscosity number $[\eta]$. For this reason, we give in Table 2.16 some numerical values of $[\eta]$ and k' for polyisobutylene of weight average molecular weight 1,460,000 in two solvents at several temperatures.

TABLE 2.16. VALUES OF $[\eta]$ AND k'
FOR POLYISOBUTYLENE
$(\bar{M}_w = 1,460,000)$[9]

Solvent	t °C	$[\eta]$ cm³g⁻¹	k'
Benzene	25	137	0·47
	35	190	0·37
	50	251	0·35
	65	280	0·35
Cyclohexane	20	515	0·36
	30	515	0·36
	45	515	0·36
	60	515	0·36

Two points from this table deserve comment. Firstly, the values of $[\eta]$ in cyclohexane, a "good" solvent for this polymer, are rather greater than those in benzene, a "poor" solvent, at comparable temperatures. Secondly, the values of $[\eta]$ in the "poor" solvent are appreciably temperature dependent unlike those in the "good" solvent. This behaviour is quite general.

To understand these results, we shall have to understand the physical significance of the limiting viscosity number and the underlying reason why it increases with molecular weight. For this purpose, we re-examine the simplified form of eqn. (2.29):

$$\frac{\eta_2}{\eta_1} = 1 + [\eta]c + kc^2.$$

The first term, unity, expresses the condition that, when no polymer is present, the viscosity is necessarily that of the pure solvent. The significance of the second and third terms can be deduced most simply by first replacing c in terms of N, the number of molecules per unit volume, and differentiating the resulting equation with respect to N. Thus

$$\frac{\eta_2}{\eta_1} = 1 + \frac{[\eta]\overline{M}_n}{N_0} \cdot N + \frac{k(\overline{M}_n)^2}{N_0^2} \cdot N^2 \qquad (2.30)$$

and therefore,

$$\frac{d(\eta_2/\eta_1)}{dN} = \frac{[\eta]\overline{M}_n}{N_0} + \frac{2k(\overline{M}_n)^2}{N_0^2} \cdot N.$$

The differential form of eqn. (2.30) shows that the addition of 1 molecule to unit volume of the solution increases the viscosity ratio by

1. a constant quantity $\dfrac{[\eta]\overline{M}_n}{N_0}$;

2. an amount which depends directly on the number of molecules already present.

Thus the second term of eqn. (2.29) expresses the fact that a proportion of the viscosity ratio arises as a result of each polymer molecule present in unit volume making its own particular contribution of $[\eta]\overline{M}_n/N_0$. The third term shows that the remainder of the viscosity ratio arises as a result of the interaction between polymer molecules for, on its account, the increase in the viscosity ratio on addition of 1 molecule to unit volume of the solution depends on the number of molecules present.

To proceed further, we shall restrict our attention to polymer solutions in which the polymer molecules are separated from one another by large numbers of solvent molecules; that is, we shall not consider the problems which arise from polymer entanglements. The approximate upper limit of the concentration for which this restriction holds is calculable as follows. Suppose in unit volume of solution, we have a weight

c of polymer of number average molecular weight $\overline{M}_n$—we then have $cN_0/\overline{M}_n$ molecules present per unit volume. Suppose we put each molecule in a cubical box of side d with its centre at the centre of the box. Obviously, we must have $cN_0/\overline{M}_u$ such boxes in our unit volume and therefore

$$d = \left(\frac{\overline{M}_n}{cN_0}\right)^{1/3}$$

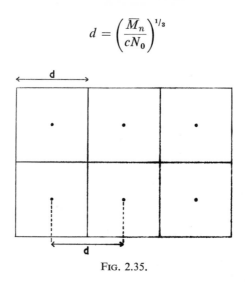

FIG. 2.35.

If we refer to Fig. 2.35, it is clear that the length of the side of each box is equal to the average distance between the centres of the molecules. The situation which we shall consider corresponds to d being greater than the root mean square end-to-end distance of the polymer chain. The values of d calculated for various concentrations are plotted as a function of molecular weight in Fig. 2.36. On this same figure is drawn the variation of the root mean square end-to-end distance with molecular weight for polymethyl methacrylate in acetone at 20°C.[10] In that these end-to-end distances are typical of many polymers, Fig. 2.36 shows that, in dilute solutions, molecular entanglements can be neglected.

Now the viscosity of a liquid is a measure of the rate of energy dissipation occurring in unit volume when the liquid flows. When a velocity gradient is set up in a pure solvent, solvent molecules move relative to one another and consequently work is done against the intermolecular forces of attraction.

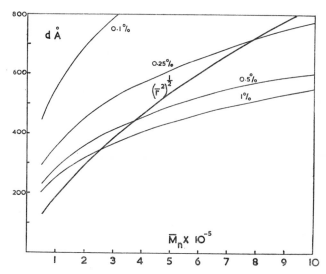

FIG. 2.36. A plot showing the approximate concentrations for a series of molecular weights below which molecular entanglements are unimportant. The lightly drawn family of curves shows the distances between molecular centres as a function of molecular weight for a series of concentrations (w/v). The prominent curve shows the corresponding root mean square end-to-end distances for a typical polymer–solvent system. The area to the left of the prominent curve corresponds to conditions where entanglements are unimportant

The rate at which this work is done, that is, the rate of energy dissipation, determines the solvent viscosity. When a polymer is dissolved in a solvent, additional molecular motions must be considered and it is these which give rise to the enhanced viscosity.

To understand this more clearly, let us consider the motion of a particular polymer molecule as the solution flows down a tube. For simplicity, let us simulate the molecule by the model shown in Fig. 2.37, each sphere representing one segment; this model is sometimes called the "pearl necklace" model.

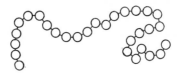

FIG. 2.37.

As a consequence of its large size, the polymer molecule experiences a torque due to the different solvent velocities at different points along its length. Consequently a continuous rotation is superimposed on the downward motion of the molecule;[†] that is, the polymer molecule "tumbles" down the tube. This is shown in Fig. 2.38.

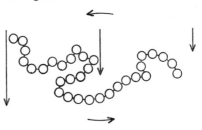

FIG. 2.38.

This rotation constitutes an additional source of energy dissipation as polymer segments sweep across the flow lines and hence the presence of the polymer molecules results in an increased viscosity relative to the pure solvent. For low velocity gradients where it may be assumed that the average dimen-

† Compare the motion of a fairly large irregularly shaped body in a river.

sions of the polymer molecules are unaffected by the solvent motion, the effect is directly proportional to the number of polymer molecules present per unit volume, the constant of proportionality (essentially the limiting viscosity number) being dependent on the dimensions of the molecules themselves. From this, it follows that any factor which increases the polymer dimensions necessarily increases $[\eta]$. Thus an increase in the molecular weight of a given polymer resulting as it does in an increase in the polymer dimensions is necessarily accompanied by an increase in $[\eta]$. For the same reason, a change in the solvent type from a "poor" solvent to a "good" solvent results in an increase in $[\eta]$. Finally, the considerable increase in $[\eta]$ in the case of "poor" solvents resulting from an increase in temperature is understandable in these terms for once again the fundamental effect is the increase in the polymer dimensions as the solvent "improves".

Quantitatively, the effects cannot be so easily accounted for because of the difficulty of writing down the appropriate velocity gradient within the polymer molecule itself. If it is assumed that the velocity gradient is unchanged in the vicinity of a polymer molecule, then we have what is termed the "free-draining" coil model; in this model, the velocity of a solvent molecule at any point in the polymer is identical with that which it would have had at the same point, had the polymer molecule not been present. The analysis of such a model produces the result that $[\eta]$ should be almost directly proportional to the molecular weight; i.e. doubling the molecular weight should produce just over twice the value of $[\eta]$. Another alternative is to regard the polymer molecule as impermeable to the flow of solvent through it; that is, the solvent molecules within the polymer coil move at the same velocity as the polymer molecule itself. Analysis of this model produces the result that $[\eta]$ should be almost directly proportional to $M^{1/2}$. The experimental results clearly indicate that neither of these ex-

treme descriptions of the solvent flow in the presence of polymer molecules is correct. The real situation is that which we
would expect on general grounds, namely that the solvent flow
is perturbed from that in the pure solvent by the presence of
the polymer molecules but not to such an extent as to be immo-
bilized relative to them. A proper account of such effects is
clearly extremely difficult. Furthermore if this perturbation of
the solvent flow pattern extends into the solvent regions separating the polymer molecules, we can account for what we have
termed "interaction between polymer molecules" without involving entanglement as the cause. This again is a difficult
problem to set down properly and consequently the prediction
of the third term of eqn. (2.29) under our chosen conditions
cannot be successfully accomplished. Nevertheless Flory has
given an account of the viscosity of such solutions which leads
to the very simple expression for the limiting viscosity number
for polymers of molecular weight 10,000 and over

$$[\eta] = \Phi \, \frac{(\overline{r^2})^{3/2}}{\overline{M}_n},$$

where Φ is a universal constant independent of solvent, molecular weight and temperature and equal to $2 \cdot 5 \times 10^{23}$ mole^{-1}.
This expression shows that the limiting viscosity number is
determined by the dimensions of the polymer molecule in solution.

CHAPTER 3

CONDENSATION POLYMERIZATION

IN THIS chapter we propose to examine the process of condensation polymerization in some detail. As its name implies, the formation of polymer is accompanied by the production of a simple, low molecular weight substance such as water, hydrogen chloride, etc. Typical of condensation polymers are the polyesters, polyamides and polyurethanes in which the linkages formed in the condensation reaction are:

$$-\overset{\underset{\displaystyle \parallel}{}}{C}-O-$$
$$\overset{O}{}$$

$$-NH-\overset{\underset{\displaystyle \parallel}{}}{C}-$$
$$\overset{O}{}$$

$$-NH-\overset{\underset{\displaystyle \parallel}{}}{C}-O-$$
$$\overset{O}{}$$

The reactions by which such polymers are prepared are the familiar condensation reactions described in the standard texts of organic chemistry, the only special requirement being that the monomers used must be *polyfunctional*. If each monomer possesses two functional groups only, linear polymers are produced; three-dimensional network structures, on the other hand, are formed when the functionality of one or more of the reactants exceeds two. The following examples illustrate the above points more explicitly.

PRODUCTION OF LINEAR POLYMERS

The polyesters

Polyesters are formed by the reactions between an alcohol and an acid or an acid chloride and by ester interchange. For example, the reaction between adipic acid and ethylene glycol to produce polymer proceeds by a series of successive condensations. The first stage is the formation of an hydroxy carboxylic acid in which the difunctionality of the reactants is preserved in the product.

$$HOOC(CH_2)_4CO\,\vdots OH + H\,\vdots O(CH_2)_2OH$$

adipic acid　　↓　　ethylene glycol

$$HOOC(CH_2)_4COO(CH_2)_2OH + H_2O$$

This product can then react with either adipic acid or ethylene glycol to produce a dicarboxylic acid or a diol, thus

$$HOOC(CH_2)_4COO(CH_2)_2OOC(CH_2)_4COOH + H_2O$$

$+$ adipic acid　↗

$$HOOC(CH_2)_4COO(CH_2)_2OH$$

$+$ ethylene glycol　↘

$$HO(CH_2)_2OOC(CH_2)_4COO(CH_2)_2OH + H_2O$$

In addition it can react with another similar molecule to produce a polymer containing four monomer residues

$$HOOC(CH_2)_4COO(CH_2)_2O\,\vdots H + HO\,\vdots OC(CH_2)_4COO(CH_2)_2OH$$

$$\downarrow$$

$$HOOC(CH_2)_4COO(CH_2)_2OOC(CH_2)_4COO(CH_2)_2OH + H_2O$$

In these and subsequent similar reactions it should be noted that the molecule produced possesses two end groups both capable of further condensation. At the early stages, the latter reaction is less likely than the previous two since the concentrations of the adipic acid and ethylene glycol are so much greater than that of the hydroxy acid. Obviously, as the reaction proceeds and water is eliminated from the system, the greater is the probability of formation of molecules containing a large number of ester linkages—the average molecular weight, therefore, increases as the functional groups are converted to ester groups. Consequently, the molecular weight increases with conversion. If the original mixture contained exactly equimolar quantities of adipic acid and ethylene glycol, the molecular weight approaches infinity as the conversion approaches 100%; on the other hand, an excess of, say, adipic acid restricts the average molecular weight of the mixture to a finite value.

In addition to using stoichiometric equivalent amounts of the two reactants as far as is practicable, polyesterification reactions of this type are usually carried out:

(1) using a catalyst of the acid-base type (e.g. p-toluene sulphonic acid or antimony trioxide);

(2) with the reactants at fairly high temperatures in the molten state;

(3) with an efficient arrangement for continuously removing the water produced (e.g. by pumping off the water under high vacuum).

The use of catalysts, elevated temperatures and high concentrations (as in the melt) ensures that the large extents of reaction required are obtained in reasonable periods of time. The reason for the removal of water is perhaps less obvious. In all esterification reactions of this type, the amount of product formed is determined by the position of an equilibrium involving water; an elementary example of such an equilibrium is that set up between ethyl acetate, water, ethyl alcohol and acetic acid, thus:

$$CH_3COOC_2H_5 + H_2O \rightleftharpoons CH_3COOH + C_2H_5OH$$

Exactly similar equilibria are set up at each step of the poly-esterification reaction and unless the concentration of water is deliberately maintained at a low level, the conversion of reactants to high molecular weight polymer is limited.

Rather less demanding from the experimental point of view (and for that matter from a theoretical aspect) is the esterification of an ω-hydroxy carboxylic acid. For, if such a substance can be obtained in the pure state, the stoichiometric equivalence of the OH and COOH groups is assured. An example to which we shall refer later is the polymerization of 12-hydroxy stearic acid,

$$HOCH(CH_2)_{10}COOH.$$
$$C_6H_{13}$$

The reaction between a diol and a diacid chloride rather than a diacid has the advantage of greater speed—otherwise very similar considerations apply to this case as to the one just discussed. A particular example is the reaction between tetramethylene glycol and isophthaloyl chloride where the first stage is as follows:

tetramethylene glycol   ↓ isophthaloyl chloride

Subsequent stages are exactly analogous so that the polymer finally is

Finally, there is the process of ester interchange or alcoholysis. When an alcohol and an ester are mixed together, interchange of the alkoxy groups takes place. For example, methyl acetate and ethyl alcohol react together to give ethyl acetate and methyl alcohol; an equilibrium involving all four species is finally reached, thus

$$CH_3CO \vdots OCH_3 + H \vdots OC_2H_5 \rightleftharpoons CH_3COOC_2H_5 + CH_3OH$$

The rate of approach of the system to equilibrium is increased by the presence of acid catalysts as is the analogous ester hydrolysis reaction already mentioned which occurs when water replaces one of the alcohols. To adapt this general reaction to the production of polymer, the starting material has to be an ester formed from a diacid and an excess of a volatile diol. An example will make the process clearer. The commercial polymer "terylene", polyethylene terephthalate, is made from the compound bis-(β-hydroxy ethyl) terephthalate

by arranging the experimental conditions so that any ethylene glycol formed by ester interchange is continuously removed. The first step of the polymerization is the reaction between two molecules of the above monomer, one of which can be regarded as the ester and the other as the alcohol.

† This material is also made by an ester interchange reaction; dimethyl terephthalate is reacted with ethylene glycol giving the monomer and methanol, the methanol being continuously removed to obtain high yields.

If no attempt were made to remove the ethylene glycol so formed, the equilibrium mixture would contain only small amounts of dimer; as it is, the displacement of the equilibrium ensures that this product is formed initially in considerable amounts. We use the word *initially* advisedly because, if the structure of this product is examined carefully, it is apparent that it too can undergo an exactly similar interchange reaction with the monomer or with an exactly similar molecule to itself or with any other molecule possessing the end group $HO(CH_2)_2$. Consequently, provided that ethylene glycol is continuously removed from the reaction system, the reaction does not stop at this first stage but continues on and on to produce polymer of substantial molecular weight—as the amount of ethylene glycol removed approaches one-half of the amount originally used to form the monomer, so the average molecular weight of the polymer approaches infinity.[†]

The occurrence of this ester interchange reaction has two other consequences in addition to its adaptation to polymer production. Firstly, the point made earlier (p. 121) regarding the necessity of taking stoichiometric equivalent amounts of a diacid and a diol requires qualification. If the diol can be removed conveniently from the reaction system, then the presence of an excess initially is not particularly serious. In such an event the di-hydroxy-ended, low molecular weight polymer produced in the early stages will continue to polymerize as a result of the elimination of the diol by ester interchange. Secondly, in any polyester sample containing molecules with hydroxy end groups, a set of exchange equilibria will be set up between the various molecules if the temperature is high enough for the interchange reactions to proceed with sufficient speed. The characteristics of the molecular weight distribution of the sample are, however, unaltered by these reactions. On

[† In commercial practice, the molecular weight is limited by the addition of a small amount of acetic acid, a monofunctional reagent.

the other hand, if two different samples of such a polymer with differing molecular weights are mixed together, the occurrence of these ester interchange reactions results in a relaxation of the distribution to that appropriate to the number of molecules in the mixture. For example, suppose we take 100 g of a polymer of number average molecular weight 10,000 and the same amount of a polymer of number average molecular weight 30,000. The sequence of events following mixing is illustrated schematically below, n indicating the number of moles actually present in the sample. We shall assume that the distribution of molecular weights in the two samples and in the final mixture conforms to the most probable distribution equation discussed in Chapter 2; in such a case, we can assume that the weight average molecular weight is twice the number average value without serious error.

$$\boxed{100 \text{ g}} \qquad\qquad \boxed{100 \text{ g}}$$

$$\bar{M}_n = 10,000 \qquad\qquad \bar{M}_n = 30,000$$

$$\bar{M}_w = 20,000 \qquad\qquad \bar{M}_w = 60,000$$

$$n = \frac{100}{10,000} \text{ mole} \qquad\qquad n = \frac{100}{30,000} \text{ mole}$$

mixing without ester interchange

$$\boxed{200 \text{ g}}$$

$$n = \frac{100}{10,000} + \frac{100}{30,000} = \frac{400}{30,000} \text{ mole}$$

$$\bar{M}_n = \frac{200}{400/30,000} = 15,000$$

$$\bar{M}_w = \frac{100 \times 20,000 + 100 \times 60,000}{200} = 40,000$$

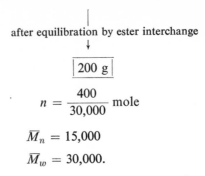

$$n = \frac{400}{30,000} \text{ mole}$$

$$\overline{M}_n = 15,000$$

$$\overline{M}_w = 30,000.$$

The number of molecules or moles does not alter as a result of the interchange reactions—two molecules which exchange alkoxy groups necessarily produce another two molecules. All that happens is that a redistribution of chain lengths takes place to conform with the most probable distribution equation. Thus in the example given, where the weight of the mixture and the number of moles present fix the number average molecular weight at 15,000, the weight average molecular weight alters from its initial value of 40,000 to a value of 30,000, twice the number average molecular weight of the mixture.

The polyamides

The preparation of polyamides is usually achieved through the condensation of amino groups with carboxylic acid or acid chloride groups. Thus, the usual reactants are:

1. diamines + dicarboxylic acids;
2. ω-amino carboxylic acids;
3. diamines + dicarboxylic acid chlorides.

The first two reactions are exemplified by the processes used to prepare commercial nylons. Nylon 6.6†—the common

† The designation 6.6 indicates the number of carbon atoms in firstly the diamine chain and secondly the carboxylic acid chain from which the

nylon—is made in the melt from hexamethylene diamine and adipic acid. In this particular case, the stoichiometric equivalence of the functional groups is achieved very conveniently by isolating the 1:1 salt before allowing the condensation to take place. The process can be represented as follows:

$$n \text{ H}_2\text{N(CH}_2)_6\text{NH}_2 \quad + \quad n \text{ HOOC(CH}_2)_4\text{COOH}$$

hexamethylene diamine $\qquad$ adipic acid
$$\downarrow \text{ crystallization from solution}$$

$$n \text{ H}_3\overset{+}{\text{N}}(\text{CH}_2)_6\overset{+}{\text{N}}\text{H}_3 \cdot \overset{-}{\text{O}}\text{OC(CH}_2)_4\text{CO}\overset{-}{\text{O}}$$

nylon salt
$$\downarrow \text{ in the melt}$$

$$\text{H}\{\text{NH(CH}_2)_6\text{NHCO(CH}_2)_4\text{CO}\}_n\text{OH} + (2n-1)\text{H}_2\text{O}$$

polyhexamethylene adipamide (nylon 6.6)

Another polyamide with useful fibre-forming properties is that formed from ε-amino caproic acid (the resulting polymer, nylon 6, can also be made from caprolactam). The reaction is simply

$$n \text{ H}_2\text{N(CH}_2)_5\text{COOH} \rightarrow \text{H}\{\text{HN(CH}_2)_5\text{CO}\}_n\text{OH} + (n-1)\text{H}_2\text{O}$$

ε-amino caproic acid $\qquad\qquad$ nylon 6

which is exactly analogous to the condensation of an ω-hydroxy carboxylic acid.

The third reaction, that between a diamine and a dicarboxylic acid chloride, has the advantage of proceeding with rather greater speed than the previous two under comparable conditions. In fact the reaction rate is sufficiently rapid in general that the process of *interfacial condensation* can be used to prepare the polymer. To explain this very convenient preparative method, we shall take a specific example—the formation of nylon 6.10 from hexamethylene diamine and sebacoyl chloride. The diamine is dissolved in water and the diacid chloride

polymer is formed. Thus nylon 4.10 indicates the polyamide formed from tetramethylene diamine and sebacic acid. Where only one number is given, it is taken that only a single monomer is involved, either an ω-amino acid or a lactam.

in some solvent such as carbon tetrachloride which is immiscible with water. The less dense aqueous solution is then poured carefully on to the solution in carbon tetrachloride and immediately a film of nylon 6.10 is formed at the interface. To produce polymer continuously, it is only necessary to draw off

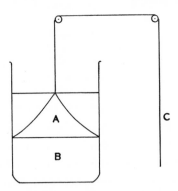

FIG. 3.1. An example of interfacial condensation; A is an aqueous solution of hexamethylene diamine, and B a solution of sebacoyl chloride in carbon tetrachloride. The polymer formed at the interface is drawn off in the form of a fibre as at C

the film so formed and regenerate a fresh interface as shown in Fig. 3·1. The reaction is

$$n \, H_2N(CH_2)_6NH_2 \quad + \quad n \, ClOC(CH_2)_8COCl$$
hexamethylene diamine   sebacoyl chloride
$$\downarrow$$
$$H\{HN(CH_2)_6NHCO(CH_2)_8CO\}_nCl + (2n-1)HCl$$
nylon 6.10

To prevent the depletion of the diamine concentration at the interface due to the secondary reaction with HCl, it is usual to work with an excess of the diamine in the aqueous phase. The fact that this is a practicable procedure shows that in interfacial condensation it is not necessary to have exact equivalence of functional groups. Apart from this advantage over melt condensation, the method has the additional merit that it can be employed at much lower temperatures thus permitting the use of monomers relatively unstable to heat.

The polyurethanes

Finally in this brief account of the reactions employed in linear condensation polymerization, we mention one method of preparing the polyurethanes. These compounds contain the linkage —NH—C—O— and can be formed by the reaction
$$\overset{\|}{O}$$
between a diamine and a bis-chloroformate made from an appropriate diol and phosgene. For example, the reaction between hexamethylene diamine and ethylene bis-chloroformate produces a polyurethane in accordance with the following scheme.

$$n \, H_2N(CH_2)_6NH_2 \quad + \quad n \, ClCO(CH_2)_2OCCl$$
$$\overset{\|}{O} \qquad \overset{\|}{O}$$

hexamethylene diamine   ethylene bis-chloroformate
$$\downarrow$$

$$H\left\{HN(CH_2)_6NHCO(CH_2)_2OC \atop \qquad\quad \overset{\|}{O} \qquad\quad \overset{\|}{O}\right\}_n Cl+(2n-1)HCl$$

Ring formation

These formulations of the reactions of difunctional monomers have ignored the possibility of ring formation. Taking as an example the ω-hydroxy carboxylic acids, lactone formation may take place as well as the polymer producing reaction already discussed, thus:

$$n \, HO(CH_2)_m COOH \nearrow \begin{array}{l} n \, O(CH_2)_m CO + n \, H_2O \\ \underline{|\qquad\qquad|} \end{array}$$
$$\searrow H\{O(CH_2)_m CO\}_n OH+(n-1)H_2O$$

In principle, any of the hydroxy carboxylic acids produced in the polymerization process may undergo a similar cyclization reaction. For example, the product of the first stage of the polymer forming reaction

$$HO(CH_2)_mCOO(CH_2)_mCOOH$$

could form the lactone

$$O(CH_2)_mCOO(CH_2)_mCO$$

instead of reacting with another hydroxy carboxylic acid molecule. The extent to which ring as opposed to chain formation takes place is determined largely by the size of the ring so formed. Five- and six-membered rings (counting the oxygen atoms) are particularly favoured structures since very little deformation of the bond angles is required in their formation. Consequently, the production of rings of this size often proceeds to the exclusion of polymerization; on the other hand, rings containing a larger number of atoms are not usually obtained. Thus γ-hydroxy butyric acid cannot be polymerized, the stable compound γ-butyrolactone being produced instead.

$$HO(CH_2)_3COOH \rightarrow O(CH_2)_3CO + H_2O$$

Very similar considerations apply to lactam formation from the analogous amino carboxylic acids.

PRODUCTION OF THREE-DIMENSIONAL
NETWORK POLYMERS

We have already stated that, as soon as the functionality of one of the monomers exceeds two, the possibility arises of the formation of branched polymers and thence structures extending in three dimensions. A particularly simple example of such a monomer is glycerol

$$CH_2OH$$
$$|$$
$$CHOH$$
$$|$$
$$CH_2OH$$

Each of the hydroxy groups can be esterified and so after a few condensations with a suitable dibasic acid, the resulting molecule could have the structure shown schematically below:

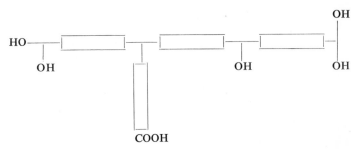

In this representation, only the unreacted functional groups are shown explicitly, the glycerol and dibasic acid skeletons being symbolized by ⌐ and ▭ respectively. It will be apparent that every time the trifunctional monomer is incorporated into the polymer, the number of functional groups attached to the polymer increases by one. Consequently, as the conversion of the monomers into polymer proceeds, the number of possible ways in which the monomers may add on to the growing polymer increases rapidly. Complex structures are thus produced from the earliest stages of the reaction. As the size of the polymers increases, there arises a strong probability that condensation may take place either between two functional groups situated at different points on the same molecule or in such a way as to link one polymer molecule with another. Since a relatively small number of such cross-links results in the formation of a three-dimensional network, it is not surprising that this effect is observed to take place quite suddenly at a particular percentage conversion in a polymerizing system of this type. The stage at which a polymer network is set up throughout the polymerizing system is called the "gel point" since at this point the mixture changes from a viscous liquid to a gel showing no tendency to flow. As would be expected from our account, the polymer formed in the polymerization before the "gel point" is soluble whereas once the space network structure is produced the polymer becomes quite insoluble in any solvent. Although the preparation of these branched and network polymers is not difficult to understand, it is not our intention to examine these reactions in more detail. Suffice it to say that the polymers so produced are of considerable industrial importance.

THE KINETICS OF POLYMERIZATION

To illustrate the principles used in formulating the kinetics of condensation polymerization, we shall consider the special case of the acid-catalysed self-condensation of an ω-hydroxy carboxylic acid. By this choice, we eliminate a number of complicating factors which, we hope, will help to clarify the kinetic treatment. If we write the ω-hydroxy carboxylic acid as HORCOOH, where R represents the hydrocarbon skeleton, the stoichiometry of the reaction is

$$n \text{ HORCOOH} \rightarrow \text{H(ORCO)}_n\text{OH} + (n-1)\text{H}_2\text{O}$$

The course of the reaction may be described as follows: initially, the monomer disappears by reaction with itself to form dimers[†]; as the dimer concentration builds up, trimers are formed in the reaction mixture from the condensation of monomer with dimer. Further reaction in the mixture of monomer, dimer and trimer results in the appearance of tetramer, pentamer and hexamer, and as these species in turn react, the mixture becomes increasingly complex. At any time after the reaction has commenced, the polymerization can be represented by the series of elementary steps shown below.

[†] We use the words dimer, trimer, etc., in this context to indicate the number of monomer residues present in the molecule. Since water is eliminated at each condensation step, their molecular weights are not simple multiples of the monomer molecular weight.

$$\text{HORCOOH} + \begin{cases} \text{HORCOOH} \rightarrow \text{H(ORCO)}_2\text{OH} & + \text{H}_2\text{O} \\ \text{H(ORCO)}_2\text{OH} \rightarrow \text{H(ORCO)}_3\text{OH} & + \text{H}_2\text{O} \\ \vdots \\ \text{H(ORCO)}_i\text{OH} \rightarrow \text{H(ORCO)}_{i+1}\text{OH} & + \text{H}_2\text{O} \\ \vdots \end{cases}$$

$$\text{H(ORCO)}_2\text{OH} + \begin{cases} \text{HORCOOH} \rightarrow \text{H(ORCO)}_3\text{OH} & + \text{H}_2\text{O} \\ \text{H(ORCO)}_2\text{OH} \rightarrow \text{H(ORCO)}_4\text{OH} & + \text{H}_2\text{O} \\ \vdots \\ \text{H(ORCO)}_i\text{OH} \rightarrow \text{H(ORCO)}_{i+2}\text{OH} & + \text{H}_2\text{O} \\ \vdots \end{cases}$$

and so on.

More briefly, this set of equations can be summarized as

$$\text{H(ORCO)}_i\text{OH} + \text{H(ORCO)}_j\text{OH} \rightarrow \text{H(ORCO)}_{i+j}\text{OH} + \text{H}_2\text{O}$$

where any value of i can be taken with any value of j.

To proceed further, we have to make an important assumption. We assume that the reactivity of the two functional groups is unaltered by the length of the chain to which they are attached. This argument has been tested by measuring the rate constants for the esterification of the lower members of a homologous series of monobasic acids with a particular alcohol. The results demonstrate that the assumption is valid except for the early members of the series. Nevertheless, the extension of the principle to functional groups attached to polymers has been challenged on the grounds that the slow diffusion of the molecules and the shielding of the reaction sites from one another by coiling both tend to prevent the maintenance of the same *effective* collision rate as that which obtains between the same functional groups at the same concentration attached to simple molecules. The success of the subsequent kinetic analysis in accounting for the experimental observations shows that these objections are not justified,[†] the diffusion rate of functional groups attached to polymers being quite adequate under normal polymerization conditions to give comparable rates of reaction to those found when they are attached to simple molecules.

We define a rate constant k in such a way that it relates the rate of disappearance of the total carboxyl (or hydroxyl) group concentration to the total concentrations of carboxyl and hydroxyl groups.

$$-\frac{d[\text{total COOH}]}{dt} = -\frac{d[\text{total OH}]}{dt}$$

$$= k[\text{total COOH}][\text{total OH}]. \quad (3.1)$$

Thus, in a mixture containing monomer and dimer only, the total loss of carboxyl groups is

$$-\frac{d[\text{total COOH}]}{dt} = k[\text{monomer} + \text{dimer}][\text{monomer} + \text{dimer}],$$

which on multiplying out gives

$$k[\text{monomer}]^2 + 2k[\text{monomer}][\text{dimer}] + k[\text{dimer}]^2.$$

The factor of two arises because the probability of reaction between monomer and dimer is twice that between monomer and monomer when the concentrations of monomer and dimer are equal. Although the rate of loss of carboxyl groups by the monomer–dimer reaction is thus twice that in the monomer–monomer reaction, the rate of disappearance of monomer is the same in each case.

It should be noted that the constant k is a composite quantity. In fact

$$k = k'f([\text{catalyst}]),$$

where k' is the fundamental rate constant and $f([\text{catalyst}])$

[†] Support for the general argument is also obtained from the success of the kinetic treatment of free radical addition polymerization given in Chapter 4.

represents some function of the catalyst concentration. k is thus only a constant if the substance added is a true catalyst and does not alter in concentration as the reaction proceeds. In the derivations that follow, it should be understood that the equations given are only valid in so far as the reaction conditions conform to this proviso.

It is convenient at this stage to contract our notation. We write M_1 for the monomer HORCOOH, M_2 for the dimer HORCOORCOOH and so on; M_i thus represents the i-mer $H(ORCO)_iOH$ containing $(i-1)$ ester linkages. Using this symbolism, let us think about the instantaneous rate of disappearance of COOH groups from a reaction system composed of a mixture of M_1, M_2, M_3, ..., M_i, ... According to our definition of the rate constant k, this is given by

$$-\frac{d[COOH]}{dt} = k[COOH][OH],$$

where [COOH] and [OH] represent the total concentrations of carboxyl and hydroxyl groups present in the reaction mixture at the particular instant of time. Since the disappearance of each carboxyl group is accompanied by the disappearance of an hydroxyl group, the same expression gives the instantaneous rate of diminution of the hydroxyl group concentration. Now because we took a pure hydroxy carboxylic acid to exemplify our kinetic analysis not only did we ensure that the initial concentrations of the two functional groups were equal but also that they remained so throughout the polymerization. That is,

$$[COOH] = [OH]$$

at all stages of the reaction. The previous rate equation thus simplifies to a simple second order equation

$$-\frac{d[COOH]}{dt} = k[COOH]^2 \tag{3.2}$$

which on integration gives

$$\frac{1}{[COOH]} - \frac{1}{[COOH]_0} = kt \tag{3.3}$$

$$\text{or} \quad [COOH] = \frac{[COOH]_0}{1 + k[COOH]_0 t}, \tag{3.4}$$

where $[COOH]_0$ is the initial concentration of COOH groups (under the usual experimental conditions, this would be equal to the initial number of moles of monomer per litre of melt).

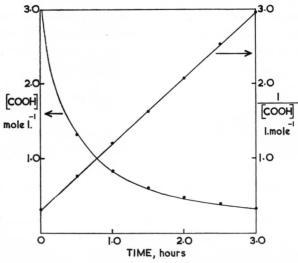

FIG. 3.2. The total carboxyl group concontration and its reciprocal plotted as a function of time for the condensation of 12-hydroxy stearic acid at 160·5°C catalysed by p-toluene sulphonic acid at a concentration of $3·31 \times 10^{-2}$ mole l.$^{-1}$

Figure 3.2 shows some numerical data obtained from the experimental study of the condensation of 12-hydroxy stearic acid[11]

$$HOCH(CH_2)_{10}COOH$$
$$|$$
$$C_6H_{13}$$

catalysed by p-toluene sulphonic acid in the melt at $160.5°C$ plotted in accordance with eqns. (3.3) and (3.4). These data were obtained by sampling the reaction mixture at various times; the samples were then titrated with ethanolic sodium hydroxide to obtain the concentration of carboxyl groups. From the slope of the straight line of $1/[COOH]$ against t,

$$k = 2.47 \times 10^{-4} \text{ l. mole}^{-1} \text{ sec}^{-1}$$

at the particular catalyst concentration employed, 3.31×10^{-2} mole l.$^{-1}$

Equations (3.3) and (3.4) can be transformed to show the dependence of the extent of reaction p, on time. The extent of reaction is the fractional equivalent of the percentage conversion and is defined by the equation

$$p = \frac{\text{number of COOH (or OH) groups reacted}}{\text{number of COOH (or OH) groups taken originally}} \cdot \quad (3.5)$$

In terms of concentrations, the extent of reaction becomes

$$p = \frac{[COOH]_0 - [COOH]}{[COOH]_0}$$

$$\text{or} \quad [COOH] = [COOH]_0(1-p) \quad (3.6)$$

Thus eqn. (3.3) becomes

$$\frac{1}{1-p} - 1 = k[COOH]_0 t, \quad (3.7)$$

while the time dependence of p is given by

$$p = \frac{k[COOH]_0 t}{1 + k[COOH]_0 t}. \quad (3.8)$$

We shall see later that this quantity p is a most useful parameter.

These equations, of course, tell us nothing about the time dependence of the concentrations of the various components $M_1, M_2, \ldots, M_i, \ldots$ making up the reaction system. Qualitatively, we know what to expect. At the early stages of the reaction, the mixture consists mainly of low molecular weight species, dimers, trimers, etc., with only a few molecules of polymeric size. As the reaction proceeds, these low molecular weight condensates link together with the elimination of water to give higher and higher molecular weight products. The concentration of each species with the exception of the monomer thus rises to a maximum value at some point in time after the reaction has commenced and then decreases as the particular species is consumed in further condensations.

To see the effects precisely, we write separate equations for the instantaneous rates of disappearance of the various species,

$$-d[M_1]/dt, -d[M_2]/dt, \ldots, -d[M_i]/dt, \ldots$$

Let us take the monomer first. It can disappear by reaction with any one of the other species present, thus:

Series 1.
$$M_1 + M_1 \rightarrow M_2 + H_2O \qquad\qquad 1$$
$$M_1 + M_2 \rightarrow M_3 + H_2O \qquad\qquad 2$$
$$M_1 + M_3 \rightarrow M_4 + H_2O \qquad\qquad 3$$
$$\vdots$$
$$M_1 + M_i \rightarrow M_{i+1} + H_2O \qquad\qquad i$$
$$\vdots$$

Let us consider each separate reaction. The rate of loss of carboxyl groups in the first reaction of this series is by our definition of the rate constant k

$$\left\{ -\frac{d[COOH]}{dt} \right\}_{\substack{\text{reaction 1} \\ \text{of series 1}}} = k[M_1]^2,$$

since [COOH] and [OH] in this reaction are both equal to the monomer concentration. But for every COOH lost by this reaction two monomer molecules disappear from the system.

Therefore
$$\left\{ -\frac{d[M_1]}{dt} \right\}_{\substack{\text{reaction 1} \\ \text{of series 1}}} = 2k[M_1]^2.$$

Taking reaction 2 of this series next, our problem is to calculate its contribution to the rate of monomer disappearance in terms of this same rate constant, k. The simplest way to do this is to consider a mixture consisting solely of M_1 and M_2. For then,

$$\left\{ -\frac{d[COOH]}{dt} \right\}_{\substack{\text{in a mixture} \\ \text{of } M_1 \text{ and } M_2}} = k[M_1+M_2][M_1+M_2],$$

since in such a mixture each molecule contributes one COOH and one OH group to the total. Multiplying out, we have

$$\left\{ -\frac{d[COOH]}{dt} \right\}_{\substack{\text{in a mixture} \\ \text{of } M_1 \text{ and } M_2}} = k[M_1]^2 + 2k[M_1][M_2] + k[M_2]^2.$$

The first term on the right-hand side of this equation represents the loss of COOH groups from the combination of two M_1 molecules in the mixture, the second term represents the loss of COOH groups resulting from the reaction in which we are interested, namely M_1+M_2, and the final term the contribution of the M_2, M_2 reaction. Extracting the second term, we have

$$\left\{ -\frac{d[COOH]}{dt} \right\}_{\substack{\text{reaction 2} \\ \text{of series 1}}} = 2k[M_1][M_2]$$

and since one M_1 molecule disappears every time a COOH group is lost, the same quantity represents the rate of disappearance of the monomer by this reaction.

$$\left\{ -\frac{d[M_1]}{dt} \right\}_{\substack{\text{reaction 2} \\ \text{of series 1}}} = 2k[M_1][M_2]$$

If we were to repeat this argument for every other reaction of this first series, it should be clear that

$$\left\{ -\frac{d[M_1]}{dt} \right\}_{\substack{\text{reaction } i \\ \text{of series 1}}} = 2k[M_1][M_i]$$

and hence by addition

$$-\frac{d[M_1]}{dt} = 2k[M_1] \sum [M_i], \qquad (3.9)$$

since only the reactions in series 1 cause the monomer to disappear. Now every molecule in the system contains one COOH group and hence the summation above is nothing more than the total concentration of COOH groups, a quantity which we have already evaluated in eqn. (3.4), i.e.

$$[COOH] = \sum [M_i]. \qquad (3.10)$$

Taking eqns. (3.4) and (3.10) together, eqn. (3.9) transforms to

$$-\frac{d\ln[M_1]}{dt} = \frac{2k[COOH]_0}{1+k[COOH]_0 t}.$$

For brevity, we shall write

$$a_0 = [COOH]_0$$

and so

$$-\frac{d\ln[M_1]}{dt} = \frac{2ka_0}{1+ka_0 t}. \qquad (3.11)$$

On integration, we obtain

$$[M_1] = \frac{a_0}{(1+ka_0 t)^2}. \qquad (3.12)$$

There is some advantage in rewriting these equations in terms of the extent of reaction p. The result looks somewhat simpler, eqn. (3.12) becoming

$$[M_1] = a_0(1-p)^2. \qquad (3.13)$$

Having solved the problem of the rate of disappearance of the monomer, we can now turn our attention to the dimer M_2. The point we have to remember is that not only does the dimer disappear by reaction with every other species present as set out in series 2

Series 2.
$$M_2+M_1 \to M_3+H_2O \qquad 1$$
$$M_2+M_2 \to M_4+H_2O \qquad 2$$
$$M_2+M_3 \to M_5+H_2O \qquad 3$$
$$\vdots$$
$$M_2+M_i \to M_{i+2}+H_2O \qquad i$$
$$\vdots$$

but also it is formed in the reaction

$$M_1+M_1 \to M_2+H_2O.$$

Its rate of disappearance by the reactions comprising series 2 follows from arguments exactly similar to those employed previously

$$\left\{ -\frac{d\,[M_2]}{dt} \right\}_{\text{series 2}} = 2k[M_2] \sum [M_i].$$

Its rate of appearance in the M_1+M_1 reaction (reaction 1 of series 1) is just one-half of the rate of loss of M_1 in the same reaction—2 monomer molecules disappear for every dimer molecule formed.

$$\left\{ \frac{d\,[M_2]}{dt} \right\}_{\substack{\text{reaction 1} \\ \text{of series 1}}} = 1/2 \left\{ -\frac{d\,[M_1]}{dt} \right\}_{\substack{\text{reaction 1} \\ \text{of series 1}}}$$
$$= k[M_1]^2.$$

Hence the total rate of disappearance of the dimer is given by

$$-\frac{d\,[M_2]}{dt} = 2k[M_2] \sum [M_i] - k[M_1]^2. \qquad (3.14)$$

Since $[M_1]$ and $\sum[M_i]$ are both known as functions of time, eqn. (3.14) can be integrated to give the time dependence of the dimer concentration. Alternatively, eqn. (3.14) can be transformed into an equation giving the dependence of $[M_2]$ on the extent of reaction p. The resulting equation can be integrated to give the rather simple result

$$[M_2] = a_0 p(1-p)^2. \qquad (3.15)$$

It is not too difficult to see how to generalize the above arguments to calculate the concentration of the i-mer at any time or at any extent of reaction. This species disappears from the reaction system at a rate $2k[M_i]\sum[M_i]$ as a result of the series of reactions M_i+M_1, M_i+M_2, ..., M_i+M_i...
It is formed by the reactions M_1+M_{i-1}, M_2+M_{i-2}, ..., at a rate $k\sum_{s=1}^{s=i-1}[M_s][M_{i-s}]$ in which every product with the exception of that corresponding to $s=i/2$ appears twice in the above summation.

Therefore
$$-\frac{d[M_i]}{dt} = 2k[M_i]\sum[M_i]-k\sum_{s=1}^{s=i-1}[M_s][M_{i-s}].$$
(3.16)

On replacing the variable t in terms of p and integrating, we obtain the general formula

$$[M_i] = a_0 p^{i-1}(1-p)^2.$$
(3.17)

The extent of reaction at which the concentration of the ith species passes through a maximum is thus found by differentiating the above equation with respect to p and putting the result equal to zero.

$$p_{[M_i]_{max}} = \frac{i-1}{i+1}.$$
(3.18)

For example, the trimer reaches its maximum concentration when 50% of the COOH groups have disappeared from the reaction system; the 9-mer, on the other hand, does not reach its maximum concentration until 80% of the reaction is completed. These maximum concentrations are $0.0625a_0$ and $0.00671a_0$ respectively as can be seen from eqn. (3.17). Figure 3.3 shows the actual time variation in the concentrations of the oligomers of 12-hydroxy stearic acid when it is allowed to polymerize in the melt at 160.5°C using the same catalyst concentration as employed in our previous example.

To conclude this brief account of the rates of formation

of the various species, dimers, trimers, etc., we subject the set of equations generalized by (3.16) to a cross-check. From this equation we write

$$-\frac{d[M_1]}{dt} = 2k[M_1]^2 + 2k[M_1][M_2] + 2k[M_1][M_3] + \ldots$$

$$-\frac{d[M_2]}{dt} = 2k[M_2][M_1] + 2k[M_2]^2 + 2k[M_2][M_3] + \ldots$$
$$- k[M_1]^2$$

$$-\frac{d[M_3]}{dt} = 2k[M_3][M_1] + 2k[M_3][M_2] + 2k[M_3]^2 + \ldots$$
$$- 2k[M_1][M_2]$$

$$-\frac{d[M_4]}{dt} = 2k[M_4][M_1] + 2k[M_4][M_2] + 2k[M_4][M_3] + \ldots$$
$$- 2k[M_1][M_3] - k[M_2]^2$$

$$\vdots$$

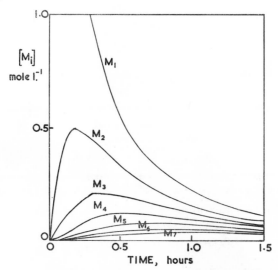

FIG. 3.3. The time dependence of the concentrations of a number of oligomers of 12-hydroxy stearic acid formed during its polymerization at 160·5° C in the presence of *p*-toluene sulphonic acid at a concentration of $3·31 \times 10^{-2}$ mole l.$^{-1}$

Adding these equations together gives

$$-\frac{d([M_1]+[M_2]+[M_3]+\ldots+[M_i]+\ldots)}{dt}$$

$$\begin{aligned}
&= k[M_1]^2 + k[M_2]^2 + k[M_3]^2 + \ldots \\
&\quad + 2k[M_1][M_2] + 2k[M_1][M_3] + \ldots \\
&\quad + 2k[M_2][M_3] + 2k[M_2][M_4] + \ldots \\
&\quad + \ldots \\
&= k([M_1]+[M_2]+[M_3]+\ldots)([M_1]+[M_2]+[M_3]+\ldots) \\
&= k([M_1]+[M_2]+[M_3]+\ldots)^2
\end{aligned}$$

Recalling that as in eqn. (3.10)

$$[COOH] = [M_1]+[M_2]+[M_3]+\ldots$$

we recover eqn. (3.2), thus:

$$-\frac{d[COOH]}{dt} = k[COOH]^2$$

THE MOLECULAR WEIGHT

The number and weight average molecular weight of the polymer can be derived from the distribution equation (3.17). The appropriate procedure has already been outlined in Chapter 2 (p. 41) where the properties of this equation[†] were dealt with in some detail. In particular, we proved that the number average degree of polymerization is $1/(1-p)$. This kinetic approach to the distribution equation, while extremely powerful, has the disadvantage in the particular case of condensation polymerization of obscuring its essential simplicity. Our object in this section is to present the alternative arguments which bring out this point more clearly.

[†] At first sight, eqns. (3.17) and (2.1) may not appear to be identical. The difference is that (3.17) relates the molar concentration of the i-mer to the initial concentration of the monomer whereas (2.1) refers essentially the same quantity to the actual number of molecules present in the mixture at time t.

In the first place we shall derive the expression for the number average degree of polymerization by a very simple argument. We take once again our ω-hydroxy carboxylic acid as an example. As before, we suppose its initial concentration to be a_0 so that in one litre of melt, there are a_0 COOH groups present at the start of the reaction. Some time later, we suppose that the number of COOH groups in this same volume of melt has decreased to a (in previous arguments, this same quantity has been symbolized by [COOH] or $\sum[M_i]$). Consequently, at this particular time, there are (a_0-a) moles of ester groups present in a reaction mixture containing a total of a moles; on average, therefore, there are $(a_0-a)/a$ moles of ester groups per mole of mixture. In other words there are, on average, $(a_0-a)/a$ ester groups per molecule. But, since one ester group is formed from the condensation of two monomer molecules, two ester groups from three monomer molecules and so on, the actual number of monomer residues in a particular chain is always one greater than the number of ester groups. Consequently, the average number of monomer residues per molecule, that is, the number average degree of polymerization n is

$$n = \frac{a_0 - a}{a} + 1$$

$$= \frac{a_0}{a}.$$

In terms of the extent of reaction p we have the expression

$$a = a_0(1-p)$$

and so the number average degree of polymerization

$$n = \frac{1}{1-p}. \tag{3.19}$$

This equation is the basis of our earlier statement that high percentage conversions of monomer to polymer are necessary in order to obtain high molecular weight polymers. As an example, let us take $p = 0.5$ and calculate the number average degree of polymerization of the mixture. The answer from eqn. (3.19) is obviously two and so when 50% of the original carboxylic acid groups have reacted, the average degree of polymerization has only doubled. For other values of p, the number average degree of polymerization can be calculated similarly with results as shown in Table 3.1

TABLE 3.1. NUMBER AVERAGE DEGREE
OF POLYMERIZATION OF THE POLYMERS
FORMED AT VARIOUS PERCENTAGE
CONVERSIONS

Percentage conversion	p	n
50	0·50	2
90	0·90	10
99	0·99	100
99·9	0·999	1000

In the particular case of 12-hydroxy stearic acid, the corresponding number average molecular weights of the polymers are: 582·9; 2,842·5; 28,263; 282,468.[†] In the general case, it should be clear that it is necessary to achieve extents of reaction greater than 0·99 to obtain polymer molecular weights greater than, say 10,000.

We have stated earlier in this chapter that such high extents of reaction can only be achieved in finite periods of time by the use of catalysts, elevated temperatures, and high initial concentrations. The combination of eqns. (3.7) and (3.19) to

[†] These molecular weights are not precisely in the ratio of 2: 10: 100: 1000 because of the effect of the end groups of the polymer; in this case, the molecular weight is related to n by the formula: mol.wt. $= 282·45n + 18·02$.

give the time dependence of the number average degree of polymerization shows this explicitly. The equation obtained is

$$n = 1 + ka_0t, \qquad (3.20)$$

which shows that n increases linearly with time at a rate

$$\frac{dn}{dt} = ka_0.$$

Thus the higher the values of k and a_0 the greater the rate of increase of the molecular weight with time. The use of high temperatures and high catalyst concentrations is the means by which high values of the rate constant k are obtained, while carrying out the condensation in the melt ensures the use of the highest initial concentrations possible. In any specific instance, of course, limits on the first two reaction variables may be imposed by the necessity of avoiding decomposition or other side reactions which remove one of the functional groups at a greater rate than the other. The general conclusions, however, are illustrated in Fig. 3.4 where the dependence of the number average degree of polymerization on time for the case of the catalysed condensation of 12-hydroxy stearic acid is given for two different temperatures and two different catalyst concentrations. From this figure, it can be seen that the greater the value of the product ka_0 the shorter the time in which a given degree of polymerization is attained.

The number average degree of polymerization is not the only quantity which can be derived without going through a detailed kinetic analysis. The distribution equation (3.17), in fact, is readily obtained by the following statistical argument. Consider a reaction mixture at any one time and in particular the carbonyl groups $C=O$. Such groups are present either as part of an ester linkage or as part of an unreacted carboxyl group. Consequently the probability that a particular carbonyl group is part of an ester group is simply the ratio

number of carbonyl groups in the mixture as part of ester groups
―――
total number of carbonyl groups in both ester and carboxyl groups

But the number of carbonyl groups in the mixture which are present in ester groups is equal to the number of COOH groups which have reacted while the number of carbonyl groups present all told either in ester or carboxyl groups is equal to the number of COOH groups taken originally. Therefore the

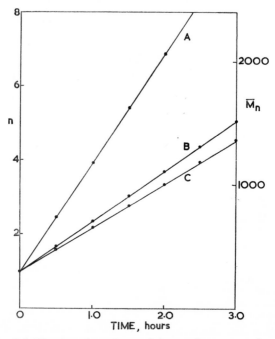

FIG. 3.4. The time dependence of the number average degree of polymerization of the reaction mixture formed as a result of the polymerization of 12-hydroxy stearic acid. The data have been calculated for three different conditions; A, [Catalyst] $= 3{\cdot}31 \times 10^{-2}$ mole l.$^{-1}$ at 160·5°C; B, [Catalyst] $= 1{\cdot}66 \times 10^{-2}$ mole l.$^{-1}$ at 160·5°C; C, [Catalyst] $= 3{\cdot}31 \times 10^{-2}$ mole l.$^{-1}$ at 133·5°C

previous expression defining the probability that a particular carbonyl group is part of an ester group becomes

$$\frac{\text{number of COOH groups reacted}}{\text{number of COOH groups originally present}}$$
$$= \text{the extent of reaction } p.$$

The probability that a particular carbonyl is part of a COOH group is then,

$$1-p$$

In a polymer formed from the condensation of i monomer molecules, there are $(i-1)$ ester linkages, one COOH and one OH group. Hence the probability of finding such a molecule in the reaction mixture, that is

$$\frac{\text{number of molecules containing } i \text{ monomer residues, } N_i}{\text{total number of molecules of all sizes, } N(= \sum N_i)}$$

is simply the probability of selecting a sequence of $(i-1)$ carbonyl groups which are incorporated into ester groups and 1 carbonyl group which is part of an unreacted carboxyl. This is

$$p^{i-1}(1-p)$$

and so from our definition of this particular probability

$$N_i = Np^{i-1}(1-p), \tag{3.21}$$

where
$$N = \sum N_i.$$

This equation is the number distribution equation (2.1). To transform it into the equivalent form (3.17), we make the volume of the reaction mixture 1 litre; consequently we can replace the numbers of molecules N_i and N by the corresponding molar concentrations $[M_i]$ and $\sum[M_i]$. It is particularly important to remember that the total number of molecules in the reaction mixture is changing with time so that the summation $\sum[M_i]$ is replaced by a not a_0. In these symbols eqn. (3.21) becomes

$$[M_i] = ap^{i-1}(1-p).$$

Since we know that a is related to a_0 by the very simple expression

$$a = a_0(1-p),$$

the above expression becomes

$$[M_i] = a_0 p^{i-1}(1-p)^2.$$

Equation (3.17) is thus recovered by statistical arguments without recourse to the integration of the series of differential equations given previously.

EXTENSION OF THESE ARGUMENTS
TO OTHER CONDENSATION REACTIONS

It should be apparent that the account of the kinetics of the condensation of an ω-hydroxy carboxylic acid and the statistical derivation of the molecular weight distribution equation can be adapted to other condensation reactions. Only minor modifications of the arguments are necessary for other reactions such as those between diols and diacids, diamines and diacids, etc., provided that the fundamental principle of the equal reactivity of all functional groups is assumed. This same principle ensures that no special problems are encountered in condensation copolymerization. If a mixture of several different monomers all of the same chemical type is polymerized, a copolymer results containing the monomers in the same proportion as in the mixture.

CHAPTER 4

FREE RADICAL ADDITION POLYMERIZATION

THE essential reaction in addition polymerization is, as we have already stated,

$$n\text{M} \rightarrow \text{M}_n$$

n representing the average number of monomer molecules which join together to form a polymer molecule. Since this number is usually very large, a polymer molecule must be formed by the series of consecutive reactions

$$\text{M}_1^* + \text{M} \rightarrow \text{M}_2^*$$
$$\text{M}_2^* + \text{M} \rightarrow \text{M}_3^*$$
$$\text{M}_3^* + \text{M} \rightarrow \text{M}_4^*$$
$$\vdots$$
$$\text{M}_i^* + \text{M} \rightarrow \text{M}_{i+1}^*$$
$$\vdots$$

In this representation of the growth process, M_i^* stands for a polymeric molecule containing i monomer units which is potentially capable of reacting with a monomer molecule. These polymeric *active centres*, as they are called, may or may not be identical with the final polymer produced; this depends simply on the specific chemical nature of the active centres and on the reaction conditions.

In this chapter we shall consider the case where each active centre is a *free radical*—that is, a molecule containing an un-paired electron—and quite distinguishable from the polymer finally produced. We shall have to consider, therefore,

(1) reactions which lead to the production of free radicals capable of reaction with monomer;

(2) the reaction already outlined in which monomer molecules add successively to radical active centres with the formation of further radicals;

(3) reactions by which the radicals are destroyed with the production of polymer unreactive towards monomer.

These three reactions are referred to as the initiation, propagation and termination reactions respectively, and the whole process is an example of a wider class of reactions known as *chain* reactions. It must not be thought that these are the only types of reaction which occur in free radical addition polymerization for we shall see later that the polymeric free radicals can take part in other reactions. For the time being, however, we shall confine our attention to this simplest of cases.

THE INITIATION REACTION

The usual procedure employed to produce the radicals containing one monomer unit is to add to the monomer a substance or substances which produce radicals capable of reacting with it. These additives are termed *initiators*, the reaction being the composite process

$$I \rightarrow \alpha R \cdot$$
$$R \cdot + M \rightarrow M_1 \cdot$$

where I represents the initiator, $R \cdot$ the radical produced therefrom and α the number of such radicals obtained; the presence of the dot to the right of a symbol indicates an unpaired electron and its radical nature.

Probably the simplest of all polymerization initiators are the organic peroxides and azo compounds. These substances decompose spontaneously into free radicals in the common organic solvents at a finite rate at temperatures between, say, 50 and 140°C. For example, benzoyl peroxide in benzene at

60°C decomposes into two benzoyloxy radicals by simple scission of the weak peroxy bond:

$$C_6H_5-\underset{\underset{O}{\|}}{C}-O-O-\underset{\underset{O}{\|}}{C}-C_6H_5 \rightarrow 2\ C_6H_5-\underset{\underset{O}{\|}}{C}-O\cdot$$

The benzoyloxy radicals so produced may either decompose to give a phenyl radical and CO_2 or they may undergo reaction with solvent or further benzoyl peroxide. In the presence of a vinyl monomer, these latter reactions are unimportant, most of the benzoyloxy or phenyl radicals reacting with the monomer;† thus in the case of styrene

$$C_6H_5-\underset{\underset{O}{\|}}{C}-O\cdot +CH_2=\underset{\underset{C_6H_5}{|}}{CH} \rightarrow C_6H_5-\underset{\underset{O}{\|}}{C}-O-CH_2-\underset{\underset{C_6H_5}{|}}{CH}\cdot$$

or

$$C_6H_5\cdot +CH_2=\underset{\underset{C_6H_5}{|}}{CH} \rightarrow C_6H_5-CH_2-\underset{\underset{C_6H_5}{|}}{CH}\cdot$$

Another example is afforded by the azo compound, azo-bis-isobutyronitrile (AZBN), which similarly decomposes into radicals at easily accessible temperatures:

$$\underset{CH_3}{\overset{CH_3}{>}}\underset{\underset{CN}{|}}{C}-N=N-\underset{\underset{CN}{|}}{C}\underset{CH_3}{\overset{CH_3}{<}} \rightarrow 2\ \underset{CH_3}{\overset{CH_3}{>}}\underset{\underset{CN}{|}}{C}\cdot\ +N_2$$

These radicals react with monomer in an exactly similar way to that described for benzoyloxy or phenyl radicals.

Instead of adjusting the temperature to obtain sufficient activated initiator molecules to maintain a suitable rate of decomposition, the necessary energy may be provided by irradiating the initiator system with ultraviolet light. Obviously, it is necessary that the initiator molecules absorb in the spectral region supplied. The initiator already mentioned, azo-bis-iso-

† If styrene is the monomer and if the initiation is carried out at 60°C in benzene, about 85 % of the benzoyloxy radicals produced by simple scission are captured by the monomer before decomposing.[12]

butyronitrile, may be decomposed in this way by simply irradiating with ultraviolet light of wavelength 3650 Å.

$$\begin{array}{c} CH_3 \\ \diagdown \\ C-N=N-C \\ \diagup \quad | \qquad | \quad \diagdown \\ CH_3 \;\; CN \;\;\; CN \;\; CH_3 \end{array} \xrightarrow{h\nu} 2 \begin{array}{c} CH_3 \\ \diagdown \\ C\cdot \\ \diagup \;\; | \\ CH_3 \;\; CN \end{array} + N_2$$

In this way, radicals can be generated at a finite rate at considerably lower temperatures than are necessary if purely thermal excitation is used. The point to remember is that the absorption of 1 mole of photons equivalent to this wavelength raises the energy of the system by 78 kcal, a value much greater than that necessary to decompose the molecule.

Finally, bimolecular reactions may produce radicals capable of initiating polymerization. Particularly important are the redox reactions commonly occurring in aqueous media involving electron transfer processes. For example,

$$Fe(II) + H_2O_2 \rightarrow Fe(III) + OH^- + HO\cdot$$
$$Ag(I) + S_2O_8^{--} \rightarrow Ag(II) + SO_4^{--} + SO_4^-\cdot$$

These reactions are particularly important in initiating the polymerization of emulsified monomers, a process which is of some industrial importance.

Not all unsaturated monomers, however, react at a significant rate with these primary radicals to produce the first active centre $M_1\cdot$. For example isobutene cannot be polymerized using free radical initiation. In general, those monomers which do react can do so in more than one way. For example, if we write a vinyl monomer as $CH_2=CH$ where X represents the
$\qquad\qquad\qquad\qquad\qquad\qquad\qquad\qquad |$
$\qquad\qquad\qquad\qquad\qquad\qquad\qquad\quad X$
substituent C_6H_5, Cl, $COOCH_3$, etc., then there are two possibilities:

$$R\cdot + CH_2=CH \Big\langle \begin{array}{c} R-CH_2-CH\cdot \qquad\qquad \text{I} \\ | \qquad\qquad\quad \\ X \\ R-CH-CH_2\cdot \qquad\qquad \text{II} \\ | \\ X \end{array}$$
$$\qquad\qquad | \\ \qquad\qquad X$$

In the case of the symmetrical diene, butadiene,

$$CH_2=CH-CH=CH_2$$
$$1 \quad 2 \quad 3 \quad 4$$

there are four ways of representing the product radical:

$$
\begin{array}{c}
R-CH_2-CH\cdot \\
| \\
CH \\
\parallel \\
CH_2
\end{array}
\qquad \text{III}
$$

$$
\begin{array}{c}
R-CH_2 \qquad\qquad CH_2\cdot \\
\diagdown \quad C=C \quad \diagup \\
H \diagup \qquad\qquad \diagdown H
\end{array}
\qquad \text{IV}
$$

$$
\begin{array}{c}
R-CH_2 \qquad\qquad H \\
\diagdown \quad C=C \quad \diagup \\
H \diagup \qquad\qquad \diagdown CH_2\cdot
\end{array}
\qquad \text{V}
$$

$$
\begin{array}{c}
R-CH-CH_2\cdot \\
| \\
CH \\
\parallel \\
CH_2
\end{array}
\qquad \text{VI}
$$

Although structures III, IV and V are essentially alternative representations of the same product radical (since one can be obtained from the other by rearrangement of the valence electrons), the formal distinction is useful in that this molecule reacts subsequently with monomer as if all three forms had a separate existence.

Let us consider the reaction between the radical $R\cdot$ and a vinyl monomer as represented in reactions I and II. The relative amounts of the two product radicals depend on the difference between the activation energies of the two reactions. We can write

$$
\frac{d\left[\begin{array}{c} RCH_2CH\cdot \\ | \\ X \end{array}\right]}{dt} = k_I[R\cdot][CH_2=CHX],
$$

$$
\frac{d\left[\begin{array}{c} RCHCH_2\cdot \\ | \\ X \end{array}\right]}{dt} = k_{II}[R\cdot][CH_2=CHX],
$$

where k_I and k_{II} represent the rate constants of the two paths.

Therefore
$$\frac{d\left[\begin{array}{c}RCH_2CH\cdot\\ |\\ X\end{array}\right]}{d\left[\begin{array}{c}RCHCH_2\cdot\\ |\\ X\end{array}\right]} = \frac{k_I}{k_{II}}.$$

Each of these rate constants can be written

$$k_I = A_I \exp(-E_I/RT),$$
$$k_{II} = A_{II} \exp(-E_{II}/RT),$$

so that integration of the previous equation gives

$$\frac{\left[\begin{array}{c}RCH_2CH\cdot\\ |\\ X\end{array}\right]}{\left[\begin{array}{c}RCHCH_2\cdot\\ |\\ X\end{array}\right]} = \frac{A_I}{A_{II}} \exp\left(\frac{E_{II}-E_I}{RT}\right)$$

for the relative concentrations of the two products at any particular time. For such similar reactions, it is reasonable to assume $A_I = A_{II}$. If this is so, the relative concentration of the two products is determined solely by the difference $E_{II}-E_I$ and the temperature; for example at 60°C, a 1·5 kcal difference in the activation energies of the two parallel reactions results in the formation of 9·6 times as much $RCH_2CH\cdot$ as $RCHCH_2\cdot$.

This activation energy difference arises on two accounts. In the first place, since the substituent group X usually hinders the approach of the radical $R\cdot$ to the carbon atom to which it is attached, some energy is required to distort the monomer sufficiently to permit the formation of a bond between $R\cdot$ and the substituted carbon atom. In the second place, at the instant of collision less energy will usually be required to re-organize the electrons in one of the two alternative ways than in the other. Both of these directing influences in the case of the majority of vinyl monomers tend to operate in the same sense to make $E_{II} > E_I$ and hence to result in the preponderance of the radical

For this reason, we shall usually write this step of the initiation process as the single reaction I even though a few additions will take place in the converse manner. Exactly similar arguments can be put up to rationalize the differing proportions of the two radicals (III/IV/V) and VI formed between a primary radical and butadiene; that is, the predominant mode of addition of the primary radical to the diene takes place on the terminal carbon atom.

Finally, it should be noted that each active centre contains an initiator fragment as an end group and therefore the polymers finally produced contain these same portions of initiator. Consequently, if these end groups can be estimated quantitatively and if it is known how many are present per polymer molecule, the number average molecular weight of the polymer can be found directly. As explained previously, the accuracy which can be achieved by this method is limited by the accuracy of the normal analytical methods; it is, however, clearly possible to use radioactive initiators to push the limits of end group detection to very low levels.

THE PROPAGATION REACTION

The propagation reaction is really the series of reactions

$$M_1 \cdot + M \rightarrow M_2 \cdot$$
$$M_2 \cdot + M \rightarrow M_3 \cdot$$
$$\vdots$$
$$M_i \cdot + M \rightarrow M_{i+1} \cdot$$
$$\vdots$$

If we write out the first reaction in more detail for the case where M represents a vinyl monomer,

$$RCH_2CH \cdot + CH_2 = CH \rightarrow M_2 \cdot$$
$$\quad\; |\qquad\qquad\; |$$
$$\quad\; X \qquad\qquad\; X$$

we have a similar problem to that already discussed in the second step of the initiation reaction; that is whether the radical $RCH_2CH \cdot$ attaches itself to the CH_2 group of the
$$\qquad\qquad |$$
$$\qquad\qquad X$$
reacting monomer or to the CH group. It should be clear that
$$\qquad\qquad\qquad\qquad |$$
$$\qquad\qquad\qquad\qquad X$$
precisely similar considerations apply to this case and to the general case $M_i \cdot + M \rightarrow M_{i+1} \cdot$ as were applied to the problem of the attachment of the primary radical $R \cdot$ to the monomer. In other words, the reaction proceeds almost exclusively to produce what is termed the "head-to-tail" arrangement

$$RCH_2CHCH_2CH \cdot$$
$$\quad\; |\qquad\quad\; |$$
$$\quad\; X \qquad\quad\; X$$

rather than the "head-to-head" arrangement

$$RCH_2CHCHCH_2 \cdot$$
$$\quad\; |\; |$$
$$\quad\; X\; X$$

Of course a few "head-to-head" additions will take place during the growth of the polymer depending on the magnitude of the activation energy difference between the two reactions producing the alternative forms. For practical purposes, however, we may regard the ordinary vinyl polymer produced as consisting predominantly of monomer units arranged in a "head-to-tail" fashion

$$RCH_2CHCH_2CHCH_2CHCH_2CH \ldots$$
$$\quad\; |\qquad\; |\qquad\; |\qquad\; |$$
$$\quad\; X\qquad X\qquad X\qquad X$$

If M represents the diene, butadiene, each of the steps symbolized by the equation

$$M_i \cdot + M \rightarrow M_{i+1} \cdot$$

represents a number of quite different reactions. If we take the first active centre $M_1 \cdot$ as an example, we have to consider that this may react as any one of the three forms

$$\begin{array}{c} R-CH_2-CH \cdot \\ | \\ CH \\ \| \\ CH_2 \end{array}$$

$$\begin{array}{c} R-CH_2 \diagdown \quad \diagup CH_2 \cdot \\ C=C \\ H \diagup \quad \diagdown H \end{array}$$

$$\begin{array}{c} R-CH_2 \diagdown \quad \diagup H \\ C=C \\ H \diagup \quad \diagdown CH_2 \cdot \end{array}$$

Provided that we restrict our attention to additions taking place on the terminal carbon atom, each of these may react with the next monomer molecule in any one of three ways to give radicals for which we can write nine formal structures:

$$\begin{array}{c} R-CH_2-CH-CH_2-CH \cdot \\ | \qquad\qquad | \\ CH \qquad\qquad CH \\ \| \qquad\qquad \| \\ CH_2 \qquad\qquad CH_2 \end{array}$$

$$\begin{array}{c} R-CH_2-CH-CH_2 \diagdown \quad \diagup CH_2 \cdot \\ | \qquad\qquad C=C \\ CH \qquad H \diagup \quad \diagdown H \\ \| \\ CH_2 \end{array}$$

$$\begin{array}{c} R-CH_2-CH-CH_2 \diagdown \quad \diagup H \\ | \qquad\qquad C=C \\ CH \qquad H \diagup \quad \diagdown CH_2 \cdot \\ \| \\ CH_2 \end{array}$$

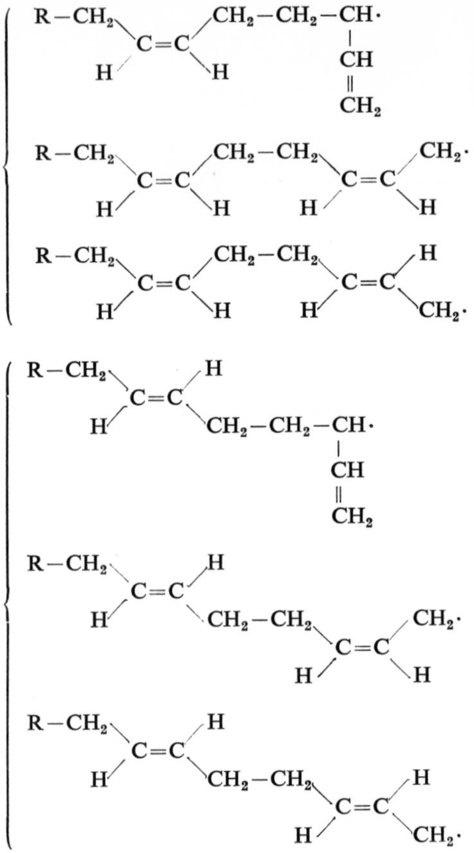

$$
\left\{
\begin{array}{l}
\text{R—CH}_2\text{—C=C—CH}_2\text{—CH}_2\text{—CH·} \\
\qquad\qquad\quad\text{CH} \\
\qquad\qquad\quad\text{CH}_2 \\[1em]
\text{R—CH}_2\text{—C=C—CH}_2\text{—CH}_2\text{—C=C—CH}_2\text{·} \\[1em]
\text{R—CH}_2\text{—C=C—CH}_2\text{—CH}_2\text{—C=C—CH}_2\text{·}
\end{array}
\right.
$$

Although only three of these are distinct chemical entities, the nine possibilities appear as soon as the next step $(M_2\cdot + M \rightarrow M_3\cdot)$ takes place. Since these alternatives occur at all subsequent steps, it is clear that the polybutadiene molecules produced vary widely in structure. Nevertheless, the propagation reaction can be regarded as one of three types according to the structure produced in the penultimate monomer unit in the polymer chain:

$$M_i \cdot + M \to \begin{cases} M_{i+1} \cdot & \text{1,2 placement} \\ M_{i+1} \cdot & \textit{cis} \text{ 1,4 placement} \\ M_{i+1} \cdot \textit{trans} \text{ 1,4 placement} \end{cases}$$

As before, the relative proportions of the three types of placement found in the final polymer are determined by the activation energy differences in the rate constants of these three reactions and the temperature.

It will be obvious that had we chosen an unsymmetrical diene such as isoprene

$$\overset{\displaystyle CH_3}{\underset{\displaystyle |}{CH_2}} = \underset{2}{C} - \underset{3}{CH} = \underset{4}{CH_2}$$
$$\underset{1}{CH_2} = \underset{2}{C} - \underset{3}{CH} = \underset{4}{CH_2}$$

the propagation reaction would be considerably more complex because not only are there four modes of addition (*cis* and *trans* 1,4, 1,2 and 3,4) but also there are two possible points of attachment of the radical in each case, analogous to the "head-to-head" and "head-to-tail" arrangements possible with the vinyl polymers.

Returning to the comparatively simple vinyl monomers, we have stated that the effective propagation reaction is the single step

$$\underset{X}{R'CH_2 - CH} \cdot + \underset{X}{CH_2 = CH} \to \underset{X}{R'CH_2 - CH} - \underset{X}{CH_2 - CH} \cdot$$

where R' represents either the initiator fragment R or a long sequence of monomer units terminating in this entity. This process is not just as simple as it appears at first sight. Let us consider the reaction three-dimensionally. Our starting point is the knowledge that the three bonds of the carbon atom of the radical are disposed in a single plane. Since three different substituents $R'CH_2$, H and X are attached to these three bonds, we can distinguish two sides of this plane which for convenience we might call "front" and "back". For example, if we draw the bonds and substituents in the plane of the paper, we can define quite arbitrarily the front view of the plane as

$$
\begin{array}{c}
R'CH_2 \\
| \\
C \\
H \diagup \quad \diagdown X
\end{array}
$$

the essential feature of the front view being that the sequence H, $R'CH_2$, X appears in a clockwise sense. Thus the arrangement

$$
\begin{array}{c}
X \\
| \\
C \\
R'CH_2 \diagup \quad \diagdown H
\end{array}
$$

also represents a front view for it can obviously be superimposed on the first drawing by appropriate rotation. On the other hand, the mirror image arrangement

$$
\begin{array}{c}
R'CH_2 \\
| \\
C \\
X \diagup \quad \diagdown H
\end{array}
$$

we shall regard as the back view of the plane, its characteristic being that the chosen sequence H, $R'CH_2$ and X now appears in the anticlockwise sense. The reader should verify that this distinction between the two sides of the plane can only be made if all three groups attached to the central carbon atom are distinguishable.

Now if we can distinguish two sides to the plane containing the three bonds of the carbon atom associated with the unpaired electron, it follows that the incoming monomer can react with the radical in one of two ways; one way we can regard as a frontal attack and the other way as an attack from the rear. The consequence of this choice is shown in the accompanying three-dimensional diagrams.

1. *Frontal attack*

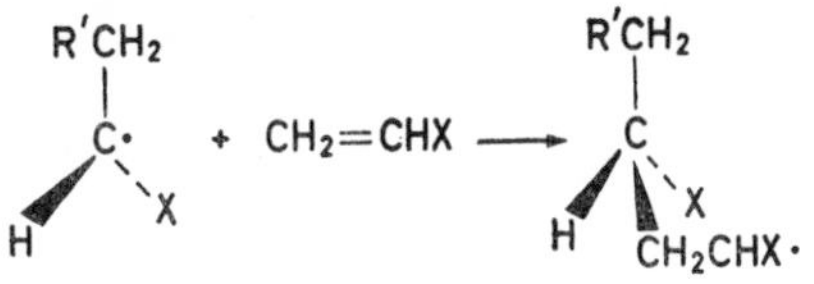

2. *Rear attack*

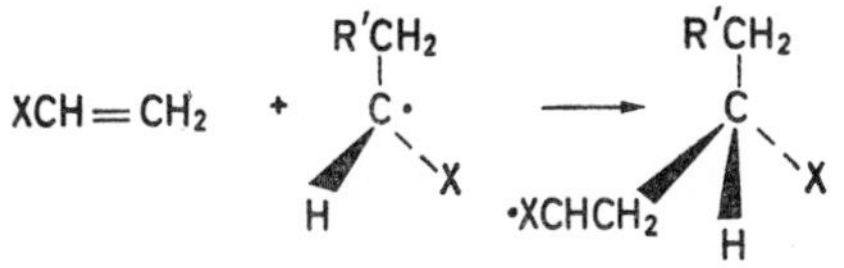

As a result of the reaction, the three bonds originally in a single plane are redirected towards the corners of a tetrahedron with the important consequence that there are two possible products which are mirror images of one another; that is, the carbon atom *originally* associated with the unpaired electron becomes *asymmetric*. Therefore, the reaction of any particular radical with monomer to produce another radical is one or other of two separate reactions which are distinguishable according to the configurations of the terminal asymmetric carbon atom in the radical so formed. These two configurations are commonly termed '*d*' or '*l*' following the nomenclature employed to describe simple optical isomers. According to whether the adopted configuration is the same as or different from that of the preceding asymmetric carbon atom, different energies of activation are involved. This means that the rate constant for the formation of an adjacent pair of asymmetric carbon atoms of the same configuration ('*dd*' or '*ll*') is different from the rate constant for the formation of an adjacent pair of opposite configuration ('*dl*' or '*ld*'). If we call these two rate constants k_a and k_b, the propagation reaction can be conveniently formalized as follows

$$
\text{\wwww } dp\cdot + M \begin{cases} \xrightarrow{k_a} \text{\wwww } ddp\cdot \\ \xrightarrow{k_b} \text{\wwww } dlp\cdot \end{cases}
$$

$$
\text{\wwww } lp\cdot + M \begin{cases} \xrightarrow{k_a} \text{\wwww } llp\cdot \\ \xrightarrow{k_b} \text{\wwww } ldp\cdot \end{cases}
$$

where the symbols d, l and p represent the configuration of the carbon atoms bearing the substituent X, p indicating the planar form adopted when this carbon atom is associated with the unpaired electron. From this representation, it follows immediately that

$$
\frac{\text{number of '}dd\text{' or '}ll\text{' pairs formed}}{\text{number of '}dl\text{' or '}ld\text{' pairs formed}} = \frac{k_a}{k_b}
$$
$$
= \exp\left(\frac{E_b - E_a}{RT}\right),
$$

where E_a and E_b are the corresponding activation energies. In other words the preference for one of the two types of reaction is determined as in the other cases by the activation energy difference and the temperature. Obviously, the difference between the two activation energies is going to be rather small, and so at high temperatures, the exponent tends to zero; consequently the number of pairs of like configuration formed is equal to the number of pairs of unlike configuration. At low temperatures, one or other of the two types of reaction will predominate since the quantity RT will become of the same order as the difference, $E_b - E_a$; which is preferred is determined by the sign of this latter quantity. When $E_b > E_a$, the tendency is for long sequences of asymmetric carbon atoms of the same configuration to be formed,

i.e. $dddddd\ldots$ or $llllll\ldots$

Such polymers are termed *isotactic*. The converse situation $E_a > E_b$ results in the formation of long sequences of alternating configurations,

i.e.   *dldldldl . . .*

These polymers are termed *syndiotactic*. When the arrangement of the monomer units is random as

dlldddlldlddl . . . ,

the polymer is termed *atactic*. The precise significance to be attached to the terms isotactic and syndiotactic will be dealt with later under copolymerization when the problem of sequence length distribution in such polymers is dealt with more fully. For the time being, it is sufficient to understand that in any vinyl polymerization involving a monosubstituted ethylene the propagation reaction necessarily introduces an asymmetric carbon atom into the chain on the addition of each monomer unit.† As a result, polymers of different steric structure can be produced in principle by controlling the temperature at which the polymerization is carried out.

It should be noted that since the 1,2 polymerization of butadiene can be regarded as a vinyl polymerization (the pendant $-CH=CH_2$ group acting as the substituent X) it is possible in principle to produce isotactic and syndiotactic 1,2 polybutadiene.

Whilst the experimental evidence available at present suggests that free radical propagation in homogeneous media is adequately described by the above considerations, it must not be thought that the development of stereoregularity in polymers is always determined by such simple factors. These more complex, stereoregular polymerizations will be dealt with in Chapter 5.

---

† The same conclusion applies to the case of a 1,1 disubstituted ethylene provided that the two substituents are different.

THE TERMINATION REACTION

The radicals must be destroyed in a reaction system by a bimolecular process since their disappearance involves spin pairing. There are two ways of achieving this result. Firstly, two radicals can simply combine together according to the equation

$$R'-CH_2-CH\cdot +R''-CH_2-CH\cdot \rightarrow R'-CH_2-CH-CH-CH_2-R''$$
$$\underset{X}{|} \qquad\qquad \underset{X}{|} \qquad\qquad \underset{X}{|}\ \underset{X}{|}$$

This process is termed *combination termination* and results in the formation of a "head-to-head" linkage. Alternatively, a hydrogen atom can be transferred from one radical to the other giving two polymer molecules, one saturated and the other possessing an olefinic double bond at one end—this process being termed *disproportionation termination*.

$$R'-CH_2-CH\cdot +R''-CH_2-CH\cdot \rightarrow R'-CH=CH+R''-CH_2-CH_2$$
$$\underset{X}{|} \qquad\qquad \underset{X}{|} \qquad\qquad \underset{X}{|} \qquad\qquad \underset{X}{|}$$

It should be noted that, in contrast to combination termination where polymer with two initiator fragments per molecule is produced, each molecule formed by disproportionation contains a single initiator end group.

In general both processes take place but to unequal extents; the competition between the two is governed as in the other analogous cases by the activation energy difference and the temperature. In the case of polystyryl radicals the energy difference is such that radical–radical combination is almost entirely responsible for the disappearance of radicals from a polymerizing system; on the other hand, polymethyl methacrylate radicals react together almost exclusively by disproportionation termination.

In either case the termination reaction in simple free-radical polymerization can be written as

$$M_i\cdot +M_j\cdot \rightarrow polymer,$$

it just being a question of whether one or two polymer molecules are produced.

A KINETIC ANALYSIS OF THE BASIC
POLYMERIZATION MECHANISM

The first object of a kinetic analysis of the simple mechanism of free radical polymerization outlined on previous pages is the prediction of the rates of monomer and initiator disappearance in terms of their concentrations at any time and the rate constants for the three elementary reactions, initiation, propagation, and termination. For simplicity we shall consider the case where the initiator decomposes into two identical radicals and the polymer is formed exclusively by combination termination. In such a case the stoichiometric equation for the reaction can be written as

$$I + nM \rightarrow M_n,$$

where n is the average number of monomer units in a polymer molecule.

Mechanism

$$I \rightarrow 2R\cdot \qquad \text{rate constant } k_i$$
$$R\cdot + M \rightarrow M_1\cdot \qquad \text{rate constant } k_r$$
$$M_1\cdot + M \rightarrow M_2\cdot$$
$$M_2\cdot + M \rightarrow M_3\cdot$$
$$\vdots \qquad \vdots \qquad \text{rate constant } k_p$$
$$M_i\cdot + M \rightarrow M_{i+1}\cdot$$
$$\vdots$$
$$M_i\cdot + M_j\cdot \rightarrow M_{i+j} \qquad \text{rate constant } k_t$$

Two comments are necessary on the rate constants. Firstly, we shall always define rate constants in terms of the reactants; quite generally

$$-\frac{d\,[\text{reactant}]}{dt} = (\text{rate constant})\,[\text{reactant 1}]\,[\text{reactant 2}]\ldots$$

Thus for the initiation step

$$I \rightarrow 2R\cdot$$

with rate constant k_i, we would write

$$-\frac{d\,[I]}{dt} = k_i[I]$$

but
$$\frac{d[R\cdot]}{dt} = -2\frac{d\,[I]}{dt} = 2k_i[I].$$

Secondly, we have attributed the same rate constant k_p to all reactions between polymer radicals and monomer molecules. Strictly speaking, this is untrue since the radicals $M_1\cdot$, $M_2\cdot$, up to say $M_5\cdot$ will certainly differ from one another in their reactivity towards the monomer. As the length of the chain increases, the radicals will become more and more alike in this respect and consequently for polymerizations producing high molecular weight polymer, the assumption of the same rate constant k_p for all propagation steps does not lead to any serious error. We have, however, distinguished the reaction between the primary radical $R\cdot$ and monomer from the subsequent propagation reactions since this radical is chemically quite different from the polymer radicals.

KINETIC EQUATIONS

$$-\frac{d\,[I]}{dt} = k_i[I].\dagger \tag{4.1}$$

$$-\frac{d[M]}{dt} = k_r[R\cdot][M] + k_p[M_1\cdot][M] + k_p[M_2\cdot][M] +$$
$$\ldots + k_p[M_i\cdot][M] + \ldots$$

† If the initiation process were photochemical the rate of decomposition of the initiator would be $-d[I]/dt = k[I]$ where k is proportional to the incident light intensity $\mathcal{I}_0$ when only a small fraction of the incident energy is absorbed by the initiator.

The amount of monomer consumed in the reaction with the primary radicals is quite negligible compared with that consumed in the propagation reaction if high molecular weight polymer is produced. Consequently, the first term on the right-hand side of the previous equation can be neglected in comparison with the remainder and hence

$$-\frac{d[M]}{dt} = k_p \left(\sum [M_i \cdot]\right)[M]. \tag{4.2}$$

Equation (4.1) is a simple first order equation which can be integrated to give

$$[I] = [I]_0 \exp{(-k_i t)},$$

where $[I]_0$ is the initial concentration of the initiator. The second equation is not quite so simple because it contains the total concentration of polymer radicals in the system, $\sum[M_i \cdot]$, a quantity which we shall now proceed to evaluate. What we do is this: we write a separate equation for the rate of increase of the concentration of each particular radical bearing in mind that there are destructive or termination processes as well as creative processes. Thus

$$\frac{d[R \cdot]}{dt} = 2k_i[I] - k_r[R \cdot][M] - k_t[R \cdot]^2 - k_t[R \cdot][M_1 \cdot]$$

$$- k_t[R \cdot][M_2 \cdot] - \ldots - k_t[R \cdot][M_i \cdot] - \ldots$$

$$= 2k_i[I] - k_r[R \cdot][M] - k_t[R \cdot]([R \cdot] + \sum [M_i \cdot]).$$

Note that we have considered that the radicals $R \cdot$ can be lost from the system by reaction with any one of the other radicals present $R \cdot$, $M_1 \cdot$, $M_2 \cdot$, etc., and hence the total radical concentration $[R \cdot] + \sum[M_i \cdot]$ enters naturally into our equation for $d[R \cdot]/dt$. For the next radical a similar equation applies

$$\frac{d[M_1 \cdot]}{dt} = k_r[R \cdot][M] - k_p[M_1 \cdot][M] - k_t[M_1 \cdot]([R \cdot] + \sum[M_i \cdot]),$$

and for the next

$$\frac{d[M_2\cdot]}{dt} = k_p[M_1\cdot][M] - k_p[M_2\cdot][M] - k_t[M_2\cdot]([R\cdot] + \sum[M_i\cdot]),$$

and so on. If we add all the equations together, we obtain

$$\frac{d([R\cdot] + [M_1\cdot] + [M_2\cdot] + \ldots + [M_i\cdot] + \ldots)}{dt}$$

$$\begin{aligned}
= {}& 2k_i[I] - k_t[R\cdot]([R\cdot] + \sum[M_i\cdot]) \\
& - k_t[M_1\cdot]([R\cdot] + \sum[M_i\cdot]) \\
& - k_t[M_2\cdot]([R\cdot] + \sum[M_i\cdot]) \\
& \qquad\qquad \vdots \\
& - k_t[M_i\cdot]([R\cdot] + \sum[M_i\cdot]) \\
& \qquad\qquad \vdots
\end{aligned}$$

which simplifies to

$$\frac{d([R\cdot] + \sum[M_i\cdot])}{dt} = 2k_i[I] - k_t([R\cdot] + \sum[M_i\cdot])^2. \quad (4.3)$$

We can assume that the concentration of primary radicals [R·] is very small compared to the total concentration of polymer radicals and so we can rewrite eqn. (4.3) as

$$\frac{d(\sum[M_i\cdot])}{dt} = 2k_i[I] - k_t(\sum[M_i\cdot])^2$$

without serious error. Simply for convenience, we shall henceforth represent the summation by a special symbol [C·],

i.e. $$[C\cdot] = \sum[M_i\cdot],$$

which enables the three equations governing the kinetic behaviour of the system to be neatly expressed as

$$-\frac{d[I]}{dt} = k_i[I], \qquad (4.4)$$

$$-\frac{d[M]}{dt} = k_p[C\cdot][M], \tag{4.5}$$

$$\frac{d[C\cdot]}{dt} = 2k_i[I] - k_t[C\cdot]^2. \tag{4.6}$$

If we substitute the integrated form of eqn. (4.4) into (4.6), there remain two equations which govern the monomer disappearance

$$-\frac{d[M]}{dt} = k_p[C\cdot][M]$$

and $\qquad \dfrac{d[C\cdot]}{dt} = 2k_i[I]_0 \exp(-k_it) - k_t[C\cdot]^2.$

Now the decomposition of an initiator into free radicals can be studied in the absence of a monomer and consequently k_i can be evaluated. For the initiators and temperatures normally employed, k_i is of the order of 10^{-6} sec^{-1} which means that the initiator concentration remains effectively constant at its initial value $[I]_0$ for the first few hours of a polymerization. Suppose we take the specific instance of AZBN. Suppose we employ it as an initiator for a polymerization in benzene at 60° C at an initial concentration of 10^{-3} mole l.$^{-1}$ Then since the value of k_i is $1\cdot2\times10^{-5}$ sec^{-1} under these conditions,[13] its concentration at the end of 1 hr is given by

$[I] = [I]_0 \exp(-k_it)$

$\qquad = 1\times10^{-3} \exp(-1\cdot2\times10^{-5}\times3600 \text{ sec}^{-1} \text{ sec}) \text{ mole l.}^{-1}$

$\qquad = 0\cdot958\times10^{-3} \text{ mole l.}^{-1}$

Its concentration is thus 96% of its original value at the end of this period and consequently its concentration over this time approximates without serious error to its initial value.

The effect of restricting our attention to the period over which the initiator concentration remains effectively constant (an hour or two for the common initiators) is a tremendous simplification of the second of the two differential equations.

It now reads

$$\frac{d[C\cdot]}{dt} = 2k_i[I]_0 - k_t[C\cdot]^2. \tag{4.7}$$

This equation integrates simply to give

$$[C\cdot] = \left\{\frac{2k_i[I]_0}{k_t}\right\}^{1/2} \frac{\exp\left\{(8k_ik_t[I]_0)^{1/2}t\right\}-1}{\exp\left\{(8k_ik_t[I]_0)^{1/2}t\right\}+1}. \tag{4.8}$$

This latter equation brings out the significant point that the concentration of active centres builds up asymptotically to a maximum value

$$[C\cdot]_{\max} = \left\{\frac{2k_i[I]_0}{k_t}\right\}^{1/2} \tag{4.9}$$

To illustrate the consequences of these equations, let us consider a particular example — the polymerization of styrene initiated by AZBN in benzene at 60°C. We shall take the initiator concentration to be 1×10^{-3} mole l.$^{-1}$, as in our previous example, and the termination rate constant as $7\cdot2 \times 10^7$ l. mole^{-1} sec^{-1}. Under these conditions, the general build-up in the radical concentration is as shown in Fig. 4.1. The absolute values of the concentrations attained are very low, as would be expected for such reactive species; taking the maximum value as an example, we have from eqn. (4.9)

$$[C\cdot]_{\max} = \left\{\frac{2 \times 1\cdot2 \times 10^{-5} \times 1 \times 10^{-3}}{7\cdot2 \times 10^7}\right\}^{1/2} \left\{\frac{\text{sec}^{-1} \text{ mole l.}^{-1}}{\text{l. mole}^{-1} \text{ sec}^{-1}}\right\}^{1/2}$$
$$= 1\cdot83 \times 10^{-8} \text{ mole l.}^{-1}$$

Since, as can be seen from Fig. 4.1, the radical concentration reaches this value for practical purposes a few seconds after the start of the reaction and thereafter remains constant, the monomer disappears to all intents and purposes by reaction with radicals at this concentration. The expression for the rate of disappearance of monomer then becomes

$$-\frac{d[M]}{dt} = k_p \left\{\frac{2k_i[I]_0}{k_t}\right\}^{1/2} [M]. \tag{4.10}$$

The same result can be obtained in a rather different way by making use of what is termed the *steady state approximation*. To understand this procedure, let us return to eqn. (4.7) for $d[C\cdot]/dt$.

$$\frac{d[C\cdot]}{dt} = 2k_i[I]_0 - k_t[C\cdot]^2.$$

According to this equation, the concentration of $C\cdot$ is initially increasing entirely as a result of the production of free radicals from the initiator (at a rate $2k_i[I]_0$); once a finite number of radicals have been formed, a significant fraction of them be-

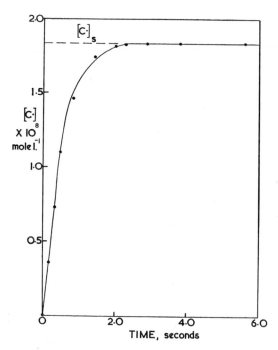

FIG. 4.1. The total radical concentration as a function of time for the polymerization of styrene in benzene at 60°C initiated by AZBN at a concentration of 1×10^{-3} mole l.$^{-1}$

gin to disappear in the termination reaction and so, although their actual concentration is increasing, the rate of increase begins to slow down; eventually, a state of balance is achieved when as many radicals are lost per second by mutual destruction in the termination reaction as are produced per second by the decomposition of the initiator. As long as the initiator concentration remains effectively constant, the concentration of the radicals at this state of balance remains constant. Because this position normally persists for a finite period of time, we describe the situation as the *steady* or *stationary* state. If we represent the radical concentration at this steady or stationary state by the symbol $[C \cdot]_s$, then

$$\frac{d[C \cdot]_s}{dt} = 0$$

and
$$[C \cdot]_s = \left\{ \frac{2k_i[I]_0}{k_t} \right\}^{1/2}. \tag{4.11}$$

This result is identical with the maximum value given by the more rigorous treatment. It only remains to assume that this is the effective radical concentration during the monomer disappearance to recover eqn. (4.10) by substitution of (4.11) in (4.5).

The validity of this argument is best seen by rearranging eqn. (4.8) to give the time t_f at which the radical concentration reaches a fraction f of its maximum or steady state value. The equation is

$$t_f = \frac{1}{(8k_ik_t[I]_0)^{1/2}} \ln \frac{1+f}{1-f}, \tag{4.12}$$

where
$$f = \frac{[C \cdot]}{[C \cdot]_{max}} = \frac{[C \cdot]}{(2k_i[I]_0/k_t)^{1/2}}.$$

Using the same numerical values as before, the radical concentration attains 99% of its maximum or steady state value in a time

$$t_{0\cdot99} = \frac{1}{(8 \times 1\cdot2 \times 10^{-5} \times 7\cdot2 \times 10^7 \times 1 \times 10^{-3})^{1/2}} \ln \frac{1+0\cdot99}{1-0\cdot99}$$

$$\frac{1}{(\text{sec}^{-1} \text{ l. mole}^{-1} \text{ sec}^{-1} \text{ mole l.}^{-1})^{1/2}} = 2\cdot01 \text{ sec.}$$

In other words 2 sec after the polymerization has commenced under the conditions which we have specified, the steady state approximation gives the value of the total radical concentration to an accuracy of 1 %. This result is quite general under the normal conditions of polymerization and so we shall write in future that the total radical concentration $[C\cdot]$ at any time is simply $[C\cdot]_s$.

Equation (4.10) shows that the rate of monomer disappearance is first order with respect to the monomer concentration and half-order with respect to the initial concentration of initiator subject to the condition that this latter quantity represents the effective initiator concentration at the time when the rate of monomer disappearance is being calculated. Integration gives

$$\frac{[M]}{[M]_0} = \exp\left\{-k_p\left(\frac{2k_i}{k_t}\right)^{1/2}[I]_0^{1/2}t\right\} \qquad (4.13)$$

from which we can find the concentration of monomer at any time after the start of the polymerization. Table 4.1 gives the concentration of monomer remaining after 1 hr for several monomers using different concentrations of initiator. Since the initiator decomposition is a first order process, the same fraction of the initiator is consumed in each case.

Our next problem is the calculation of the number average degree of polymerization n and the corresponding molecular weight of the polymer. This quantity appears in our simple formulation of the stoichiometry of the reaction

$$I + nM \rightarrow M_n.$$

TABLE 4.1. CONCENTRATION OF MONOMER REMAINING IN A
POLYMERIZATION SYSTEM AFTER 1 HR USING AZBN
INITIATION AT 60°C

$[M]_0 = 1$ mole l.$^{-1}$

Monomer	k_p[14] l. mole^{-1} sec^{-1}	$k_t \times 10^{-7}$[14] l. mole^{-1} sec^{-1}	$[I]_0$ mole l.$^{-1}$	$[C\cdot]_s \times 10^8$ mole l.$^{-1}$	$[M]_{1 \text{ hr}}$ mole l.$^{-1}$
Styrene	176	7·2	1×10^{-3}	1·83	0·989
			1×10^{-2}	5·78	0·964
			1×10^{-1}	18·3	0·891
Methyl methacrylate	734	3·7	1×10^{-3}	2·53	0·935
			1×10^{-2}	8·01	0·809
			1×10^{-1}	25·3	0·513
Vinyl acetate	3700	14·8	1×10^{-3}	1·27	0·844
			1×10^{-2}	4·03	0·585
			1×10^{-1}	12·7	0·184

There is rather more in this equation than appears at first sight; taken in conjunction with the mechanism we have under consideration, it means that the two radicals formed from the decomposition of each initiator molecule react on average with $n/2$ monomer molecules before terminating by combination; thus one initiator molecule produces one polymer molecule.† From this equation, we can see that monomer molecules must disappear from the reaction system n *times* as fast as initiator molecules,

i.e.
$$-\frac{d[M]}{dt} = -n\frac{d[I]}{dt}$$

or
$$n = \frac{-d[M]/dt}{-d[I]/dt}. \qquad (4.14)$$

† If termination were by disproportionation, each initiator molecule would produce *two* polymer molecules and so the stoichiometric equation would read

$$I + 2nM \rightarrow 2M_n$$

Hence we can calculate n from eqn. (4.14) knowing the rates of disappearance of monomer and initiator.

An alternative method of calculating n is based on the following argument. If, say, 1000 monomer molecules disappear from the reaction system every second and if in the same time only 10 polymer molecules appear, then each polymer molecule must contain, on average, 100 monomer units. This proposition can be simply formalized as follows

$$n = \frac{-d[M]/dt}{d[P]/dt}, \tag{4.15}$$

where $d[P]/dt$ represents the rate of production of polymer.

Strictly these equations only apply at the steady state. This can be seen by writing down two conservation equations, one for initiator fragments and one for monomer units. Since there are two initiator fragments per polymer molecule but only one attached to each radical, the equation showing that no initiator fragments are destroyed in the reaction reads

$$2[I]_0 = 2[I] + 2 \sum [M_i] + [R \cdot] + \sum [M_i \cdot],$$

where $[M_i]$ stands for the concentration of the i-mer (this must not be confused with the concentration of the radical containing i monomer units $[M_i \cdot]$). Similarly, the conservation equation in the monomer units is

$$[M]_0 = [M] + \sum i[M_i] + \sum i[M_i \cdot].$$

If we write

$$\sum [M_i] = [P]$$

so that $[P]$ stands for the total concentration of polymer molecules of all types, then by definition the average number of monomer units in a polymer n is given by

$$n = \frac{\sum i[M_i]}{[P]}.$$

Our two conservation equations thus become

$$2[I]_0 = 2[I]+2[P]+[R\cdot]+\sum [M_i\cdot],$$
$$[M]_0 = [M]+n[P]+\sum i[M_i\cdot].$$

Differentiating these equations with respect to time gives

$$0 = 2\frac{d[I]}{dt}+2\frac{d[P]}{dt}+\frac{d[R\cdot]}{dt}+\sum \frac{d[M_i\cdot]}{dt},$$

$$0 = \frac{d[M]}{dt}+n\frac{d[P]}{dt}+\sum i\frac{d[M_i\cdot]}{dt}.$$

In the special case of the steady state $d[R\cdot]/dt$ and $d[M_i\cdot]/dt$ are zero and so we obtain

$$-\frac{d[I]}{dt} = \frac{d[P]}{dt}$$

and

$$-\frac{d[M]}{dt} = n\frac{d[P]}{dt}$$

from which eqns. (4.14) and (4.15) follow at once.

Returning to eqn. (4.14) we can obtain an explicit value for n from eqns. (4.10) and (4.4); in the latter equation, we shall replace [I] by $[I]_0$ since (4.10) only applies when the initiator concentration remains essentially unchanged.

$$n = \frac{k_p\left(\dfrac{2k_i}{k_t}\right)^{1/2}[I]_0^{1/2}[M]}{k_i[I]_0}$$
$$= k_p\left(\frac{2}{k_ik_t}\right)^{1/2}\frac{[M]}{[I]_0^{1/2}}. \qquad (4.16)$$

There is an advantage in restricting our attention to small fractional conversions of monomer to polymer; that is, to the period of time where between 1 and 5% of the monomer originally present has been converted into polymer. By so doing, we can regard the monomer concentration as remaining effectively constant at its initial value $[M]_0$ which means that neither the rate of monomer disappearance nor the average degree of polymerization varies with time over this period. From equation (4.16), the number average degree of polymerization of the polymer formed at low percentage conversion is

$$n = k_p \left(\frac{2}{k_i k_t} \right)^{1/2} \frac{[M]_0}{[I]_0^{1/2}}. \tag{4.17}$$

Thus for a particular monomer–initiator system, increasing the initial monomer concentration increases the molecular weight of the polymer while an increase in the initiator concentration has the opposite result. Qualitatively, these two effects can be easily understood. If we fix the initiator concentration while raising that of the monomer, the total radical concentration remains unchanged but the probability of a given radical reacting with monomer is increased. Each radical therefore grows rather larger before termination and the molecular weight of the polymer so produced is correspondingly enhanced. The converse procedure of raising the initiator concentration while keeping that of the monomer constant is simply a method of raising the stationary radical concentration. With the same number of monomer molecules to compete for, each radical can therefore only grow to a lesser size and the resulting polymer molecular weight falls.

Returning to equation (4.17), we shall now calculate the numerical value of n for the system styrene–AZBN in benzene. We shall take $[I]_0 = 1 \times 10^{-3}$ mole l.$^{-1}$ as before and $[M]_0 = 1$ mole l.$^{-1}$

$$n = 176 \left(\frac{2}{1 \cdot 2 \times 10^{-5} \times 7 \cdot 2 \times 10^7} \right)^{1/2} \cdot \frac{1}{(1 \times 10^{-3})^{1/2}}$$

$$\text{l. mole}^{-1} \text{ sec}^{-1} \left(\frac{1}{\text{sec}^{-1} \text{ l. mole}^{-1} \text{ sec}^{-1}} \right)^{1/2} \cdot \frac{\text{mole l.}^{-1}}{\text{mole}^{1/2} \text{l.}^{-1/2}}$$

$$= 268.$$

Since the molecular weight of the styrene repeat unit is 104, the number average molecular weight of the resulting poly-styrene is equal to 268×104, i.e. 27,900, the end-group contribution being neglected.

Our calculations so far have been concerned with the macroscopic parameters of the reacting system: the polymerization rate and the average molecular weight. But we can learn more about the processes occurring if we extend our enquiries to what we might call the "life-histories" of the individual reacting species. In particular we propose to calculate:

(a) the time which, on average, elapses between consecutive additions of monomer molecules to a particular radical, and

(b) the average lifetime of a polymer radical at the steady state; that is, the time which, on average, elapses between its creation and its destruction under these conditions.

For the first problem we consider the rate at which the monomer concentration decreases by reaction with a particular type of radical $M_i \cdot$. The appropriate expression is

$$\left\{ -\frac{d[M]}{dt} \right\}_{\substack{\text{by reaction with} \\ \text{radicals } M_i \cdot}} = k_p[M_i \cdot][M],$$

which takes this form because each of the $M_i \cdot$ radicals present in unit volume causes the disappearance of $k_p[M]$ monomer molecules in unit time. If $k_p[M]$ monomer molecules disappear in unit time by reaction with a particular radical, a single monomer molecule must disappear by reaction with this same radical in a time

$$\frac{1}{k_p[M]}, \tag{4.18}$$

which in our example at a monomer concentration of

1 mole l. $^{-1}$ is

$$\frac{1}{176 \times 1} \frac{1}{\text{l. mole}^{-1} \text{sec}^{-1} \text{mole l.}^{-1}}$$

$$= 5 \cdot 68 \times 10^{-3} \text{ sec}$$

$$= 5 \cdot 68 \text{ msec.}$$

If the argument is re-examined, it will be clear that this conclusion applies to every other radical in the system and so the growth process can be described as spasmodic, a monomer molecule adding on to an active centre every 5–6 msec. It should be realized that this quiescent period of 5–6 msec of the radical's life is a very long time on the molecular time scale; during this period the radical will have collided up to one thousand million times with monomer molecules without reaction and rather more times with solvent molecules—the relative numbers depending on the relative concentrations. That such a low proportion of the radical–monomer collisions result in reaction is a consequence of the special energy and orientation requirements of a reacting pair.

On average each radical must add on $n/2$ monomer molecules between its "birth" and "death"—the factor of two arising because its "death" results from combination[†] with another radical also containing an average of $n/2$ monomer residues (n is as before the number average degree of polymerization). Consequently, the average *radical lifetime* τ is given by

τ = (time between consecutive monomer additions) $\times$
(average number of monomer additions between "birth" and "death")

$$= \frac{1}{k_p[\text{M}]} \cdot \frac{n}{2}. \tag{4.19}$$

If we confine our attention to low percentage conversion of

[†] In disproportionation termination this factor of two would not be present.

monomer to polymer so that $[M] = [M]_0$ without serious error, we can substitute for n from eqn. (4.17).

Therefore
$$\tau = \frac{1}{k_p[M]_0} \cdot \frac{k_p}{2} \left(\frac{2}{k_i k_t} \right)^{1/2} \frac{[M]_0}{[I]_0^{1/2}}$$

$$= \frac{1}{(2k_i k_t)^{1/2}} \cdot \frac{1}{[I]_0^{1/2}} \cdot \tag{4.20}$$

Under the conditions chosen in our example

$$\tau = \frac{1}{(2 \times 1 \cdot 2 \times 10^{-5} \times 7 \cdot 2 \times 10^7)^{1/2}} \cdot \frac{1}{(1 \times 10^{-3})^{1/2}}$$

$$\frac{1}{(\text{sec}^{-1} \text{ l. mole}^{-1} \text{ sec}^{-1})^{1/2}} \cdot \frac{1}{(\text{mole l.}^{-1})^{1/2}} = 0 \cdot 76 \text{ sec.}$$

(A cross-check can easily be carried out without going through the formal equation derived above. We know that a monomer molecule adds on to a radical every 5·7 msec and that each radical adds on 134 monomers before termination by combination with another radical also containing 134 monomer units to give a polymer of degree of polymerization 268. The time taken for 134 monomer molecules to add on is clearly $5 \cdot 7 \times 10^{-3} \times 134$ sec $= 0 \cdot 76$ sec as before.)

Equation (4.20) for the radical lifetime can be transformed into an equation containing the stationary radical concentration $[C \cdot]_s$ without any difficulty; the product $(2k_i[I]_0)^{1/2}$ is simply replaced by $k_t^{1/2}[C \cdot]_s$ giving

$$\tau = \frac{1}{k_t[C \cdot]_s}. \tag{4.21}$$

This equation emphasizes the important point that the radical lifetime depends on the stationary radical concentration.

An alternative method of deriving eqn. (4.21) is as follows. Suppose we fix our attention on a particular group of radicals at some instant in time and follow their fate. If we confine our attention to one litre of reaction mixture at the steady state, the initial number of these selected radicals is $[C\cdot]_s$. Following our selection, some of these radicals disappear and are replaced by other radicals originating in the initiation reaction so that the total number of radicals remains constant. If we write $[\mathcal{C}\cdot]$ for the number of radicals originally members of our selected group which remain at time t following our selection, then

$$-\frac{d[\mathcal{C}\cdot]}{dt} = k_t[\mathcal{C}\cdot][C\cdot]_s,$$

since the members of our group disappear in the presence of a constant radical concentration $[C\cdot]_s$.

Therefore $[\mathcal{C}\cdot] = [C\cdot]_s \exp(-k_t[C\cdot]_s t).$

Now if our problem were to find the average lifetime of a group of radicals which could be broken down into a set of subgroups such that n_1 radicals survived for a time t_1, n_2 radicals for a time t_2 and so on, we should have no difficulty in defining an average lifetime—we should write

$$\tau = \frac{n_1 t_1 + n_2 t_2 + \dots}{n_1 + n_2 + \dots}.$$

In our case where there is a continuous gradation in the number and survival times, we modify this general expression by dividing the original group of radicals into an infinite set of subgroups each containing an infinitesimal number of radicals $d[\mathcal{C}\cdot]$. Each subgroup survives a variable time t and so the extension of our previous averaging procedure to this more general situation gives

$$\tau = \frac{\displaystyle\int_0^{[C\cdot]_s} t\,d[\mathcal{C}\cdot]}{\displaystyle\int_0^{[C\cdot]_s} d[\mathcal{C}\cdot]} = \frac{-k_t[C\cdot]_s^2 \displaystyle\int_\infty^0 t \exp(-k_t[C\cdot]_s t)\,dt}{[C\cdot]_s}$$

$$= k_t[C\cdot]_s \int_0^\infty t \exp(-k_t[C\cdot]_s t)\,dt = \frac{1}{k_t[C\cdot]_s}.$$

The general picture of the mechanism of free radical polymerization in a simple case is thus as follows. The process is started by the decomposition of an initiator induced thermally, photochemically or by admixture of another substance. The free radicals so obtained add on monomer or react with other radicals to produce polymer. At very early times in the reaction, there are insufficient radicals present to make the second of these two processes important—consequently the radical concentration builds up and the rate of monomer disappearance increases. In a fairly short time, however (roughly a few seconds), the radical concentration reaches a sufficiently high value of about 10^{-8} mole l. $^{-1}$ that the rate of disappearance of the radicals is for practical purposes equal to the rate of their formation—a situation which we describe as a steady state. Provided that the monomer concentration remains fairly constant, the rate of monomer disappearance levels out at a steady value and the percentage conversion–time curve becomes linear. Under these conditions monomer molecules add on to the active centres at intervals of a few milliseconds and since each active centre survives on average for a second or thereabouts, the polymer formed by combination of two such active centres contains upwards of two or three hundred monomer units. The polymer molecular weight thus shows little or no variation with time being the same whether formed ten seconds or ten minutes after the start of the reaction. The actual numerical values of these quantities depend, of course, on the particular values k_i, k_p and k_t as well as on the concentrations of monomer and initiator. The effects of varying these latter two parameters are shown in Table 4.2.

Examination of Table 4.2 shows that the three rate constants k_i, k_p and k_t can be obtained by combining the results of three separate measurements:

(a) the rate of polymerization at the steady state;

(b) the number average degree of polymerization of the polymer produced at the steady state;

(c) the average radical lifetime at the steady state.

TABLE 4.2. THE DEPENDENCE OF THE VARIOUS REACTION PARAMETERS ON THE INITIAL CONCENTRATIONS OF INITIATOR AND MONOMER

Parameter	Expression	Effect of increasing $[M]_0$ 4 times at constant $[I]_0$	Effect of increasing $[I]_0$ 4 times at constant $[M]_0$
The total radical concentration at the steady state. $[C\cdot]_s$	$\left(\dfrac{2k_i}{k_t}\right)^{1/2}[I]_0^{1/2}$	No change	Increases 2 times
The time for the radical concentration to reach a given fraction, f, of its steady state value. t_f	$\dfrac{1}{(8k_ik_t[I]_0)^{1/2}}\ln\dfrac{1+f}{1-f}$	No change	Decreases by factor $1/2$
The rate of polymerization. $-d[M]/dt$	$k_p\left(\dfrac{2k_i}{k_t}\right)^{1/2}[I]_0^{1/2}[M]_0$	Increases 4 times	Increases 2 times
The number average degree of polymerization. n	$k_p\left(\dfrac{2}{k_ik_t}\right)^{1/2}\dfrac{[M]_0}{[I]_0^{1/2}}$	Increases 4 times	Decreases by factor $1/2$
The time between consecutive monomer additions to a particular radical.	$\dfrac{1}{k_p[M]_0}$	Decreases by factor $1/4$	No change
The average radical lifetime at the steady state. τ	$\dfrac{1}{(2k_ik_t)^{1/2}}\dfrac{1}{[I]_0^{1/2}}$	No change	Decreases by factor $1/2$

1. (b) gives $\dfrac{k_p}{(k_ik_t)^{1/2}}$

   (c) gives $\dfrac{1}{(k_ik_t)^{1/2}}$ $\Bigg\}$ combined together give k_p.

2. (b) and (c) give k_p

   (a) gives $k_p\left(\dfrac{k_i}{k_t}\right)^{1/2}$ $\Bigg\}$ combined together give $\left(\dfrac{k_i}{k_t}\right)^{1/2}$

3. (a), (b) and (c) give $\left(\dfrac{k_i}{k_t}\right)^{1/2}$

   (c) gives $\dfrac{1}{(k_ik_t)^{1/2}}$ $\Bigg\}$ combined together give k_i and k_t.

PRACTICAL METHODS OF
DETERMINING THESE QUANTITIES

At this point, we shall consider the experimental methods which are employed to determine the three quantities which enable the individual rate constants to be calculated. We do not need to consider the experimental procedure required to determine the number average degree of polymerization, for this has been dealt with in detail in Chapter 2. It is sufficient to say that, after a small fraction of the monomer has been converted into polymer, the polymer is normally precipitated from the reaction system by the addition of a non-solvent, washed free from adhering monomer and initiator, dried and then subjected to either end-group or osmotic methods of molecular weight determination.

The determination of the rate of polymerization does not present any conceptual difficulties. Essentially, all that is required is a clock and a procedure which can distinguish monomer molecules incorporated in the polymer from unchanged monomer. The most direct method is to take a sample of the polymerizing mixture at a series of times, precipitate the polymer contained therein and from its weight calculate the fractional conversion directly. Other methods which have been used take advantage of the difference in some physical property between the monomer and polymer. For example, all polymers formed by addition processes have a higher density than the monomers so that the volume of a polymerizing mixture decreases as the reaction proceeds. The decrease in

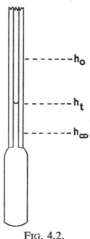

FIG. 4.2.

volume of the reaction mixture is very conveniently followed in a special vessel called a dilatometer, a simple example of which is shown in Fig. 4.2. Provided that the densities of the monomer and polymer in the solution are identical with the values appropriate to the pure substances, it is very easy to calculate the fraction of monomer converted into polymer from the contraction in volume. In addition to the density, use has been made of refractive index, dielectric constant† and heat content

† These methods were developed particularly to study the rate of polymerization in the non-stationary state period; that is, during the build-up of the radical concentration to its steady state value. These studies provide an alternative method of evaluating $\dfrac{1}{(k_t k_i)^{1/2}}$.

difference between monomer and polymer in order to detect the amount of polymerization which has taken place. The experimental arrangements employed in these latter methods are rather sophisticated and outside the scope of this book.

The determination of the average lifetime of the growing radical is less easy to explain. It is essential that the initiation process shall be photochemical so that initiation may be interrupted at will. We can imagine two ways in which we may interrupt the initiation process.

In the first case the light can be switched on for a period considerably longer than the time required for the radical concentration to build up to its stationary state concentration and then switched off for a period considerably longer than the radical lifetime which we wish to measure. In a sequence of such operations, the radical concentration would fluctuate as shown in Fig. 4.3.

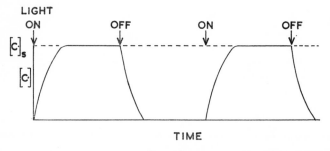

FIG. 4.3.

For example, suppose we have the light on for 1 min, off for 1 min, on for 1 min, and so on for a period of, say, 10 min all told. If we choose a light intensity of such a magnitude that with the wavelength used we obtain just the same rate of production of primary radicals as from the thermal decomposition of AZBN at $60°C$ at 1×10^{-3} mole l. $^{-1}$, then we know that the build-up of radicals must be complete in about 2 sec. Similarly, since the average lifetime of the radicals is of the order of 1 sec, then the decay period after the light has been switched off must be no more than a few seconds.† The amount of monomer consumed in the build-up and decay periods is thus only a small fraction of that consumed while the radical concentration is at its maximum value, for we have deliberately arranged that this period is considerably longer than the radical lifetime (nearly 1 min as against 1 sec). If for simplicity we restrict our attention to equal light and dark intervals of duration

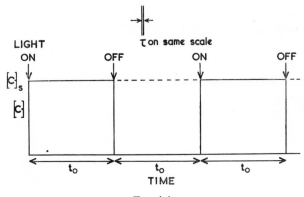

FIG. 4.4.

t_0, we can say that the greater the ratio of t_0/τ, the more completely can we ignore the effects of the non-stationary periods. Hence we can replace Fig. 4.3 by Fig. 4.4. In effect the light is only switched on for 5 min out of 10 and consequently the amount of monomer consumed is one half that which would

† The radical concentration decays according to the second-order equation $-d[C\cdot]/dt = k_t[C\cdot]^2$. By simple integration and transformation, it can be shown that the radical concentration at time t after the light has been switched off is given by $\dfrac{[C\cdot]}{[C\cdot]_s} = \dfrac{\tau}{\tau+t}$. Thus 90% of the radicals have been destroyed after a time 9τ; in our example, this would be in about 7 sec.

have disappeared under steady illumination of the same intensity over the whole period.

In the second case we can make the duration of the light and dark periods equal but very short compared to the lifetime of the polymer radicals. Figure 4.5 shows that in this case the radical concentration builds up from zero until it oscillates about a value rather less than the value it would reach under conditions of steady illumination.

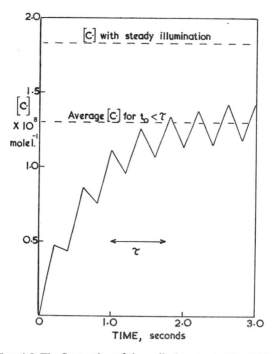

FIG. 4.5. The fluctuation of the radical concentration with time when the alternating light and dark periods are shorter than the radical lifetime. $t_0/\tau = 0.26$. This curve has been calculated for the case where steady illumination would produce just the same rate of increase of the radical concentration as found under the conditions used for Fig. 4.1

The reason is that, the radical lifetime being considerably longer than the dark periods, few radicals disappear when the light is switched off. On the other hand insufficient energy is supplied to the reaction system to maintain the radical concentration at its value corresponding to the same intensity steady illumination. For very rapid flashes of equal light and dark periods, the effect is simply to halve the effective intensity (half the energy received per unit area over the same time). The radical concentration then remains as near as makes no matter constant. The rate of production of radicals under these conditions is proportional to $\mathcal{J}_0/2$ (where $\mathcal{J}_0$ is the steady intensity) and the rate of loss of radicals as usual is $k_t[\text{C}\cdot]^2$. Consequently, the new stationary radical concentration for rapid intermittent illumination is proportional to $\mathcal{J}_0^{1/2}/\sqrt{2}$ and therefore the amount of monomer which disappears in unit time is less by a factor of $1/\sqrt{2}$ than that which would have disappeared under steady illumination of the same intensity.

Comparison of the two cases brings out the rather interesting result that although the total energy received by the reaction system is the same for each, the rates of monomer disappearance are different. When the alternate periods of illumination and darkness are considerably longer than the radical lifetime, the rate of monomer disappearance is proportional to $\mathcal{J}_0^{1/2}/2$; on the other hand, when these periods are considerably shorter, the rate becomes proportional to $\mathcal{J}_0^{1/2}/\sqrt{2}$.† Clearly, at flashing frequencies in between these two extreme cases where the periods of illumination and darkness are comparable to the radical lifetime, intermediate rates of monomer disappearance will be recorded. A full treatment of the problem enables the graph in Fig. 4.6 to be predicted.

† The dependence of the rate of monomer disappearance on the flashing frequency is one of the best pieces of evidence for bimolecular radical–radical termination. If termination only involved a single radical, the rates would be the same in the two experiments.

Experimentally, of course, the only graph that can be drawn is $R_p/(R_p)_{\text{steady illumination}}$ against t_0. This is superimposed on the theoretical graph of Fig. 4.6 and the value of t_0 is noted on the experimental graph which corresponds to the ratio $t_0/\tau = 1 \cdot 0$. This value is the required radical lifetime.

From a practical point of view, the rates of monomer disappearance can be obtained by one of the physical methods already mentioned. The time of illumination of the polymeri-

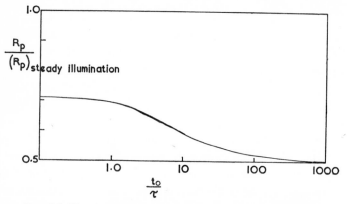

Fig. 4.6. The dependence of the rate of monomer disappearance R_p on the ratio of the time of illumination t_0 to the radical lifetime τ for equal periods of illumination and darkness

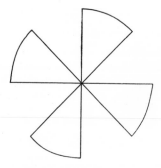

Fig. 4.7. A rotating sector suitable for equal periods of illumination and darkness

zation system is not normally controlled by switching a lamp on and off as implied in our description. The more convenient arrangement is employed whereby a disc cut out in the manner shown in Fig. 4.7 is rotated at various speeds in the path of a light beam of constant intensity. For this reason, the method is referred to as the *rotating sector technique*.

Table 4.3 gives the results obtained for three different monomers.

TABLE 4.3. NUMERICAL VALUES OF THE RATE
CONSTANTS k_p AND k_t FOR THREE DIFFERENT
MONOMERS

Temperature °C	Monomer	k_p l. mole^{-1} sec^{-1}	$k_t \times 10^{-7}$ l. mole^{-1} sec^{-1}
25	Styrene	44	4·8
	Methyl methacrylate	240	2·3
	Vinyl acetate	1000	5·9
60	Styrene	176	7·2
	Methyl methacrylate	734	3·7
	Vinyl acetate	3700	14·8

MODIFICATIONS TO THE PREVIOUS SCHEME

The three-reaction polymerization mechanism described in detail is inadequate to account for all the known features of free-radical addition polymerization. We now describe a few of the more important modifications which must be made to the ideas already developed.

1. Initiator efficiencies

We have written the initiation reaction as

$$I \rightarrow 2R \cdot$$
$$R \cdot + M \rightarrow M_1 \cdot$$

There is some evidence to suppose that a fraction of the initiator molecules which decompose do not lead to the production of radical active centres which participate in the propagation reaction; with certain initiators, the number of initiator molecules known to have decomposed in a given time exceeds the number of initiator fragments which have been incorporated into polymer chains. This means that the primary radicals can react in other ways than with monomer.

(a) A primary radical can react with an initiator molecule to give another primary radical and a decomposition product of the initiator—a process known as induced decomposition; for example, a benzoyloxy radical from benzoyl peroxide can decompose the parent peroxide

$$C_6H_5-\underset{\underset{O}{\|}}{C}-O\cdot + C_6H_5-\underset{\underset{O}{\|}}{C}-O-O-\underset{\underset{O}{\|}}{C}-C_6H_5$$

$$\rightarrow C_6H_5-\underset{\underset{O}{\|}}{C}-O-C_6H_5 + C_6H_5-\underset{\underset{O}{\|}}{C}-O\cdot + CO_2$$

(b) Alternatively a primary radical can react with a scission product from another primary radical to give a molecule different from the parent initiator; for example, two radicals from AZBN may recombine after losing nitrogen *before* diffusing apart.

$$\begin{array}{c} \underset{CH_3}{\overset{CH_3}{\diagdown}}\underset{\underset{CN}{|}}{C}-N=N-\underset{\underset{CN}{|}}{C}\underset{CH_3}{\overset{CH_3}{\diagup}} \\ \downarrow \\ \underset{CH_3}{\overset{CH_3}{\diagdown}}\underset{\underset{CN}{|}}{C}\cdot + N_2 + \cdot\underset{\underset{CN}{|}}{C}\underset{CH_3}{\overset{CH_3}{\diagup}} \\ \downarrow \\ \underset{CH_3}{\overset{CH_3}{\diagdown}}\underset{\underset{CN}{|}}{C}-\underset{\underset{CN}{|}}{C}\underset{CH_3}{\overset{CH_3}{\diagup}} \end{array}$$

tetramethyl-succinodinitrile

The two radicals produced are initially very close to one another. If they do not react within one or two jumps from their original position, they will diffuse sufficiently far apart that their chances of reacting subsequently with one another are negligible; their probable fate is then reaction with monomer.

Kinetically, these effects are not very important unless the concentration of the monomer affects the probabilities of these events occurring relative to the reaction $R \cdot + M \rightarrow M_1 \cdot$. If the monomer concentration has no effect—this appears to be the usual case—then the net result of the presence of these side reactions is that the rate constant for initiation k_i previously employed is replaced by $\beta k_i'$, where β is the *initiator efficiency* and k_i' is the first order rate constant for the decomposition of the initiator calculated from studies of the initiator concentration as a function of time. The values which β takes vary from one initiator to another but, on average, are close to unity, showing that the above considerations are of minor importance in the polymerization process as a whole.

2. The effect of additives; Inhibition, Retardation and Chain transfer

Certain substances when added to a polymerizing system affect the rate of polymerization and/or the average molecular weight of the polymer produced. Those substances which affect the rate of the polymerization are termed *inhibitors* or *retarders* according to whether the rate is reduced to zero or to a finite value. The substances which only affect the average molecular weight of the polymer but have no influence on the polymerization rate are termed *chain transfer agents*.

The action of inhibitors and retarders may be understood if we regard them as offering an alternative reaction path to the chain radicals. Schematically, their action can be represented as

$$M_i\cdot \quad \xrightarrow[+M]{} \quad M_{i+1}\cdot \tag{1}$$

$$\xrightarrow[+A]{} \quad M_iA\cdot \tag{2}$$

where A represents a molecule of inhibitor or retarder. Reaction 1 is the normal propagation reaction in which the addition of a monomer molecule to a polymer radical produces another polymer radical of exactly the same reactivity. In reaction 2 the radical $M_iA\cdot$ produced from the combination of the polymer radical and the inhibitor or retarder is incapable of reacting with further monomer and consequently there is a diminution in the concentration of active centres and a corresponding decrease in the polymerization rate. The extent to which A competes with monomer for polymer radicals determines whether it is classed as an inhibitor or a retarder. If the rate of reaction 2 is very much greater than the rate of reaction 1, the majority of the polymer radicals are removed from the system before they have time to grow to any reasonable length and therefore, if the reaction is followed by means which only permit the detection of reasonably high molecular weight polymer (viscosity, or precipitation and weighing), the rate of polymerization appears to be zero. In such a case the added substance is classed as an inhibitor. On the other hand, if the relative rates of the two reactions are such that there is a finite probability that a particular radical can grow to a reasonable length in the presence of the additive, then clearly the substance is classed as a retarder. Thus there is no essential difference between a retarder and an inhibitor for the observed effects depend as much on concentration as on chemical type. A few words need to be said about the fate of the product radical $M_iA\cdot$. Its concentration will build up until the rate at which it disappears by combination or disproportionation with another radical just balances its rate of production.

As an example of the likely processes which occur in inhibition or retardation, we list the intermediate products formed in the reaction between polystyryl radicals and benzoquinone.

These hydroquinone radicals then disappear from the reaction system by mutual combination or disproportionation; for example,

A particularly important feature is the extremely small amounts of inhibitor which are necessary to completely suppress polymerization. This is easily understandable if we consider the problem quantitatively using the example we have employed previously. According to our previous calculations, the rate of production of radicals is

$$2k_i[I]$$

which for AZBN at a concentration of 1×10^{-3} mole $1.^{-1}$ in benzene at 60°C is

$$2 \times 1 \cdot 2 \times 10^{-5} \times 1 \times 10^{-3} \text{ mole } 1.^{-1} \text{ sec}^{-1}$$
$$= 2 \cdot 4 \times 10^{-8} \text{ mole } 1.^{-1} \text{ sec}^{-1}.$$

The total number of radicals generated in 1 1. in 1 hr is

$$2 \cdot 4 \times 10^{-8} \times 3 \cdot 6 \times 10^{3} \text{ mole } 1.^{-1} \text{ hr}^{-1}$$
$$= 8 \cdot 6 \times 10^{-5} \text{ mole } 1.^{-1} \text{ hr}^{-1}.$$

Suppose every inhibitor molecule accounts for one polymer radical; then, provided that the only reaction removing polymer radicals is the inhibition reaction, we need only have a concentration of $8 \cdot 6 \times 10^{-5}$ mole $1.^{-1}$ of inhibitor to remove all the radicals generated in 1 hr. This latter proviso can never be precisely fulfilled in a real system for there is always a finite probability that a radical may disappear by the normal termination process; this probability which we would define by the ratio

$$\frac{\text{number of polymer radicals disappearing per unit time by normal termination}}{\text{total number of polymer radicals disappearing per unit time}}$$

is given by
$$\frac{k_t[\text{C·}]^2}{k_t[\text{C·}]^2 + k_A[\text{C·}][\text{A}]},$$

where $[\text{C·}]$ as before represents the total concentration of polymer radicals of all lengths and k_A represents the rate constant for the reaction of a polymer radical with an inhibitor molecule, i.e. for the reaction

$$\text{M}_i\text{·} + \text{A} \rightarrow \text{M}_i\text{A·}$$

Cancelling $[\text{C·}]$ top and bottom, the probability that a radical disappears from the system by the normal termination process is

$$\frac{k_t[\text{C·}]}{k_t[\text{C·}] + k_A[\text{A}]}.$$

Thus when $k_A[A] \gg k_t[C \cdot]$ this source of radical loss can be neglected without serious error but when a sufficient amount of the inhibitor has disappeared to reverse the inequality, the simple arguments outlined above can no longer be sustained. In some systems, the quantitative scavenging of the polymer radicals by inhibitor up to the point where practically less than 1 % of the original inhibitor remains appears to be well authenticated. Such cases are recognizable by the direct proportionality between the inhibitor concentration and the interval of time between the start of the reaction and the start of polymerization—the *induction period* as it is called. Reverting to our numerical example, if it were found that an inhibitor concentration of $8 \cdot 6 \times 10^{-5}$ mole 1. $^{-1}$ suppressed polymerization for 1 hr, a concentration of $17 \cdot 2 \times 10^{-5}$ mole 1. $^{-1}$ for 2 hr, and so on, then these data would be experimental evidence for the simple explanation of the inhibitor action. Clearly these same experiments lead to a value for the rate of initiation if the number of radicals scavenged by each inhibitor molecule is known and hence provide an alternative way of determining the rate constant k_i to that already discussed. In practice the stoichiometry of the inhibition reaction is not usually known with sufficient certainty to make this method completely reliable.

Use is made of this phenomenon when storing easily polymerizable monomers; 1 or 2 % of an inhibitor such as benzoquinone or t-butyl catechol is usually added to the monomer to suppress the slow polymerization which occurs thermally or as a result of the presence of traces of initiators. When the monomer is required, the inhibitor is removed (usually by chemical means) and the monomer fractionally distilled. At the same time, the phenomenon can have unfortunate consequences in quantitative work. If all traces of inhibitors (or retarders) are not removed from the monomer, irreproducible rates of polymerization are often found; for this reason it is the practice to "pre-polymerize" 1 or 2% of the monomer before use so that any residual impurities which react with the polymer radicals do so before the investigation proper is commenced.

In contrast to the action of inhibitors or retarders, chain transfer agents do not influence the polymerization rate but only affect the degree of polymerization of the product polymer. They, too, react with the polymer radicals but, instead of producing an inactive radical, they produce a radical capable of starting a new polymer chain *and* an inactive polymer molecule. The reaction may be represented

$$M_i\cdot + TH \rightarrow M_iH + T\cdot\dagger$$

where TH stands for the transfer agent and $T\cdot$ represents a radical which can react with monomer thus

$$T\cdot + M \rightarrow M_1\cdot$$

The basic principle to appreciate is that the stationary radical concentration is unaffected by the introduction of a chain transfer agent and hence the polymerization rate is unaltered; the chain transfer agent simply provides a second route to the production of polymer in addition to the straightforward bimolecular termination reaction. Consequently, more polymer molecules are produced per unit time and since the rate of monomer disappearance is unaltered, the average number of monomer molecules in each polymer chain is reduced. In other words these substances produce a lowering of the molecular weight. Quantitatively, the number average degree of polymerization of the polymers produced at the steady state can be calculated using eqn. (4.15), i.e.

$$n = \frac{-d[M]/dt}{d[P]/dt}.$$

† This is the most common case. There are, however, transfer agents which transfer atoms other than hydrogen to polymer radicals, e.g. CCl_4.

Since we know $-d[M]/dt$, the problem reduces to the calculation of $d[P]/dt$ which is simply the sum of the two separate rates of polymer production.

If we consider combination termination as the sole radical destroying reaction, then every time two radicals disappear one polymer molecule appears. So, in this process,

$$\left\{\frac{d[P]}{dt}\right\}_{\substack{\text{combination} \\ \text{termination} \\ \text{reaction}}} = -1/2 \left\{\frac{d[C\cdot]_s}{dt}\right\}^{\dagger}_{\substack{\text{combination} \\ \text{termination} \\ \text{reaction}}}$$

We have already shown that the rate of disappearance of radicals of all types in the bimolecular termination reaction is $k_t[C\cdot]^2$ and so the contribution of this reaction to the rate of production of polymer is

$$\left\{\frac{d[P]}{dt}\right\}_{\substack{\text{combination} \\ \text{termination} \\ \text{reaction}}} = \frac{k_t}{2}\,[C\cdot]_s^2$$

The second route by which polymer is produced is, of course, the chain transfer process which we are at present examining. Since all radicals can react with the transfer agent, the reaction is really a series of parallel reactions all leading to the formation of polymer.

$$M_1\cdot + TH \;\rightarrow\; M_1H + T\cdot$$
$$M_2\cdot + TH \;\rightarrow\; M_2H + T\cdot$$
$$\vdots$$
$$M_i\cdot + TH \;\rightarrow\; M_iH + T\cdot$$
$$\vdots$$

If as usual we suppose that each reaction has the same rate

† The rate of radical disappearance in the termination reaction which is required in this calculation must not be confused with the overall rate of radical disappearance. At the stationary state, this latter quantity is zero though obviously polymer is being produced at a finite rate.

constant k_{tr}, then

$$\left\{\frac{d[P]}{dt}\right\}_{\text{transfer}} = k_{tr}[M_1\cdot][TH]+k_{tr}[M_2\cdot][TH]+\dots$$
$$\dots k_{tr}[M_i\cdot][TH]\dots$$
$$= k_{tr}([M_1\cdot]+[M_2\cdot]+\dots[M_i\cdot]+\dots)[TH]$$
$$= k_{tr}[C\cdot]_s[TH].$$

It only remains to add these two results together in order to obtain an expression for the total rate of production of polymer.

$$\frac{d[P]}{dt} = \frac{k_t}{2}[C\cdot]_s^2+k_{tr}[C\cdot]_s[TH].$$

Recalling that $-d[M]/dt$ is $k_p[C\cdot]_s[M]$, we can now calculate the number average degree of polymerization n.

$$n = \frac{k_p[C\cdot]_s[M]}{\dfrac{k_t}{2}[C\cdot]_s^2+k_{tr}[C\cdot]_s[TH]} = \frac{k_p[M]}{\dfrac{k_t}{2}[C\cdot]_s+k_{tr}[TH]}.$$

This equation is usually rearranged as follows

$$\frac{1}{n} = \frac{k_t}{2k_p}\cdot\frac{[C\cdot]_s}{[M]}+\frac{k_{tr}}{k_p}\cdot\frac{[TH]}{[M]}.$$

From eqn. (4.11), we obtain the value of $[C\cdot]_s$ and by confining our attention to the early stages of the polymerization so that the instantaneous values of the two concentrations [M] and [TH] can be replaced by their initial values, we obtain

$$\frac{1}{n} = \frac{1}{k_p}\cdot\left(\frac{k_i k_t}{2}\right)^{1/2}\cdot\frac{[I]_0^{1/2}}{[M]_0}+\frac{k_{tr}}{k_p}\cdot\frac{[TH]_0}{[M]_0}. \qquad (4.22)$$

The ratio k_{tr}/k_p is called the transfer constant $\mathcal{C}$ and so eqn. (4.22) is often rewritten as

$$\frac{1}{n} = \frac{1}{k_p}\cdot\left(\frac{k_i k_t}{2}\right)^{1/2}\cdot\frac{[I]_0^{1/2}}{[M]_0}+\mathcal{C}\cdot\frac{[TH]_0}{[M]_0} \qquad (4.23)$$

In this form, eqn. (4.23) enables the transfer constant to be obtained from experimental measurements of n at different $[TH]_0/[M]_0$ ratios; a plot of $1/n$ against $[TH]_0/[M]_0$ is clearly linear of slope numerically equal to the transfer constant $\mathscr{C}$. Note that by putting $[TH]_0 = 0$, eqns. (4.22) and (4.23) reduce to the expression given in (4.17) for the number average degree of polymerization appropriate to the simple mechanism.

A wide variety of substances have been found to act as transfer agents in polymerization including the monomers themselves, some of the solvents employed, and sometimes the initiators. Particularly important are the mercaptans, RSH, which are used industrially to control the average molecular weights of some commercially produced polymers. Table 4.4 lists a few values of the transfer constants for various substances with styrene at 60° C.

TABLE 4.4

Transfer agent	$\mathscr{C}^{(15)}$
Styrene	6×10^{-5}
Benzoyl peroxide	0·055
Benzene	$1·8 \times 10^{-6}$
Chloroform	5×10^{-5}
n-Butyl Mercaptan	22

If, as often happens, there is more than one transfer agent present in the system at any one time, an extension of the arguments which lead to eqn. (4.23) simply replaces the term

$$\mathscr{C} \frac{[TH]_0}{[M]_0}$$

by

$$\sum \mathscr{C}_i \frac{[TH_i]_0}{[M]_0},$$

each type of transfer agent having its own particular value of the transfer constant and making its own contribution to the formation of polymer. In order to see the effect of transfer, we shall now calculate the average degree of polymerization of the polystyrene produced at 60° C in benzene under the usual conditions in the presence of n-butyl mercaptan at a concentration of 10^{-3} mole l. $^{-1}$ Equation (4.23) modified to include transfer to monomer, solvent and n-butyl mercaptan (BuSH) reads

$$\frac{1}{n} = \frac{1}{k_p}\left(\frac{k_i k_t}{2}\right)^{1/2}\frac{[I]_0^{1/2}}{[M]_0} + \mathcal{C}_M + \mathcal{C}_{C_6H_6}\frac{[C_6H_6]_0}{[M]_0} + \mathcal{C}_{BuSH}\frac{[BuSH]_0}{[M]_0},$$

where the subscripts to the transfer constants indicate the substances to which they apply. We have already calculated the value of the first term (p. 179), the second term we read from Table (4.4), and the third and fourth terms we calculate as follows taking the concentration of benzene under the conditions employed to be 10 mole l. $^{-1}$

$$\frac{1}{n} = \frac{1}{268} + 6\times10^{-5} + 1\cdot8\times10^{-6}\times10 + 22\times10^{-3}$$
$$= 10^{-3}(3\cdot7 + 0\cdot06 + 0\cdot018 + 22).$$

Therefore $n = 38\cdot8$.

Thus instead of a molecular weight of 27,900 (268×104), the polymers produced only reach a value of 4030 ($38\cdot8\times104$). Clearly, transfer to monomer and solvent under these conditions has a negligible influence on the polymer molecular weight. In fact, the molecular weight is almost entirely determined by the concentration of n-butyl mercaptan employed.

To conclude this section, we refer briefly to a further type of transfer process in which a growing polymer radical abstracts a hydrogen atom from a preformed polymer molecule. For example, in a polymerizing system containing both styrene and polystyrene, there is a finite probability that a polystyryl radical abstracts a hydrogen atom from the backbone of the polymer, as follows:

$$M_i \cdot \; + \; \text{\small\leavevmode}CH_2CHCH_2CHCH_2CH\text{\small\leavevmode}$$
$$\hspace{2cm} | \hspace{1.2cm} | \hspace{1.2cm} |$$
$$\hspace{2cm} C_6H_5 \hspace{0.6cm} C_6H_5 \hspace{0.6cm} C_6H_5$$

$$\rightarrow M_iH \; + \; \text{\small\leavevmode}CH_2CHCH_2\overset{\cdot}{C}CH_2CH\text{\small\leavevmode}$$
$$\hspace{2.5cm} | \hspace{1.2cm} | \hspace{1.0cm} |$$
$$\hspace{2.5cm} C_6H_5 \hspace{0.6cm} C_6H_5 \; C_6H_5$$

Of course, there are other sites from which the abstraction of hydrogen could have occurred—the above choice is simply the most likely. The net result is the same, however, irrespective of the point of radical attack; that is, a radical active centre is created somewhere along the backbone of the polymer molecule. This grows in the usual way by successive monomer addition, eventually terminating by either combination or disproportionation. Consequently, this sequence of reactions results in the formation of *branched polymers*.

$$HC-C_6H_5$$
$$|$$
$$CH_2$$
$$|$$
$$HC-C_6H_5$$
$$|$$
$$CH_2$$
$$|$$
$$\text{\small\leavevmode}CH_2-CH-CH_2-C-CH_2-CH\text{\small\leavevmode}$$
$$\hspace{1cm} | \hspace{1.8cm} | \hspace{1.5cm} |$$
$$\hspace{1cm} C_6H_5 \hspace{1.2cm} C_6H_5 \hspace{1.0cm} C_6H_5$$

Obviously, the probability of this process increases as the polymer concentration increases, the concentration at which it becomes important depending on the numerical value of the corresponding transfer constant.

A slight variation of this reaction is that employed to produce *graft copolymers*. In this process, polymerization of

monomer A is carried out in the presence of a preformed
polymer ⌇⌇BBBBBBBB⌇⌇. In addition to the homopolymer
of A which is formed in the usual way, the transfer reaction
under discussion produces a certain amount of graft copolymer
of the type

C representing the mer at the branch point. For example, if
methyl methacrylate is polymerized in the presence of polystyrene using benzoyl peroxide as initiator, a graft copolymer
of styrene and methyl methacrylate is formed together with a
large amount of polymethyl methacrylate. A portion of the
copolymer structure is as follows:

$$
\begin{array}{c}
\text{\LARGE\}} \\
CH_3C-COOCH_3 \\
| \\
CH_2 \\
| \\
CH_3C-COOCH_3 \\
| \\
CH_2 \\
| \\
\text{⌇⌇}CH_2-CH-CH_2-C-CH_2-CH\text{⌇⌇} \\
\quad\quad | \quad\quad\quad | \quad\quad\quad | \\
\quad\quad C_6H_5 \quad\quad C_6H_5 \quad\quad C_6H_5
\end{array}
$$

Finally, we refer to the reaction known as "backbiting" in
which the transfer process occurs intramolecularly. This reaction is well illustrated by the process producing the short chain
branches in the radical polymerization of ethylene.

The initial radical is drawn in the rather unusual way to suggest the conformation in which the hydrogen atom transfer occurs.

3. The effect of temperature

For the simple three-reaction polymerization scheme which has formed the basis of our account, the effect of temperature on the various parameters can be predicted by replacing the rate constants by the appropriate Arrhenius expressions:

$$k_i = A_i \exp\left(-E_i/RT\right),$$

$$k_p = A_p \exp\left(-E_p/RT\right),$$

$$k_t = A_t \exp\left(-E_t/RT\right),$$

where A_i, A_p and A_t are the temperature independent factors for initiation, propagation and termination, and E_i, E_p and E_t are the corresponding activation energies. The values of A_p, A_t, E_p and E_t for the same three monomers used in the previous examples are shown in Table 4.5. The quantities A_i and E_i are specific to a given initiator system; for the case of AZBN in benzene,[16]

$$A_i = 5 \cdot 6 \times 10^{14} \text{ sec}^{-1},$$

$$E_i = 30 \text{ kcal mole}^{-1}.$$

TABLE 4.5

Monomer	A_p l. mole^{-1} sec^{-1}	E_p kcal mole^{-1}	A_t l. mole^{-1} sec^{-1}	E_t kcal mole^{-1}
Styrene	$2 \cdot 2 \times 10^7$	$7 \cdot 8$	$2 \cdot 6 \times 10^9$	$2 \cdot 4$
Methyl methacrylate	$1 \cdot 0 \times 10^7$	$6 \cdot 3$	$2 \cdot 7 \times 10^9$	$2 \cdot 8$
Vinyl acetate	$2 \cdot 4 \times 10^8$	$7 \cdot 3$	$4 \cdot 2 \times 10^{11}$	$5 \cdot 2$

Taking, for example, the polymerization rate

$$-\frac{d[M]}{dt} = k_p \left(\frac{2k_i}{k_t}\right)^{1/2} [I]_0^{1/2}[M]_0,$$

we obtain

$$-\frac{d[M]}{dt} = A_p \left(\frac{2A_i}{A_t}\right)^{1/2} \exp\left(\frac{E_t/2 - E_i/2 - E_p}{RT}\right) [I]_0^{1/2}[M]_0$$

in which the only temperature dependent factor is the exponential term

$$\exp\left(\frac{E_t/2 - E_i/2 - E_p}{RT}\right).$$

In general the individual values of the activation energies are such that the exponent is negative and hence the rate of polymerization usually increases with increasing temperature. In the case of styrene initiated by AZBN, the values of Table 4.5 show that the temperature dependence of the rate of polymerization is governed by the term

$$\exp\left(\frac{-21 \cdot 6 \text{ kcal mole}^{-1}}{RT}\right)$$

Under otherwise constant conditions, this means that a change in the temperature from 60 to 70°C increases the rate by a factor of 2·59.

However, at sufficiently high temperatures it is no longer permissible to regard the propagation reaction as the composite process

$$M_1\cdot + M \rightarrow M_2\cdot$$
$$M_2\cdot + M \rightarrow M_3\cdot$$
$$M_3\cdot + M \rightarrow M_4\cdot$$
$$\vdots$$
$$M_i\cdot + M \rightarrow M_{i+1}\cdot$$
$$\vdots$$

For each radical, the reverse reaction must be considered

$$\vdots$$
$$M_{i+1}\cdot \rightarrow M_i\cdot + M$$
$$\vdots$$
$$M_4\cdot \rightarrow M_3\cdot + M$$
$$M_3\cdot \rightarrow M_2\cdot + M$$
$$M_2\cdot \rightarrow M_1\cdot + M$$

a reaction known as *depropagation*. If we ascribe the same rate constant to each of these depropagation steps and represent it by k_{dp}, the proper expression for $-d[M]/dt$ becomes

$$-\frac{d\,[M]}{dt} = k_p[C\cdot]_s[M] - k_{dp}[C\cdot]_s$$

assuming, as usual, that the radical concentration is at its steady state value. This equation reduces to the equation which we have previously used at those temperatures where $k_{dp} \ll k_p[M]$. At temperatures where k_{dp} is comparable with $k_p[M]$, the rate of monomer disappearance is less than it would have been, had depropagation not occurred. Indeed there are conditions where this rate is zero for clearly built into the above expression is the possibility of the rates of propagation and depropagation becoming equal to one another. In fact $-d[M]/dt$ becomes zero at a monomer concentration $[M]_e$ given by

$$k_p[C\cdot]_s[M]_e = k_{dp}[C\cdot]_s$$

or

$$k_p[M]_e = k_{dp}.$$

The subscript e denotes that monomer at this particular concentration is in equilibrium with its polymer. The temperature corresponding to this situation is termed the *ceiling temperature* T_c for the particular monomer concentration. It can be found from the above condition by simply replacing the two rate constants by their Arrhenius equivalents $A_p \exp(-E_p/RT)$ and $A_{dp} \exp(-E_{dp}/RT)$ with T_c substituted for T.

$$\frac{A_p}{A_{dp}} [M]_e = \exp\left(\frac{E_p - E_{dp}}{RT_c}\right).$$

Therefore

$$T_c = \frac{E_{dp} - E_p}{R\ln A_{dp}/A_p - R\ln[M]_e}.$$

The basic reason why depropagation only comes into play at higher temperatures is because $E_{dp} > E_p$; that is, more energy has to be provided to decompose a polymer radical into monomer and another radical than to cause the reaction to take place in the reverse manner. In consequence k_{dp} increases more rapidly with temperature than does k_p and so the term $k_{dp}[C\cdot]_s$ becomes increasingly important compared to $k_p[C\cdot]_s[M]$ as the temperature is raised.

Some idea of the magnitude of the ceiling temperature for, say, a monomer concentration of 1 mole l.$^{-1}$ can be obtained by (1) equating the activation energy difference $E_{dp} - E_p$ to the heat evolved on polymerization, and (2) guessing the values of A_p and A_{dp}. Polymerization is usually exothermic to the extent of about 20 kcal mole^{-1} of monomer units reacted, though there is the special case of α-methyl styrene where the heat of polymerization is much lower[17] at 9 kcal mole^{-1} due to the severe steric problems which arise in the polymer. A_p is usually of the order of 10^7 l. mole^{-1} sec^{-1}, that is, a factor of 10^4 to 10^5 less than the pre-exponential factor for simple bimolecular reactions. A_{dp} can be taken as around 10^{13} sec^{-1} as in the majority of unimolecular reactions. Thus for most of the common vinyl monomers

$$T_c \sim \cfrac{20,000 \quad \text{cal mole}^{-1}}{2 \ln \left(\cfrac{10^{13}}{10^7 \times 1} \cfrac{\text{sec}^{-1}}{\text{l. mole}^{-1} \text{ sec}^{-1} \text{ mole l.}^{-1}} \right) \text{cal mole}^{-1}\,{}^\circ\text{K}^{-1}}$$

$$\sim \frac{10,000}{2 \cdot 303 \times 6} \, {}^\circ\text{K}$$

$$\sim 725^\circ\text{K}.$$

This means that at 725°K a system of polymer and monomer at monomer concentrations less than 1 mole l. $^{-1}$ is inherently unstable in the presence of free radicals; the polymer would decompose until the concentration of monomer attained its equilibrium value of 1 mole l. $^{-1}$ Conversely at higher concentrations of monomer, polymerization would ensue until sufficient monomer were converted into polymer for this same equilibrium concentration to be attained.[†]

On the other hand, the corresponding ceiling temperature for α-methyl styrene at a concentration of 1 mole l. $^{-1}$ is about 330°K using the same estimates for A_p and A_{dp}. The actual value found experimentally is 280°K which agrees rather well with that calculated. Before this principle was properly appreciated, a good deal of fruitless experimental work was carried out in an attempt to find suitable initiators for the polymerization of α-methyl styrene at the common temperatures employed; the reader will now realize that the difficulty lies not in the initiation process but in the near equality of the propagation and depropagation rates under the normal conditions.

[†] The lower the temperature, the lower the equilibrium concentration of monomer which can co-exist with polymeric radicals. Using the same numerical values as in the example, the equilibrium monomer concentration at the normal polymerization temperatures around 60°C is about 10^{-7} mole l. $^{-1}$ Consequently, there is no difficulty in polymerizing the common vinyl monomers to almost 100% conversion under these conditions.

Finally in this connection, attention should be drawn to the analogous process of the condensation of a gas to a liquid—the similarity being that both liquefaction and polymerization involve an aggregation of molecules. As in the case discussed, the temperature fixes the equilibrium concentration of the non-aggregated species (i.e. the vapour pressure); the lower the temperature, the lower the concentration of vapour which can co-exist with liquid. The similarity extends to the situtation arising when, at a particular temperature, the concentration of molecules in the vapour phase is less than the equilibrium value. Just as in the analogous situation when polymer breaks up into monomer (assuming that free radicals are present to provide a reaction path), the liquid vaporizes to increase the number of molecules in the gas phase.

4. Other complications

The modifications to the basic polymerization mechanism which we have just discussed are essentially modifications to the initiation and propagation steps. As might be expected, the termination reaction is not free from complications either and it is our purpose in this section to draw attention to these effects.

If we consider the termination reaction as we have already written it

$$M_i \cdot + M_j \cdot \ \rightarrow \ M_{i+j},$$

the kinetics of this process are straightforwardly described by the equation

$$-\frac{d[M_i\cdot]}{dt} = k_t[M_i\cdot][M_j\cdot],$$

which generalizes to

$$-\frac{d[C\cdot]}{dt} = k_t[C\cdot]^2$$

when account is taken of all possible combinations of the values of i and j. On a simple view of the termination process, the rate constant k_t represents the number of fruitful collisions occurring between radical ends at unit concentration. On this basis k_t is determined by the corresponding collision number and the factors $\exp(-E_t/RT)$ and P giving the probability that a given collision has the correct energy and orientation for reaction to occur. For the situation where the reactant molecules can be regarded as small spheres moving independently of one another through a continuum, this interpretation is reasonably satisfactory. In the case of polymer radicals of finite size in solutions containing reasonable amounts of polymer, these rather naive pictures do not even approach the physical reality. In such cases, the polymer radicals are embedded in a tangled web of polymer chains so that the chance of two ends coming together is dependent on the co-operative movement of the molecular entanglement. To examine this problem in a proper fashion is well outside the scope of this book. Nevertheless, with the above ideas as a guide, we can foresee that when entanglement of polymer chains is very high—a situation associated with high solution viscosities and occurring particularly at high percentage conversion in systems containing little or no solvent—the termination rate constant may well be decreased by one or two orders of magnitude. Such indeed is found to be the case, the phenomenon showing in a considerably increased rate of polymerization at high conversion; the reader should verify that a reduced value of k_t will result in a higher value of the stationary radical concentration and a correspondingly higher rate. This acceleration in rate may be so marked that, if precautions are not taken to remove efficiently the heat produced on polymerization, explosion may occur.

One final word in this connection: although there is a marked reduction in k_t under the conditions described, one would not expect a similar reduction in the value of k_p. This is because the propagation reaction is between a small molecule (the monomer) and a single radical—as far as the monomer molecules are concerned, the intermeshing polymer chains present no real obstacle to their gaining access to the radical ends.

COPOLYMERIZATION

The ideas already elaborated can be extended to cover the case where two or more monomers are present in the reaction system. In the presence of a free radical initiator, each monomer will give rise to its own particular type of radical. Each radical will react, in general, with any of the other monomers to produce a second radical which may or may not be similar in chemical structure to the original. If, for example, we consider two monomers A and B about to react with the corresponding radicals $A_1\cdot$ and $B_1\cdot$, then there are clearly four possible reactions:

$$A_1\cdot + A \rightarrow A_2\cdot$$
$$A_1\cdot + B \rightarrow A_1B_1\cdot$$
$$B_1\cdot + B \rightarrow B_2\cdot$$
$$B_1\cdot + A \rightarrow B_1A_1\cdot$$

Each of the radicals formed in the second step may react in the same number of ways as there are monomer types and since this choice is present at all the propagation steps, there results a complete spectrum of structures for the polymeric radicals; it is, however, highly unlikely that a significant number of radicals of the type $A_i\cdot$ or $B_i\cdot$ are produced if i is large, for the chance of a given radical $A_1\cdot$ or $B_1\cdot$ reacting with the same monomer type at each of $(i-1)$ propagation steps is negligibly small. The growth process is terminated when two polymeric radicals react together—the diversity of radical structures leading to a corresponding variety of polymer molecules differing from one another in the arrangement of the two monomers in the chains.

To fully characterize the process of copolymerization, we have to consider, therefore:

(1) the proportion of each monomer type incorporated into the polymer chains;

(2) the average sequence length of each monomer type over all chains;

(3) the rates at which the various monomers disappear from the reaction system and the molecular weight of the copolymer produced.

The problems in 3 bear close similarities to the problems already discussed in the first part of this chapter under the headings of polymerization kinetics and molecular weight. Problems 1 and 2, on the other hand, involve principles peculiar to copolymerization. All are sufficiently difficult that we shall only attempt a proper discussion of the first two problems for the special case when only two monomers A and B are involved.

1. The proportion of each monomer type present in the polymer chains

The basic principle by which we proceed is to regard the reactivity of a radical as being determined solely by the chemical nature of the terminal group containing the unpaired electron. By this, we mean that the rate constants for a given reaction for the two radicals

ABAAABA·

BBABBAA·

are identical despite the difference in the structure of the chains. With this simplification, propagation in copolymerization reduces to four simultaneous reactions.

1. $A\cdot + A \rightarrow A\cdot$ rate constant k_{11}
2. $A\cdot + B \rightarrow B\cdot$ rate constant k_{12}
3. $B\cdot + B \rightarrow B\cdot$ rate constant k_{22}
4. $B\cdot + A \rightarrow A\cdot$ rate constant k_{21}

$A\cdot$ represents a molecule ending in the free radical grouping derived from monomer A, its concentration $[A\cdot]$, including molecules of all lengths and structures. k_{11} is the rate constant for its reaction with a monomer of similar type (radical type 1 with monomer type 1) to produce a similar radical and, if our basic argument is correct, is identical with the propagation rate constant k_p appropriate to the polymerization of the single monomer A. k_{12} on the other hand, is the rate constant for the reaction between radical type 1 $A\cdot$ and the second monomer B to produce a radical of different type $B\cdot$. The ratio r_1 defined by

$$r_1 = \frac{k_{11}}{k_{12}} \tag{4.24}$$

termed the *reactivity ratio* thus measures the relative affinities of different monomers for the same radical. For if we were to introduce the two monomers A and B at the same concentration into a system containing a certain number of radicals of type $A\cdot$, the instantaneous rates of disappearance of the two monomers (before any radicals of the second type had appeared) would be

$$\left\{-\frac{d[A]}{dt}\right\}_{\text{reaction 1}} = k_{11}[A\cdot][A],$$

$$\left\{-\frac{d[B]}{dt}\right\}_{\text{reaction 2}} = k_{12}[A\cdot][B],$$

which on division gives

$$\frac{-d[A]}{-d[B]} = \frac{k_{11}}{k_{12}}$$

$$= r_1,$$

since we deliberately made [A] and [B] identical. Taking the styrene–methyl methacrylate system as an example, r_1 is found to be 0·52; this means that polystyryl type radicals react with methyl methacrylate at nearly twice the rate at which they react with styrene if both monomers are present at the same concentration.

Precisely similar interpretations are to be given to the symbols $B\cdot$, $[B\cdot]$, k_{22} and k_{21} and to the symbol r_2, defined by

$$r_2 = \frac{k_{22}}{k_{21}}. \tag{4.25}$$

For interest, r_2 in the copolymerization system just mentioned is equal to 0·46; that is polymethyl methacrylate type radicals react with styrene at just over twice the rate at which they react with methyl methacrylate at the same concentration.

The problem of the copolymer composition can now be solved. We assume that the polymer molecular weights are sufficiently high that the number of monomer molecules which disappear in the initiation reactions is quite negligible compared with the number which disappear in the reactions 1–4. In this case we can write

$$-\frac{d[A]}{dt} = k_{11}[A\cdot][A] + k_{21}[B\cdot][A], \tag{4.26}$$

$$-\frac{d[B]}{dt} = k_{22}[B\cdot][B] + k_{12}[A\cdot][B], \tag{4.27}$$

since two reactions are open to each of the two monomers A and B. Hence the ratio of the amounts of the two monomers incorporated into the copolymer in an infinitesimal period of time is given by dividing eqn. (4.26) by (4.27)

$$\begin{aligned}
\frac{d[A]}{d[B]} &= \frac{k_{11}[A\cdot][A] + k_{21}[B\cdot][A]}{k_{22}[B\cdot][B] + k_{12}[A\cdot][B]} \\
&= \frac{[A]}{[B]} \cdot \left\{ \frac{k_{11}[A\cdot]/[B\cdot] + k_{21}}{k_{12}[A\cdot]/[B\cdot] + k_{22}} \right\}.
\end{aligned} \tag{4.28}$$

It only remains to evaluate the ratio $[A\cdot]/[B\cdot]$.

In a similar fashion to the case of a single polymerizing monomer, it would be expected that the two radical concentrations $[A\cdot]$ and $[B\cdot]$ would establish themselves at such levels that their rates of loss would just balance their rates of production. By analogy with the simpler case, we would anticipate that the stationary radical concentrations would be attained almost immediately after the start of the copolymerization and so for our purpose we can write

$$\frac{d\,[A\cdot]_s}{dt} = 0,$$

$$\frac{d\,[B\cdot]_s}{dt} = 0,$$

where the subscript s denotes steady state conditions. Let us consider radicals of the first type, $A\cdot$. They are produced in the initiation process

$$\text{I} \to 2\text{R}\cdot \qquad \text{rate constant } k_i$$
$$\text{R}\cdot + \text{A} \to \text{A}\cdot \qquad \text{rate constant } k_r$$

and the cross-propagation reaction

$$\text{B}\cdot + \text{A} \to \text{A}\cdot \qquad \text{rate constant } k_{21}$$

Simultaneously with these modes of production, they are lost by bimolecular termination

$$\text{A}\cdot + \text{A}\cdot \to \text{polymer} \qquad \text{rate constant } k_{t,\text{AA}}$$
$$\text{A}\cdot + \text{B}\cdot \to \text{polymer} \qquad \text{rate constant } k_{t,\text{AB}}$$

and in the second of the cross-propagation reactions

$$\text{A}\cdot + \text{B} \to \text{B}\cdot \qquad \text{rate constant } k_{12}$$

Therefore

$$\frac{d\,[A\cdot]_s}{dt} = 2xk_i[\text{I}] + k_{21}[\text{B}\cdot]_s[\text{A}] - k_{t,\text{AA}}[\text{A}\cdot]_s^2 - k_{t,\text{AB}}[\text{A}\cdot]_s[\text{B}\cdot]_s$$
$$- k_{12}[\text{A}\cdot]_s[\text{B}] = 0, \qquad (4.29)$$

where x is the fraction of primary radicals $\text{R}\cdot$ which react with monomer A.

Little progress can be made with this equation without some further simplification; it would be advantageous obviously if some of the terms could be dropped—the only problem being which ones can be considered negligible in comparison with the others. In a case like this the replacement of symbols by numerical values is a great help; since the object is simply to ascertain which are the important terms, only orders of magnitude are required while for those quantities which are unknown, guesses based on previous experience are quite permissible. Thus there is no reason to suppose that the individual radical concentrations would be greatly different from the value of 10^{-8} mole l. $^{-1}$ previously calculated. Similarly the cross-propagation constants, k_{21} and k_{12}, can be set at about 10^2 l. mole $^{-1}$ sec $^{-1}$ and the termination constants taken to be about 10^8 l. mole $^{-1}$ sec $^{-1}$ (compare Table 4.3). Typical monomer concentrations are 1 mole l. $^{-1}$ so that substituting 10^{-8} mole l. $^{-1}$ sec $^{-1}$ for the product $2xk_i[I]$ ($x \sim 0.5$, $k_i \sim 10^{-5}$ sec^{-1}, $[I] \sim 1 \times 10^{-3}$ mole l. $^{-1}$), the contributions of the various terms listed in eqn. (4.29) are as shown in Table 4.6.

TABLE 4.6. APPROXIMATE MAGNITUDES OF THE VARIOUS
TERMS OF EQN. (4.29)

Rate process	Estimated contribution to rate, mole l.$^{-1}$ sec^{-1}
Production of radicals by initiation	10^{-8}
Production of radicals in cross-propagation	10^{-6}
Loss of radicals in termination $A \cdot + A \cdot$	10^{-8}
Loss of radicals in termination $A \cdot + B \cdot$	10^{-8}
Loss of radicals in cross-propagation	10^{-6}

These rough calculations suggest that the concentration of the particular radical type $A \cdot$ is determined primarily by the two cross-propagation reactions. Thus eqn. (4.29) reduces without serious error to

$$\frac{d[A\cdot]_s}{dt} = k_{21}[B\cdot]_s[A] - k_{12}[A\cdot]_s[B] \qquad (4.30)$$

$$= 0.$$

An identical equation for $d[B\cdot]_s/dt$ is obtained by neglect of the term for the rate of initiation $2(1-x)k_i[I]$ and the termsrepresenting the rate of termination $k_{t,BB}[B\cdot]_s^2$ and $k_{t,AB}[A\cdot]_s[B\cdot]_s$.

From eqn. (4.30), we obtain the ratio of the radical concentrations $[A\cdot]_s$ and $[B\cdot]_s$ at any time after the attainment of the steady state:

$$\frac{[A\cdot]_s}{[B\cdot]_s} = \frac{k_{21}[A]}{k_{12}[B]}.$$

Substituting this result in eqn. (4.28) gives

$$\frac{d[A]}{d[B]} = \frac{[A]}{[B]} \left\{ \frac{r_1[A]/[B]+1}{[A]/[B]+r_2} \right\} \qquad (4.31)$$

an equation which is often termed the *copolymer composition equation*.

It is important to be quite clear about the significance of eqn. (4.31). It is a differential equation and so it gives the relative numbers of the two types of monomer molecule which react to give copolymer at a particular instant in time; it thus gives the composition of the copolymer formed at that particular instant. In general the ratio of the two monomer types incorporated into the copolymer at any instant is *not* the same as the ratio of the two monomer concentrations in the reaction mixture, as can be seen from the equation. Usually more of one particular monomer copolymerizes at any instant. If, for example, we consider a reaction mixture consisting of equimolar concentrations of styrene (monomer A) and butadiene (monomer B) whose reactivity ratios at 60°C are 0·78 and

1·39 respectively, the ratio of the two monomers incorporated into the copolymer at this particular instant is

$$\frac{d\,[\text{styrene}]}{d\,[\text{butadiene}]} = \frac{0\cdot78+1}{1+1\cdot39} = 0\cdot745.$$

That is, rather more butadiene enters the copolymer than styrene and hence the reaction mixture becomes enriched in styrene. This in turn means that the copolymer formed in the next instant of time has a slightly different composition due to the displacement of the ratio [styrene]/[butadiene] from its original value of unity. In order to calculate the composition of the copolymer formed after appreciable consumption of the two monomers, eqn. (4.31) has to be integrated. A discussion of the procedure would be out of place in this book; instead we shall confine our attention to some special cases of eqn. (4.31).

These special cases can be classified according to the numerical values of the two reactivity ratios, r_1 and r_2.

(1) $r_1 = r_2 = 0$. Such a situation arises when the two monomers do not themselves polymerize but which nevertheless copolymerize. Putting it another way, k_{11} and k_{22} are both zero but the cross-propagation constants k_{12} and k_{21} are both finite though not necessarily equal.

In this case

$$\frac{d\,[\text{A}]}{d\,[\text{B}]} = 1$$

and consequently equal numbers of the two monomers are incorporated in the copolymer. Since monomer A does not react with a radical of type A· nor monomer B with radical B·, a perfectly alternating copolymer is produced

...ABABABAB...

A case which approximates to this extreme situation is the

monomer pair maleic anhydride, isopropenyl acetate where the values of r_1 and r_2 are 0·002 and 0·032 at 75°C.

(2) r_1 *finite*, $r_2 = 0$. This situation arises when the monomer B does not add on to the radical B· but reacts with the radical derived from the other monomer A; on the other hand, the resulting radical B· can react with the monomer A. In such a case the copolymer composition equation becomes

$$\frac{d[A]}{d[B]} = 1 + r_1 \frac{[A]}{[B]}.$$

Thus monomer A always disappears from the reaction system at a greater rate than monomer B whatever the value of the ratio [A]/[B]. If we take the special case of an equimolar mixture of the two monomers so that [A]=[B], the composition of the copolymer formed in the short period of time when this condition is satisfied is given by

$$\frac{d[A]}{d[B]} = 1 + r_1.$$

Thus if r_1 is considerable (10, for example) the copolymer formed contains long sequences of A units interspersed with occasional B units. At the other end of the scale where r_1 is rather small (0·05, for example), the situation is very similar to that dealt with in case (1); i.e. an almost alternating copolymer is obtained.

(3) $r_1 = 1/r_2$ *or* $r_1 r_2 = 1$.[†] This is a very special case corresponding to the identity

$$\frac{k_{11}}{k_{12}} = \frac{k_{21}}{k_{22}}.$$

This means that the relative probabilities of the two monomers reacting is just the same for one radical as for the other. It results in the considerable simplification of eqn. (4.31). We first

† This case is often referred to as "ideal copolymerization".

multiply the top and bottom of this equation by r_1 to obtain

$$\frac{d[A]}{d[B]} = \frac{r_1[A]}{[B]} \left\{ \frac{r_1[A]/[B]+1}{r_1[A]/[B]+r_1 r_2} \right\},$$

which, when $r_1 r_2 = 1$, reduces to

$$\frac{d[A]}{d[B]} = r_1 \frac{[A]}{[B]}.$$

The consequences of this latter equation are fairly obvious; for example, if $r_1 = 2$ and if we start with an equimolar mixture of the two monomers, then the copolymer formed initially contains twice as much monomer A as monomer B.

(4) r_1 *and* r_2 *any values.* We shall restrict our treatment of this general case to the calculation of the proportion of the two monomers incorporated in a copolymer at low conversion from an equimolar feed. We write

$$\left\{ \frac{d[A]}{d[B]} \right\}_{\substack{\text{low percentage} \\ \text{conversion}}} = \frac{[A]_0}{[B]_0} \left\{ \frac{r_1[A]_0/[B]_0 +1}{[A]_0/[B]_0 +r_2} \right\}$$

and substitute $[A]_0/[B]_0 = 1$.

Then

$$\left\{ \frac{d[A]}{d[B]} \right\}_{\substack{\text{low percentage} \\ \text{conversion for} \\ \text{equimolar feed}}} = \frac{1+r_1}{1+r_2}.$$

Table 4·7 gives the compositions of the copolymers formed initially for a variety of monomer pairs under these conditions. It should be noted that no initiators have been specified for, provided the free radical mechanism previously described is applicable, the composition is independent of the chemical structure of the initiator; the actual initiator used affects the rate but not the composition. On the other hand, it is necessary to specify the temperature at which the copolymerization is carried out for the simple reason that the reactivity ratios are temperature dependent; i.e. the two rate constants comprising the reactivity ratio do not, in general, have the same activation energy.

TABLE 4.7. COMPOSITIONS OF THE COPOLYMERS
FORMED INITIALLY AT
$$\frac{[A]_0}{[B]_0} = 1$$

Monomer A	Monomer B	t °C	r_1	r_2	% A in copoly-mer
Maleic anhydride	Isopropenyl acetate	75	0·002	0·032	49
Vinylidene chloride	Maleic anhydride	60	9	0	91
Styrene	Butadiene	60	0·78	1·39	34
Styrene	Methyl methacrylate	60	0·52	0·46	51

Experimentally, the numerical values of the reactivity ratios are found from the compositions of the copolymers formed using different monomer feeds. The actual calculation procedure based on eqn. (4.31) need not, however, concern us here.

2. The average sequence length of each monomer type taken over all molecules

Our discussion of the copolymer compositions which result from different values of the reactivity ratios has brought out the close connection between these quantities and the average sequence length. Thus in the simplest of cases where $r_1 = r_2 = 0$, the average sequence length of each monomer type is unity. We propose to examine the relation between the reactivity ratios and the average sequence length a little more closely in this section.

In the first place we shall have to be quite clear as to what is meant by the average sequence length of each monomer type taken over all chains. Let us consider three copolymer molecules of the structures written out below.

AAA BB AA B AAAA BBB

A B A BB AAAA B AAA BB

B AA B AA BBB AAA B AA

For simplicity, we have taken nine A and six B units in each chain, so that the only difference between them is the arrangement of A and B. Counting the sequences, we find for A

> 2 sequences containing 1 A unit
> 4 sequences containing 2 A units
> 3 sequences containing 3 A units
> 2 sequences containing 4 A units

The average number of A units *per sequence* taken over all chains is defined by the ratio

$$\frac{\text{total number of A units in the chains}}{\text{total number of A sequences}}$$
$$= \frac{2\times1+4\times2+3\times3+2\times4}{2+4+3+2} = 2\cdot45$$

For B, a similar procedure shows that the average number of B units which are to be found in sequence is 1·64. Since every A sequence must be followed by a B sequence and vice versa, the total number of A and B sequences must be equal in a chain containing an even number of sequences; for a chain with an odd number of sequences, the number of each type can only differ by one. Consequently, for chains containing a large number of sequences, we can say without serious error that the total number of A sequences must be equal to the total number of B sequences.

Returning to our numerical example, we can see that to calculate the average number of units of one type in a sequence, we have to calculate the actual number of sequences of each type. If $n_A(S)$ represents the number of sequences containing S A units, the average number of A units in each sequence, $\bar{S}_A$, is given by

$$\bar{S}_A = \frac{\sum n_A(S) \cdot S}{\sum n_A(S)}. \qquad (4.32)$$

Similarly,

$$\bar{S}_B = \frac{\sum n_B(S) \cdot S}{\sum n_B(S)}. \qquad (4.33)$$

Each summation is taken over all possible values of S from 1 to ∞.

In order to proceed with this calculation, we require the probability that a given A unit in a chain is followed by another A unit—a quantity which we shall call p_{AA}. Since an A unit can only be followed by an A or a B unit, this probability will be given by

$$p_{AA} = \frac{\text{number of AA units in all the chains}}{\text{(number of AA units} + \text{number of AB units) in all the chains}†}$$

$$= \frac{\text{rate of production of AA bonds}}{\text{rate of production of AA and AB bonds}}$$

Since AA and AB bonds are produced solely by the reactions

$$\text{A}\cdot + \text{A} \rightarrow \text{A}\cdot \qquad \text{rate constant } k_{11}$$

and

$$\text{A}\cdot + \text{B} \rightarrow \text{B}\cdot \qquad \text{rate constant } k_{12}$$

the probability that a given A unit is followed by another A

† Note that we distinguish between AB and BA units since our concern is with what unit *follows* an A unit.

unit is

$$p_{AA} = \frac{k_{11}[A\cdot][A]}{k_{11}[A\cdot][A]+k_{12}[A\cdot][B]} \dagger = \frac{r_1[A]}{r_1[A]+[B]}.$$

In a precisely similar fashion we define and calculate the remaining three probabilities p_{AB}, p_{BB} and p_{BA}.

$$p_{AB} = \frac{[B]}{r_1[A]+[B]}$$

$$p_{BB} = \frac{r_2[B]}{r_2[B]+[A]}$$

$$p_{BA} = \frac{[A]}{r_2[B]+[A]}.$$

Each of these probabilities depends on the ratio $[A]/[B]$ and, as this varies with time in the usual copolymerization reactions, the probabilities alter as the conversion of the two monomers into polymer proceeds. This complication can be avoided by restricting our subsequent arguments to such short intervals of time that the ratio $[A]/[B]$ can be taken as constant. Thus a single, constant parameter characterizes the probability that a given unit is followed by another unit in the copolymer formed in this small interval of time.

With this proviso in mind, it is a relatively straightforward matter to calculate the number of sequences containing S A units in a given copolymer mixture from the probability that any particular A unit is followed by another. Suppose that, in this mixture, there are a total of L sequences of A units; L is thus simultaneously equal to $\sum n_A(S)$ and to the number of BA links. The number of A sequences containing a single A unit is then simply the number of these BA groupings which

† We regard the number of AA and AB links formed in the termination processes as quite negligible compared to those formed in the propagation reaction; this is consistent with our previous neglect of the rate of this reaction in determining $[A\cdot]$.

are followed by a B unit, i.e. Lp_{AB}. The number of A sequences containing two A units is likewise the product of L and the probability that the original A unit is followed by a second A and then a B, i.e. $Lp_{AA}p_{AB}$. In general since the formation of a sequence of S A units involves $(S-1)$ successive additions of A units to a BA unit before being followed by a B addition, the number of such sequences is

$$Lp_{AA}^{S-1}p_{AB}. \tag{4.34}$$

The average length of an A sequence then follows directly from eqn. (4.32)

$$\begin{aligned}
\bar{S}_A &= \frac{\sum Lp_{AA}^{S-1}p_{AB} \cdot S}{\sum Lp_{AA}^{S-1}p_{AB}} \\
&= \frac{Lp_{AB}}{Lp_{AB}} \cdot \frac{(1+2p_{AA}+3p_{AA}^2+\ldots Sp_{AA}^{S-1}+\ldots)}{(1+p_{AA}+p_{AA}^2+\ldots p_{AA}^{S-1}+\ldots)} \\
&= \frac{1-p_{AA}}{(1-p_{AA})^2} = \frac{1}{p_{AB}}. \tag{4.35}
\end{aligned}$$

Similarly, the average length of a B sequence

$$\bar{S}_B = \frac{1}{p_{BA}}. \tag{4.36}$$

We see at once that our previous arguments concerning the average sequence length in certain special cases are confirmed by these two expressions. For example when r_1 and r_2 are both zero, p_{AB} and p_{BA} are unity and hence so is the average sequence length of both A and B; furthermore, since $\left.\begin{array}{c} p_{AA}^{S-1} \\ p_{BB}^{S-1} \end{array}\right\} = 0$ when $S > 1$, there are no sequences containing more than one A or B unit—the polymer is thus a strictly alternating copolymer. On the other hand when r_1 is quite large and r_2 is zero, we obtain long A sequences interspersed by an occasional B unit; taking for example the copolymer formed initially from an equimolar mixture of vinylidene chloride and maleic anhydride ($r_1 = 9$, $r_2 = 0$), $p_{AB} = 1/10$ and $p_{BA} = 1$. This means that, on average, sequences of 10 vinylidene chloride units separated from one another by a single maleic anhydride unit are found in the copolymer.

This last statement brings out the close connection between the average sequence length of A and B units and the composition of the copolymer. We can write

$$\frac{\bar{S}_A}{\bar{S}_B} = \frac{\sum S \cdot n_A(S)}{\sum n_A(S)} \cdot \frac{\sum n_B(S)}{\sum S \cdot n_B(S)},$$

which reduces to

$$\frac{\sum S \cdot n_A(S)}{\sum S \cdot n_B(S)},$$

since the number of A sequences is practically equal to the number of B sequences. But the two quantities $\sum S \cdot n_A(S)$ and $\sum S \cdot n_B(S)$ are simply the number of A and B units actually in the copolymer.

Therefore

$$\frac{\bar{S}_A}{\bar{S}_B} = \frac{\text{total number of A units in the copolymer}}{\text{total number of B units in the copolymer}} = \frac{d[A]}{d[B]},$$

since our derivations are restricted to very short intervals of time.

Therefore $$\frac{d[A]}{d[B]} = \frac{p_{BA}}{p_{AB}} = \frac{[A]}{[B]} \left\{ \frac{r_1[A]/[B]+1}{[A]/[B]+r_2} \right\},$$

and so we recover the copolymer composition equation (4.31) by a quite different method.

Finally, a few words must be said about the arrangement of the various sequences in the polymer chains. The arrangement is entirely random, the only condition being that the frequency of occurrence of each sequence length is determined by an equation essentially identical with eqn. (4.34); that is, the proportion of A sequences containing S units is

$$p_{AA}^{S-1}p_{AB} \tag{4.37}$$

The arrangement of the various sequence lengths in the chains follows the pattern that would be obtained if alternate selections were made from two bags of A and B sequences distributed in accordance with eqn. (4.37).

A special case which is suitable for private investigation by the reader is that which arises when

$$p_{AB} = p_{BA} = 1/2,$$

a case which arises when [A] = [B] and r_1 and r_2 are both equal to unity. For then, the arrangement of the two monomers in the chain can be simulated exactly by tossing a coin as many times as there are units. An A placement corresponds to a "head" and a B placement to a "tail"; a sequence of two units then occurs at the same frequency as two heads are obtained on successive tosses and so on. Four chains each 20 units long produced in this way have the structures

AABAAAABABBBAABABBAA

BBBBBBAABAAABBBBABAA

ABAABAABBBAABAABAABB

BAAAAABBBABBBBBABABB

where the sequence length distribution is as summarized in Table 4.8. Arithmetically, $\bar{S}_A = 1{\cdot}95$ and $\bar{S}_B = 2{\cdot}05$ compared with the theoretical values of $2{\cdot}0$—the discrepancy arising from the limited lengths of the chains considered.

Tacticity. In those cases of polymerization which introduce an asymmetric carbon atom into the chain on each propagation step, the product can be regarded as a copolymer formed from two sterically distinguishable monomer units. The number of sequences containing S asymmetric carbon atoms of identical

TABLE 4.8. SEQUENCE LENGTH ANALYSIS OF THE FOUR
COPOLYMERS "OBTAINED" BY TOSSING A COIN

A sequences			B sequences		
Number in sequence	Number of sequences found	Number of sequences expected	Number in sequence	Number of sequences found	Number of sequences expected
1	7	10	1	11	10
2	10	5	2	3	5
3	1	2·5	3	3	2·5
4	1	1·25	4	1	1·25
5	1	0·625	5	1	0·625
6		.	6	1	0·313
7		.	7		.
8		.	8		.
Total	20	20	Total	20	20

configuration can be found by a very similar analysis to the
above. For this purpose, we represent the polymerization as

$$\sim\!\sim\!\sim dp\cdot + M \rightarrow \sim\!\sim\!\sim ddp\cdot$$
$$\sim\!\sim\!\sim dp\cdot + M \rightarrow \sim\!\sim\!\sim dlp\cdot$$
$$\sim\!\sim\!\sim lp\cdot + M \rightarrow \sim\!\sim\!\sim llp\cdot$$
$$\sim\!\sim\!\sim lp\cdot + M \rightarrow \sim\!\sim\!\sim ldp\cdot$$

where as explained previously (p. 164) the symbolism indicates
the configuration of the relevant carbon atoms. Let the probability that a given asymmetric carbon atom is followed by
another of the same configuration be σ. Since there are only
two possibilities for the configuration of the second asymmetric
centre compared to the first, i.e. like or unlike, this probability
is necessarily given by

$$\sigma = \frac{\text{number of '}dd\text{' and '}ll\text{' pairs in the polymer sample}}{\text{number of '}dd\text{', '}dl\text{', '}ll\text{' and '}ld\text{' pairs}}$$

We have already pointed out that the two reactions

$$\sim\!\!\sim\!\!\sim\!dp\cdot + M \rightarrow \sim\!\!\sim\!\!\sim\!ddp\cdot$$
$$\sim\!\!\sim\!\!\sim\!lp\cdot + M \rightarrow \sim\!\!\sim\!\!\sim\!llp\cdot$$

proceed with the same rate constant k_a, since the same steric and energetic factors are operative in forming an adjacent pair of asymmetric carbon atoms of identical configuration irrespective of the actual way in which the pair is fixed. Similarly, the reactions producing an adjacent pair of unlike configuration

$$\sim\!\!\sim\!\!\sim\!dp\cdot + M \rightarrow \sim\!\!\sim\!\!\sim\!dlp\cdot$$
$$\sim\!\!\sim\!\!\sim\!lp\cdot + M \rightarrow \sim\!\!\sim\!\!\sim\!ldp\cdot$$

proceed with the same rate constant k_b. By considering the placements formed in unit time, the relation of σ to the two rate constants k_a and k_b follows at once as

$$\sigma = \frac{k_a}{k_a + k_b}.$$

For such processes, there will be as many 'l' as 'd' sequences produced in the final polymer. Supposing this number to be K in a given sample of polymer, we shall have

$K(1-\sigma)$	'l' sequences of the type	dld
$K\sigma(1-\sigma)$	'l' sequences of the type	$dlld$
$K\sigma^2(1-\sigma)$	'l' sequences of the type	$dllld$
$\vdots$		$\vdots$
$K\sigma^{S-1}(1-\sigma)$	'l' sequences of the type	$d\,\underbrace{l\ldots l}\,d$
		S units

and similarly

$K(1-\sigma)$	'd' sequences of the type	ldl
$K\sigma(1-\sigma)$	'd' sequences of the type	$lddl$
$K\sigma^2(1-\sigma)$	'd' sequences of the type	$ldddl$
$\vdots$		$\vdots$
$K\sigma^{S-1}(1-\sigma)$	'd' sequences of the type	$l\,\underbrace{d\ldots d}\,l$
		S units

The average length of these '*l*' or '*d*' sequences is then equal to

$$1/(1-\sigma).$$

A more important consideration than the above is the immediate environment in which a particular asymmetric carbon atom is situated. We distinguish three situations.

1. An asymmetric carbon atom placed between two other asymmetric carbon atoms of the same configuration as itself; that is, a sequence

ddd

or   *lll*

These are termed *isotactic* triads.

2. An asymmetric carbon atom placed between two asymmetric carbon atoms both of different configuration to itself; that is, a sequence

dld

or   *ldl*

These are termed *syndiotactic* triads.

3. An asymmetric carbon atom placed between two asymmetric carbon atoms of different configuration; that is, a sequence

lld

dll

ddl

or   *ldd*

These are termed *heterotactic* triads.

The importance of these distinctions is that the relative number of such triads can be measured experimentally in certain cases. The technique used is that of nuclear magnetic resonance in which hydrogen nuclei in differing chemical environments can be distinguished. It would be out of place to discuss this experimental method in more detail in this book;

suffice it to say that this powerful technique permits the determination of the fraction of isotactic, syndiotactic and heterotactic triads in certain polymers and hence, as we shall now explain, the determination of the parameter σ.

Let us return to our K 'l' sequences made up of

$$K(1-\sigma) \quad \text{sequences of type} \quad dld$$
$$K\sigma(1-\sigma) \quad \text{sequences of type} \quad dlld$$
$$K\sigma^2(1-\sigma) \quad \text{sequences of type} \quad dllld$$
$$\vdots$$
$$K\sigma^{S-1}(1-\sigma) \quad \text{sequences of type} \quad \underbrace{d\,l\ldots l\,d}_{S \text{ units}}$$

According to the definitions given above, the first line gives immediately the number of syndiotactic triads of the type *dld*. From the K 'd' sequences, an equal number of syndiotactic triads of the type *ldl* are present.

Therefore number of syndiotactic triads present $= 2K(1-\sigma)$.

To obtain the fractional syndiotactic content, viz.

$$\frac{\text{number of syndiotactic triads}}{\text{total number of triads of all types}}$$

it only remains to calculate the total number of triads of all three types. To do this we simply evaluate the total number of asymmetric carbon atoms in the polymer sample. Since we have K 'l' sequences containing on average $1/(1-\sigma)$ 'l' asymmetric carbons, the total number of 'l' asymmetric carbon atoms is $K/(1-\sigma)$. On exactly the same argument, we have $K/(1-\sigma)$ 'd' asymmetric carbon atoms and so our total number is

$$\frac{2K}{1-\sigma}$$

[Alternatively, this result could have been obtained by multiplying the number of 'l' or 'd' units in a sequence by the number of such sequences and adding up the results for all possible values of the sequence length *i.e.*, $\sum SK\sigma^{S-1}(1-\sigma)$.] Although in every chain there are two less triads than there are asymmetric carbon atoms, the latter quantity represents the required number of triads without serious error if the polymer chains are long. With this proviso in mind, we substitute in the defining expression for the fraction of syndiotactic placements in the polymer to obtain

$$\text{fraction of syndiotactic placements} = \frac{2K(1-\sigma)}{2K/(1-\sigma)} = (1-\sigma)^2.$$

Turning now to the problem of the fractional isotactic content, it is clear that a sequence of 3 say '*l*' asymmetric carbon atoms represents 1 isotactic triad, a sequence of 4 '*l*' asymmetric carbon atoms, 2 isotactic triads and so on. The total number of isotactic triads formed from '*l*' asymmetric carbon atoms is thus

$$K\sigma^2(1-\sigma)+2K\sigma^3(1-\sigma)+\ldots(S-2)K\sigma^{S-1}(1-\sigma)+\ldots$$
$$= K\sigma^2(1-\sigma)(1+2\sigma+3\sigma^2+\ldots S\sigma^{S-1}+\ldots)$$
$$=\frac{K\sigma^2}{1-\sigma}$$

An identical number of isotactic triads are formed from sequences of '*d*' asymmetric carbon atoms and so

$$\text{fraction of isotactic placements} = \frac{\text{number of isotactic triads}}{\text{total number of triads of all types}}$$
$$= \frac{2K\sigma^2/(1-\sigma)}{2K/(1-\sigma)}$$
$$= \sigma^2.$$

Finally, the heterotactic content of the polymer: every '*l*' sequence of asymmetric carbon atoms containing more than one '*l*' unit contains two heterotactic triads—one at the beginning of the sequence '*dll*' and one at the end of the sequence '*lld*'. Thus from these sequences, the total number of hetero-tactic triads is

$$2\{K\sigma(1-\sigma) + K\sigma^2(1-\sigma) + K\sigma^3(1-\sigma) + \ldots\}$$
$$= 2K\sigma$$

There are the same number of heterotactic triads arising from the '*d*' sequences and so

$$\text{fraction of heterotactic placements} = \frac{4K\sigma}{2K/(1-\sigma)}$$
$$= 2\sigma(1-\sigma)$$

As a cross-check, the reader should verify that the three fractions add up to unity.

The important point about this treatment is that it adds precision to the notion of tacticity using concepts already developed.

3. The rate of copolymerization and the molecular weight of the copolymer produced

The basic arguments by which we deduce expressions for the rates of disappearance of the two monomers and the molecular weight of the copolymer produced are similar to those employed for the case of a single monomer. First of all, we write down the expressions for $-d[A]/dt$ and $-d[B]/dt$ which on addition give an equation for the rate of copolymerization $-d([A]+[B])/dt$ containing the radical concentrations $[A\cdot]$ and $[B\cdot]$. By assuming a stationary state in the concentrations of $[A\cdot]$ and $[B\cdot]$, we obtain:

(1) the relation of $[A\cdot]_s$ to $[B\cdot]_s$ as in eqn. (4.30)

i.e.
$$\frac{[A\cdot]_s}{[B\cdot]_s} = \frac{k_{21}[A]}{k_{12}[B]}.$$

(2)
$$\frac{d\left([A\cdot]_s + [B\cdot]_s\right)}{dt} = 0.$$

This latter condition gives

$$2k_i[I] = k_{t,\,AA}[A\cdot]_s^2 + 2k_{t,\,AB}[A\cdot]_s[B\cdot]_s + k_{t,\,BB}[B\cdot]_s^2.$$

It should be noted that the total radical concentration in the system is determined by precisely those terms which we had neglected in eqn. (4.29); i.e. by the initiation and termination rates. The terms representing the cross-propagation rates cannot enter into an expression for the total radical concentration since these reactions result in no change in this quantity. The remainder of the derivation consists of replacing, say, all the $[B\cdot]_s$ factors by $k_{12}[B][A\cdot]_s/k_{21}[A]$, solving for $[A\cdot]_s$ from the above stationary state condition and substituting the result in the expressions relating $-d[A]/dt$, $-d[B]/dt$ and $-d([A]+[B])/dt$ to $[A\cdot]_s$. The equations so obtained are rather involved algebraically and a discussion of them is outside the scope of this book. Our objective in this short section is simply to indicate the way in which the problem of the rate of copolymerization can be examined by essentially similar procedures to those employed for the problem of the rate of polymerization of a single monomer.

Likewise the number average degree of polymerization of the copolymers follows from a knowledge of the rate of copolymerization and the rate of termination.

CHAPTER 5

IONIC POLYMERIZATION

ALTHOUGH a large number of polymerization processes can be understood using the conceptions developed in Chapters 3 and 4, there remain many which cannot be explained in these terms. Those which we shall discuss in this chapter fall into the general class of addition reactions and proceed, as in the case of the analogous free radical reactions, through the stepwise addition of monomer molecules to active centres. The difference between the addition reactions which form the subject matter of this chapter and those previously discussed is that the active centres are ionic rather than free radical in character.

Before proceeding further, we must emphasize that ionic compounds dissolved in solvents of low dielectric constant (2–10) as are commonly employed in polymerization work do *not* exist in the form of free ions. The predominant species present at the usual concentrations encountered ($< 10^{-1}$ mole $1.^{-1}$) are *ion-pairs* formed by the association of the positive and negative ions. In equilibrium with these ion-pairs are a small number of free ions which can move independently of one another and which cause the solution to exhibit a small electrical conductivity. The reverse situation is found in solvents of high dielectric constant such as water. In these systems the dissociation of ionic compounds into free ions is usually considerable, ion-pair formation being of much lesser importance than in the low dielectric constant solvents; for example, in an aqueous solution of potassium nitrate at a concentration of 0·1 mole $1.^{-1}$, about 3% of the potassium and nitrate ions are present in the form of $K^+NO_3^-$ ion-pairs at room temperature. Ion-pairs (and free ions where these are an important constituent of the system) are frequently *solvated*. That is to say, solvent molecules are bound to one or both of the constituents of the ion-pair so that solvent and ion-pair move and react as a single unit. In the solvents in which we are interested —aliphatic and aromatic hydrocarbons, chlorinated hydrocarbons, ethers and amines—the questions associated with solvation, its extent, the type of chemical bonding, the number of solvent molecules involved, the rates of exchange with unbound solvent, present great experimental problems and at the moment are largely unanswerable. Despite this lack of knowledge of the quantitative aspects of solvation, there is no doubt that this effect is of great importance.

In accordance with these ideas, it is found that the type of solvent employed has a profound influence on both the course and rate of an ionic polymerization. Apart from specific solvation effects, the solvent influences the reaction through its dielectric constant. This parameter influences not only the extent of dissociation of the ion-pairs but also the activation energies of the various elementary steps. Unfortunately, it is not usually possible to disentangle these three solvent effects because of the lack of information concerning the precise nature of the solvation. Generally speaking, all that can be said is that a major change in solvent type is usually accompanied by a major change in the observable characteristics of the reaction. For example, rates of ionic polymerization in, say, tetrahydrofuran

$$\begin{array}{c} CH_2-CH_2 \\ | \qquad | \\ CH_2 \quad CH_2 \\ \diagdown \quad \diagup \\ O \end{array}$$

or triethylamine $(C_2H_5)_3N$

are usually markedly different from those found in benzene or cyclohexane.

CLASSIFICATION OF IONIC
POLYMERIZATION

We classify ionic polymerizations according to whether the polymeric ions are negatively or positively charged; the former type are termed *anionic* and the latter *cationic* polymerization. To make the distinction quite clear and at the same time to summarize the previous paragraphs, we have written out below in a general fashion the types of propagation reaction which may occur.

Anionic polymerization

$$\text{\Large\sim\sim\sim} M^-\mathcal{C}^+ \cdot x\mathrm{S} + \mathrm{M} \rightarrow \text{\sim\sim\sim} M^-\mathcal{C}^+ \cdot x\mathrm{S}$$
$$\text{\sim\sim\sim} M^-\mathcal{C}^+ \qquad + \mathrm{M} \rightarrow \text{\sim\sim\sim} M^-\mathcal{C}^+$$
$$\text{\sim\sim\sim} M^- \cdot y\mathrm{S} \qquad + \mathrm{M} \rightarrow \text{\sim\sim\sim} M^- \cdot y\mathrm{S}$$
$$\text{\sim\sim\sim} M^- \qquad\quad + \mathrm{M} \rightarrow \text{\sim\sim\sim} M^-$$

The symbol $\sim\sim\sim M^-$ represents a polymer chain terminating in a negatively charged mer, $\sim\sim\sim M^- \cdot y\mathrm{S}$ represents a solvated form of this ion (S standing for the solvating species and y for the number involved), $\sim\sim\sim M^-\mathcal{C}^+$ represents the negatively charged polymeric ion associated with a positively charged counterion, $\mathcal{C}^+$, and $\sim\sim\sim \bar{M}^-\mathcal{C}^+ \cdot x\mathrm{S}$ represents its solvated form (x being the number of solvent molecules bound to the ion-pair). The proportions of these various active centres are controlled by the set of equilibria listed below

$$\text{\sim\sim\sim} M^-\mathcal{C}^+ \cdot x\mathrm{S} \qquad\qquad \rightleftharpoons \text{\sim\sim\sim} M^-\mathcal{C}^+ + x\mathrm{S}$$
$$\updownarrow \qquad\qquad\qquad\qquad\qquad \updownarrow$$
$$\text{\sim\sim\sim} M^- \cdot y\mathrm{S} + \mathcal{C}^+ \cdot (x-y)\mathrm{S} \rightleftharpoons \text{\sim\sim\sim} M^- + \mathcal{C}^+ + x\mathrm{S}$$

As we have implied the values of the various equilibrium constants in the usual solvents are such that the solvated and un-solvated ion-pairs are in much greater concentration than the free ions. One other point should be borne in mind: the values

x and y which represent the solvation numbers of the ion-pairs and free ions respectively may assume more than one value so that the corresponding reactions written out above are composite processes and not single steps.

Cationic polymerization

Formally, the situation is exactly analogous to anionic polymerization except that the polymeric species participating in the propagation reaction are positively charged. The possible types of propagation steps are thus:

$$\text{\Large\sim}M^+\mathcal{C}^- \cdot xS + M \rightarrow \text{\Large\sim} M^+\mathcal{C}^- \cdot xS$$
$$\text{\Large\sim}M^+\mathcal{C}^- \quad\ + M \rightarrow \text{\Large\sim}M^+\mathcal{C}^-$$
$$\text{\Large\sim} M^+ \cdot yS \quad + M \rightarrow \text{\Large\sim} M^+ \cdot yS$$
$$\text{\Large\sim} M^+ \quad\quad\ + M \rightarrow \text{\Large\sim} M^+$$

the various symbols for the active centres being defined in a precisely similar way to those used for the anionic active centres. These four types of active centre are in equilibrium with each other, the equilibrium constants, as before, favouring the ion-pairs.

$$\text{\Large\sim}M^+\mathcal{C}^- \cdot xS \qquad\quad \rightleftharpoons \text{\Large\sim}M^+\mathcal{C}^- + xS$$
$$\qquad\qquad\updownarrow \qquad\qquad\qquad\qquad \updownarrow$$
$$\text{\Large\sim} M^+ \cdot yS + \mathcal{C}^- \cdot (x-y)S \rightleftharpoons \text{\Large\sim}M^+ + \mathcal{C}^- + xS$$

We are now in a position to consider specific examples of these two types of polymerization. We shall see that the phenomena encountered are more diverse than those met in free radical polymerization, a result which arises from the fact that a wide variety of active centres may be formed from a particular monomer according to the type of solvent and counterion used. Very often the precise nature of these active centres is not known with complete certainty and so a detailed interpretation of the observed data is frequently impossible.

For this reason, we shall confine our attention to a limited number of fairly well-characterized systems. We shall present some of the current ideas in this field even though many are not as firmly established as one would wish.

ANIONIC POLYMERIZATION OF VINYL MONOMERS AND DIENES

A few of the monomers which fall into this category together with some of the initiators and solvents commonly employed are listed in Table 5.1.

TABLE 5.1

Monomers

Butadiene
Isoprene
Styrene
α-Methyl styrene
Methyl methacrylate
Vinyl chloride
Acrylonitrile

Initiators

Alkali metals
Sodium naphthalide
n-Butyl lithium
Potassium amide
n-Butyl magnesium bromide
mono-Potassium benzophenone
Sodium methoxide

Solvents

Hexane
Benzene
Dioxane
Diethyl ether
Tetrahydrofuran
Dimethyl formamide
Liquid ammonia

These lists are by no means exhaustive; in particular, a wide number of solvents can be used in place of those quoted provided that they are compatible with the polymeric active centres and the initiator. Of more importance is the fact that some of the initiators listed only initiate the polymerization of certain monomers—whereas n-butyl lithium initiates the polymerization of all the monomers shown in a wide variety of solvents, the alkyl Grignard reagents are only effective for those monomers containing highly electronegative substituents, e.g. methyl methacrylate, vinyl chloride and acrylonitrile. This particular example illustrates the useful generalization that the ease with which the above monomers undergo anionic polymerization increases in the order butadiene $<$ isoprene $<$ styrene $<$ methyl methacrylate $<$ vinyl chloride $<$ acrylonitrile. A further point to notice is the fact that all the initiators are compounds of the more electropositive metals. It is the ions derived from these metals, solvated or otherwise, which form the positive counterions to the growing polymer anions.

The most typical anionic initiators are compounds containing metal–carbon bonds such as n-butyl lithium and n-butyl magnesium bromide. Organometallic compounds of this sort are usually rapidly destroyed by water, alcohols, carbon dioxide and oxygen and so most work in this field is carried out under high vacuum conditions or under protective atmospheres of dry nitrogen or argon. In general, however, it is not necessary to rigorously exclude traces of free radical inhibitors since the small amounts which produce such profound changes in the rates of free radical polymerizations have no pronounced effects in ionic systems.

THE INITIATION REACTION

There are two processes by which anionic polymerizations may be initiated. The first involves the addition of a negative ion or group to the monomer molecule, a process known as *group addition*. Typical initiators which function in this way are:

> alkali metal amides;
> alkyl lithium compounds;
> Grignard reagents;
> alkali metal ketyls.

For example, potassium amide initiates the polymerization of styrene in liquid ammonia as a result of the addition of an amide ion to the monomer, thus:

$$NH_2^- + CH_2 = \underset{\underset{C_6H_5}{|}}{CH} \rightarrow NH_2CH_2\underset{\underset{C_6H_5}{|}}{CH^-}$$

In this solvent, the free ions are the kinetically important species. Another example is found in the polymerization of α-methyl styrene in benzene initiated by n-butyl lithium.

$$BuLi + CH_2 = \underset{\underset{C_6H_5}{|}}{\overset{\overset{CH_3}{|}}{C}} \rightarrow BuCH_2\underset{\underset{C_6H_5}{|}}{\overset{\overset{CH_3}{|}}{C^-}}Li^+$$

The second process by which anionic polymerization may be initiated involves the transfer of an electron to the monomer so producing a *radical-ion*. Initiators which act by *electron transfer*, as it is called, are:

> alkali metals;
> alkali metal–aromatic hydrocarbon complexes.

A particularly simple example of an electron transfer initiation

process is the sodium metal-initiated polymerization of butadiene.

$$CH_2=CH-CH=CH_2+Na \rightarrow (CH_2=CH-CH=CH_2)^-Na^+$$

The electron which is transferred occupies the lowest unfilled
molecular orbital of the monomer and is, of course, unpaired—
consequently, the anion is sometimes referred to as a radical-
ion.

THE PROPAGATION AND TRANSFER
REACTIONS

As we have already said, the active centres in the propagation reaction are either ion-pairs or free ions which may or
may not be solvated according to the type of solvent employed.
In the case of styrene, three out of the four possible types of
active centre have been shown to participate in the polymerization according to the conditions employed, thus:

(a) free ion propagation in liquid ammonia

$$\sim\sim\sim CH_2CH^- + CH_2=CH \rightarrow \sim\sim\sim CH_2CH^-$$
$$\underset{C_6H_5}{|} \qquad \underset{C_6H_5}{|} \qquad \underset{C_6H_5}{|}$$

(b) ion-pair propagation in benzene

$$\sim\sim\sim CH_2CH^-Li^+ + CH_2=CH \rightarrow \sim\sim\sim CH_2CH^-Li^+$$
$$\underset{C_6H_5}{|} \qquad \underset{C_6H_5}{|} \qquad \underset{C_6H_5}{|}$$

(c) solvated ion-pair propagation in mixtures of benzene
and tetrahydrofuran (THF)

$$\sim\sim\sim CH_2CH^-Li^+\cdot2\,THF + CH_2=CH \rightarrow \sim\sim\sim CH_2CH^-Li^+\cdot2\,THF$$
$$\underset{C_6H_5}{|} \qquad \underset{C_6H_5}{|} \qquad \underset{C_6H_5}{|}$$

In general, transfer reactions in anionic polymerization seem
to be of little importance. That is not to say that they do not
take place, for both solvent and monomer transfer are encountered in certain special systems. For example, transfer to sol-

vent takes place in the potassium amide–styrene–liquid ammonia system as shown below.

$$\text{\large\textasciitilde\textasciitilde\textasciitilde\textasciitilde}CH_2CH^- + NH_3 \rightarrow \text{\large\textasciitilde\textasciitilde\textasciitilde}CH_2CH_2 + NH_2^-$$
$$\qquad\underset{C_6H_5}{|}\qquad\qquad\qquad\qquad\underset{C_6H_5}{|}$$

Transfer to monomer occurs in the anionic polymerization of acrylonitrile in dimethyl formamide, thus:

$$\text{\textasciitilde\textasciitilde\textasciitilde}CH_2CH^-Li^+ + CH_2{=}CH \rightarrow \text{\textasciitilde\textasciitilde\textasciitilde}CH_2CH_2 + CH_2{=}C^-Li^+$$
$$\qquad\underset{CN}{|}\qquad\qquad\underset{CN}{|}\qquad\qquad\underset{CN}{|}\qquad\qquad\underset{CN}{|}$$

Both these processes are proton transfer reactions.

TERMINATION REACTIONS

Two distinct types of termination process are found: those in which the active centres spontaneously decompose and those in which the active centres are destroyed by reaction with another substance.

The first process is illustrated by polystyryl sodium which decomposes by elimination of a hydride ion to produce a polystyrene with terminal unsaturation.

$$\text{\textasciitilde\textasciitilde\textasciitilde}CH_2CH^-Na^+ \rightarrow \text{\textasciitilde\textasciitilde\textasciitilde}CH{=}CH + NaH$$
$$\qquad\underset{C_6H_5}{|}\qquad\qquad\qquad\underset{C_6H_5}{|}$$

Reactions of this type are usually unimportant in anionic polymerization.

On the other hand, termination may be brought about by many types of reagent. The most efficient are those which also destroy the initiators, i.e. water, alcohols, carbon dioxide, oxygen, etc. Some of the reactions involved are listed below for the case of a polystyryl lithium ion-pair.

1. $\qquad\text{\textasciitilde\textasciitilde\textasciitilde}CH_2CH^-Li^+ + H_2O \rightarrow \text{\textasciitilde\textasciitilde\textasciitilde}CH_2CH_2 + LiOH$
$$\qquad\qquad\underset{C_6H_5}{|}\qquad\qquad\qquad\qquad\underset{C_6H_5}{|}$$

2. $\quad \sim\sim\sim CH_2CH^-Li^+ + ROH \rightarrow \sim\sim\sim CH_2CH_2 + LiOR$
$\quad\quad\quad\quad\quad | \quad\quad\quad\quad\quad\quad\quad\quad\quad\quad | $
$\quad\quad\quad\quad\quad C_6H_5 \quad\quad\quad\quad\quad\quad\quad\quad C_6H_5$

3. $\quad \sim\sim\sim CH_2CH^-Li^+ + CO_2 \rightarrow \sim\sim\sim CH_2CHCOO^-Li^+$
$\quad\quad\quad\quad\quad | \quad\quad\quad\quad\quad\quad\quad\quad\quad\quad | $
$\quad\quad\quad\quad\quad C_6H_5 \quad\quad\quad\quad\quad\quad\quad\quad C_6H_5$
$\quad\quad\quad\quad\quad\quad\quad\quad\quad\quad\quad\quad\quad\quad\quad\quad \downarrow HCl$
$\quad\quad\quad\quad\quad\quad\quad\quad\quad\quad \sim\sim\sim CH_2CHCOOH + LiCl$
$\quad\quad\quad\quad\quad\quad\quad\quad\quad\quad\quad\quad\quad\quad | $
$\quad\quad\quad\quad\quad\quad\quad\quad\quad\quad\quad\quad\quad C_6H_5$

4. $\quad \sim\sim\sim CH_2CH^-Li^+ + CH_2-CH_2 \rightarrow \sim\sim\sim CH_2CHCH_2CH_2O^-Li^+$
$\quad\quad\quad\quad | \quad\quad\quad\quad\quad \backslash\ /\quad\quad\quad\quad\quad\quad\quad | $
$\quad\quad\quad\quad C_6H_5 \quad\quad\quad\quad\quad O \quad\quad\quad\quad\quad\quad\quad C_6H_5$
$\quad\quad\quad\quad\quad\quad\quad\quad\quad\quad\quad\quad\quad\quad\quad\quad \downarrow HCl$
$\quad\quad\quad\quad\quad\quad\quad\quad\quad \sim\sim\sim CH_2CHCH_2CH_2OH + LiCl$
$\quad\quad\quad\quad\quad\quad\quad\quad\quad\quad\quad\quad\quad\quad | $
$\quad\quad\quad\quad\quad\quad\quad\quad\quad\quad\quad\quad\quad C_6H_5$

5. $\quad \sim\sim\sim CH_2CH^-Li^+ + C_2H_5Cl \rightarrow \sim\sim\sim CH_2CHC_2H_5 + LiCl$
$\quad\quad\quad\quad\quad | \quad\quad\quad\quad\quad\quad\quad\quad\quad\quad\quad\quad | $
$\quad\quad\quad\quad\quad C_6H_5 \quad\quad\quad\quad\quad\quad\quad\quad\quad\quad C_6H_5$

These reactions can be used to obtain specific end groups on the polymer molecules.

Each of the reactions listed above proceeds much more rapidly than propagation; consequently, polymerization does not occur in the presence of the above terminating agents when their concentration is in excess of the total concentration of organometallic compounds.

We shall now consider a limited number of specific systems which have been investigated.

1. The polymerization of styrene

(a) *Initiation by potassium amide in liquid ammonia at temperatures around $-33°C$.*[18] In liquid ammonia, potassium amide is incompletely dissociated into free ions, an equilibrium existing between the ion-pair $K^+NH_2^-$ and the free ions K^+ and NH_2^-. The initiation step consists of the addition of the amide ion to the double bond of styrene in such a way that the substituted carbon atom of the monomer becomes negatively charged; the choice between the two alternative modes of addition is determined by precisely the same criteria as those discussed in Chapter 4 (p. 156). In view of the high dielectric constant of liquid ammonia (22 at $-33°C$), the active centres at the low concentrations normally encountered are thought to be free anions and not ion-pairs. The growth occurs by successive monomer addition to these carbanions to form similar carbanions one monomer unit greater. The process is terminated by transfer of a proton from an ammonia molecule giving an amide ion and a saturated polystyrene molecule containing a terminal amino group. Because this transfer process is highly competitive with propagation, the molecular weight of the polymer is very low. The whole reaction is thus:

$$K^+NH_2^- \rightleftharpoons K^+ + NH_2^-$$

$$NH_2^- + CH_2{=}\underset{\overset{|}{C_6H_5}}{CH} \rightarrow NH_2CH_2\underset{\overset{|}{C_6H_5}}{CH^-}$$

$$NH_2CH_2\underset{\overset{|}{C_6H_5}}{CH^-} + CH_2{=}\underset{\overset{|}{C_6H_5}}{CH} \rightarrow NH_2CH_2\underset{\overset{|}{C_6H_5}}{CH}CH_2\underset{\overset{|}{C_6H_5}}{CH^-}$$

$$\vdots$$

$$NH_2\left\{\underset{\overset{|}{C_6H_5}}{CH_2CH}\right\}_i \underset{\overset{|}{C_6H_5}}{CH_2CH^-} + CH_2{=}\underset{\overset{|}{C_6H_5}}{CH} \rightarrow NH_2\left\{\underset{\overset{|}{C_6H_5}}{CH_2CH}\right\}_{i+1} \underset{\overset{|}{C_6H_5}}{CH_2CH^-}$$

$$\vdots$$

$$NH_2\left\{\underset{\overset{|}{C_6H_5}}{CH_2CH}\right\}_i \underset{\overset{|}{C_6H_5}}{CH_2CH^-} + NH_3 \rightarrow NH_2\left\{\underset{\overset{|}{C_6H_5}}{CH_2CH}\right\}_i \underset{\overset{|}{C_6H_5}}{CH_2CH_2} + NH_2^-$$

The kinetic behaviour observed in this system is quite different from that found in the simple free radical case—in particular, the rate of monomer disappearance is second order with respect to the monomer because of monomer participation in the initiation reaction.

(b) *Initiation by n-butyl lithium in benzene at temperatures around 25°C.*[19] In benzene at ordinary temperatures, n-butyl lithium exists predominantly as a hexamer $(BuLi)_6$. The hexamer is in equilibrium with the lower complexes, pentamer, tetramer, and so on, the important species as far as this polymerization is concerned being the monomer BuLi.† When butyl lithium is added to a solution of styrene in benzene a red colour appears which increases in intensity over a period of an hour or so as the butyl lithium is consumed. This red colour is due to the presence of ion-pairs containing the end group

$$-CH_2CH^-Li^+$$
$$\underset{C_6H_5}{|}$$

The kinetics of the monomer disappearance indicate that these ion-pairs are the active centres and so under the usual conditions employed where the ion-pair concentration builds up with time, no stationary state in the active centre concentration is attained. The basic reason why this is so is that there is no termination reaction in this system, a fact demonstrable by two pieces of evidence. Firstly, the red coloration persists at the end of the polymerization showing that the active centres neither mutually terminate nor are destroyed in other reactions—the proton transfer reaction which we met in the polymerization in liquid ammonia is not energetically feasible with the very stable substance benzene. Secondly, if more monomer is added at the end of a polymerization, this too polymerizes even when it can be shown that all the n-butyl lithium originally present has disappeared; in other words, the active centres

---

† It is of interest that the only evidence at the present time for the existence of the monomer (and by inference the other oligomers up to the pentamer) is that obtained from the study of polymerization kinetics.

remain at the end of the polymerization.† Although there is no destruction of the active centres, they themselves associate in pairs in a reversible fashion to give inactive dimeric ion-pairs. As a result, the active centre concentration does not rise in direct accord with the amount of initiator used; in fact, the active centre concentration is *considerably* lower than it would have been in the absence of association. The full scheme for this polymerization is as follows:

$$(BuLi)_6 \rightleftharpoons 6\ BuLi$$

$$BuLi + CH_2{=}CH\!\!\underset{\displaystyle C_6H_5}{|} \rightarrow BuCH_2CH^-Li^+\!\!\underset{\displaystyle C_6H_5}{|}$$

$$BuCH_2CH^-Li^+\!\!\underset{\displaystyle C_6H_5}{|} + CH_2{=}CH\!\!\underset{\displaystyle C_6H_5}{|} \rightarrow BuCH_2CHCH_2CH^-Li^+\!\!\underset{\displaystyle C_6H_5\quad C_6H_5}{|\qquad |}$$

$$\vdots$$

$$Bu\left\{CH_2CH\!\!\underset{\displaystyle C_6H_5}{|}\right\}_i CH_2CH^-Li^+\!\!\underset{\displaystyle C_6H_5}{|} + CH_2{=}CH\!\!\underset{\displaystyle C_6H_5}{|} \rightarrow Bu\left\{CH_2CH\!\!\underset{\displaystyle C_6H_5}{|}\right\}_{i+1} CH_2CH^-Li^+\!\!\underset{\displaystyle C_6H_5}{|}$$

$$\vdots$$

$$Bu\left\{CH_2CH\!\!\underset{\displaystyle C_6H_5}{|}\right\}_i CH_2CH^-Li^+\!\!\underset{\displaystyle C_6H_5}{|} + Bu\left\{CH_2CH\!\!\underset{\displaystyle C_6H_5}{|}\right\}_j CH_2CH^-Li^+\!\!\underset{\displaystyle C_6H_5}{|}$$

$$\updownarrow$$

$$Bu\left\{CH_2CH\!\!\underset{\displaystyle C_6H_5}{|}\right\}_i CH_2CH^-Li^+\!\!\underset{\displaystyle C_6H_5}{|} . Bu\left\{CH_2CH\!\!\underset{\displaystyle C_6H_5}{|}\right\}_j CH_2CH^-Li^+\!\!\underset{\displaystyle C_6H_5}{|}$$

It will be apparent that a kinetic treatment of this scheme is complicated in part because the steady state approximation cannot be used and in part because both the propagation and

† In a polymerization process in which termination and transfer reactions are either negligibly slow or absent, the lifetime of the polymeric active centres is extremely large. When the lifetime is of the order of hours or even weeks, the polymers are often referred to as "living" polymers.

the initiation reactions may compete for monomer over the whole time scale of the reaction.

When all the n-butyl lithium has been consumed, the number of polymer chains created is equal to the number of lithium atoms originally present as butyl lithium. If we consider one litre of reaction mixture, we can equate the number of moles of lithium atoms to the formal concentration of n-butyl lithium taken initially $[I]_0$. At complete consumption of the monomer and initiator, there are $[M]_0$ moles of monomer units distributed over $[I]_0$ polymer chains, $[M]_0$ being the initial concentration of monomer. Clearly, the number average degree of polymerization of the polymer is given by

$$n = \frac{[M]_0}{[I]_0}.$$

(c) *Initiation by n-butyl lithium in mixtures of benzene and tetrahydrofuran at temperatures around 25°C.*[20] By studying the influence of small amounts of tetrahydrofuran (THF) on the previous system and thus avoiding dielectric constant effects, the importance of solvation becomes abundantly clear. In the first place it is found that the red coloration associated with structures of the type

$$-CH_2CH-Li^+$$
$$|$$
$$C_6H_5$$

reaches a maximum intensity in a few seconds or less even at concentrations of THF of the same order as the butyl lithium (10^{-3} mole l.$^{-1}$). In other words initiation is practically instantaneous. Propagation, however, takes place at a measurable rate and is found to be first order with respect to styrene irrespective of the amount of THF added. This means that the monomer disappears solely by reaction with active centres. To account for the complicated effects which occur on increasing the concentration of THF, it has been postulated that at least three types of active centre compete for monomer in three separate propagation reactions, thus:

$$M_i^- Li^+ + M \rightarrow M_{i+1}^- Li^+$$
$$M_i^- Li^+ \cdot THF + M \rightarrow M_{i+1}^- Li^+ \cdot THF$$
$$M_i^- Li^+ \cdot 2\,THF + M \rightarrow M_{i+1}^- Li^+ \cdot 2\,THF$$

M_i^- represents the ion $Bu\left\{\begin{matrix}CH_2CH \\ | \\ C_6H_5\end{matrix}\right\}_{i-1} \begin{matrix}CH_2CH^- \\ | \\ C_6H_5\end{matrix}$ and M the

monomer. Since the concentration of each active centre is governed by either an association or solvation equilibrium, thus:

$$M_i^- Li^+ + M_j^- Li^+ \quad \rightleftharpoons M_i^- Li^+ \cdot M_j^- Li^+$$
$$M_i^- Li^+ + THF \quad \rightleftharpoons M_i^- Li^+ \cdot THF$$
$$M_i^- Li^+ \cdot THF + THF \rightleftharpoons M_i^- Li^+ \cdot 2\,THF$$

the quantitative treatment of the effects is difficult. Like the system in pure benzene, there are no transfer or termination reactions.

(d) *Initiation by sodium naphthalide in tetrahydrofuran at temperatures between —78°C and 25°C.*[21, 22] Sodium naphthalide is a compound which is formed from metallic sodium and naphthalene in highly solvating media, thus:

$$C_{10}H_8 + Na \rightarrow (C_{10}H_8)^- Na^+$$

Solvent molecules are undoubtedly involved in this reaction but here again the lack of knowledge of the precise action is responsible for the omission of solvent from the stoichiometric equation. The fact that the electron transfer does not occur in benzene solution, for example, suggests that the reaction only takes place as a result of the large solvation energies which are released in strongly solvating media. A solution of sodium naphthalide is deep green in colour and unstable in the presence of any substances which react with carbanions—water, oxygen, carbon dioxide and so on. The compound exists predominantly in the form of ion-pairs in tetrahydrofuran, the naphthalide ion having the characteristics of both a free radical and a negative ion. For this reason, it is sometimes referred to as the naphthalene *radical-ion;* for brevity we shall not normally refer to the counterion in the following account except in writing down the chemical equations.

One of the important properties of the radical-ion is its ability to transfer its extra electron to another aromatic hydrocarbon—in most cases, an equilibrium is set up in which both the aromatic negative ions and the parent hydrocarbons participate. Thus when sodium naphthalide is mixed with anthracene, the following equilibrium is set up

$$(C_{10}H_8)^- Na^+ + C_{14}H_{10} \rightleftharpoons (C_{14}H_{10})^- Na^+ + C_{10}H_8$$

With styrene in THF, a similar electron transfer takes place to form the styrene radical-ion

$$(C_{10}H_8)^- Na^+ + \underset{\underset{C_6H_5}{|}}{CH_2{=}CH} \rightleftharpoons \left(\underset{\underset{C_6H_5}{|}}{CH_2{=}CH} \right)^- Na^+ + C_{10}H_8$$

The important point in the case of styrene is that the reaction does not stop at this stage. The styrene radical-ions formed in the above electron transfer process disappear from the system by two main reactions, each of which is very fast.

1.
$$\left(\underset{\underset{C_6H_5}{|}}{CH_2{=}CH} \right)^- Na^+ + \left(\underset{\underset{C_6H_5}{|}}{CH_2{=}CH} \right)^- Na^+$$
$$\rightarrow Na^+ {-} \underset{\underset{C_6H_5}{|}}{CH} {-} CH_2 {-} CH_2 {-} \underset{\underset{C_6H_5}{|}}{CH}{-} Na^+$$

2.
$$\left(\underset{\underset{C_6H_5}{|}}{CH_2{=}CH} \right)^- Na^+ + \underset{\underset{C_6H_5}{|}}{CH_2{=}CH} \rightarrow \cdot \underset{\underset{C_6H_5}{|}}{CH} {-} CH_2 {-} CH_2 {-} \underset{\underset{C_6H_5}{|}}{CH}{-} Na^+$$

The first of these reactions converts the monomer radical-ions into di-ions capable of propagating anionically at each end. In the second reaction the unpairing of the two electrons of the

π bond in the monomer results in the formation of a molecule having an unpaired electron at one end and a negative charge at the other; the product is just as much a radical-ion as the initiator but without the same degree of electron delocalization. The preference for the above configuration rather than the alternatives

$$\cdot CH_2 - \underset{\underset{C_6H_5}{|}}{CH} - CH_2 - \underset{\underset{C_6H_5}{|}}{CH^-} Na^+$$

or

$$\cdot CH_2 - \underset{\underset{C_6H_5}{|}}{CH} - \underset{\underset{C_6H_5}{|}}{CH} - CH_2^- Na^+$$

follows from similar arguments to those used before. These radical-ions, however, do not survive as radicals for any finite length of time in the reaction mixture for the simple reason that radical–radical termination is very fast.[†] In the very short lifetime of the radical ends, a few monomer additions may occur by free radical propagation as well as by anionic propagation,

$$\cdot \underset{\underset{C_6H_5}{|}}{CH} - CH_2 - \underset{\underset{C_6H_5}{|}}{CH} - CH_2 - CH_2 - \underset{\underset{C_6H_5}{|}}{CH^-} Na^+$$

free ↗ radical propagation

$$\cdot \underset{\underset{C_6H_5}{|}}{CH} - CH_2 - CH_2 - \underset{\underset{C_6H_5}{|}}{CH^-} Na^+ + CH_2 = \underset{\underset{C_6H_5}{|}}{CH}$$

↘ anionic propagation

$$\cdot \underset{\underset{C_6H_5}{|}}{CH} - CH_2 - CH_2 - \underset{\underset{C_6H_5}{|}}{CH} - CH_2 - \underset{\underset{C_6H_5}{|}}{CH^-} Na^+$$

before these radical ends are lost in the usual bimolecular ter-

† The rate constant for the mutual termination of two radicals which are anions as well as radicals should not be very much different from that appropriate to the simple radical–radical reaction; if anything, it will be somewhat lower because of the Coulombic repulsion between the two reacting radical-ions.

mination process. The point is, though, that once the monomer radical-ions have been formed, a very rapid sequence of reactions converts them to di-anions which are the species effective for the major portion of the monomer disappearance.

In this example as in the previous two cases, there is no termination reaction if the polymerization is carried out under the usual high vacuum conditions using rigorously purified materials. This property of the system taken together with the practically instantaneous initiation process has the interesting consequence of producing a polymer of very sharp molecular weight. The reason is that the number of active centres—the di-anions—remains constant throughout the polymerization. Since each has the same probability of reacting with a monomer molecule, each grows to almost the same length and so the resulting sample of polymer contains a narrow distribution of molecular weights.[†] In fact the polymer is almost monodisperse with $\bar{M}_w/\bar{M}_n$ being 1·1 or less in the high molecular weight range (100,000 or greater). The value of $\bar{M}_n$, or more simply the number average degree of polymerization n, follows directly from this account of the polymerization. If the initial concentration of sodium naphthalide is $[I]_0$ in a reaction mixture containing an initial concentration of monomer $[M]_0$, then the concentration of active centres produced is also $[I]_0$. As there are two active centres to every polymer molecule (since these are di-anions $Na^{+-}CHCH_2 \sim\sim\sim CH_2CH^-Na^+$),

$$\underset{C_6H_5}{|} \qquad \underset{C_6H_5}{|}$$

the concentration of polymer molecules is $[I]_0/2$. Taking 1 l. of reaction mixture, it therefore follows that when all the monomer molecules present have been converted to polymer, a total of $[M]_0$ moles of monomer are distributed between $[I]_0/2$ moles of polymer. Each polymer molecule thus contains $2[M]_0/[I]_0$ monomer units, i.e.

[†] The polymer formed has a Poisson distribution of molecular weights.

$$n = \frac{2[M]_0}{[I]_0}.$$

Two other points should be mentioned in connection with the propagation reaction. Firstly, there is a considerable amount of kinetic evidence that there are two types of active centre in this polymerization, one the ion-pair

$$\sim\sim\sim CH_2CH^-Na^+$$
$$|$$
$$C_6H_5$$

and the other the free ion

$$\sim\sim\sim CH_2CH^-$$
$$|$$
$$C_6H_5$$

Although the concentration of the free ions is very small, their contribution to the rate of monomer disappearance appears to be considerable. Secondly, this is yet another case where the role of the solvent is not quantitatively understood and so, although solvation is undoubtedly important in the reaction, it has been omitted from the various stoichiometric equations.

(e) *Initiation by alkali metals.* These reactions are heterogeneous unlike those discussed previously. Because of the limited surface areas of the metal films usually employed, initiation is generally a slow process. In other respects, however, the basic chemistry of these systems is very similar to that involved with the alkali metal naphthalides. Sodium naphthalide, for example, can be regarded as far as polymerization is concerned as a solution of the metal; the sequence of reactions

$$C_{10}H_8 + Na \rightarrow (C_{10}H_8)^-Na^+$$
$$(C_{10}H_8)^-Na^+ + CH_2=CH \rightarrow \left(CH_2=CH\right)^-Na^+ + C_{10}H_8$$
$$\qquad\qquad\qquad | \qquad\qquad\qquad\qquad |$$
$$\qquad\qquad\qquad C_6H_5 \qquad\qquad\qquad\quad C_6H_5$$

is in effect

$$Na + CH_2=CH \rightarrow \left(CH_2=CH\right)^-Na^+$$
$$\qquad\qquad | \qquad\qquad\qquad |$$
$$\qquad\qquad C_6H_5 \qquad\qquad\quad C_6H_5$$

The formation of radical-ion intermediates and their conversion to di-anions containing many monomer units are, thus, the basic features of alkali-metal initiated polymerizations.

2. *The polymerization of methyl methacrylate*

As we have said, styrene is not the only vinyl monomer which polymerizes by an anionic mechanism. In fact it might be argued that a substance such as methyl methacrylate with a more electron-withdrawing substituent is more typical of the monomers susceptible to anionic initiation. However, with this monomer, side reactions so complicate the interpretation of the observed experimental behaviour that the essential features of anionic polymerization tend to be obscured. For example, the initiators which act by group addition often not only add across the double bond but also react with the other functional groups in the molecule. Thus n-butyl lithium reacts in three different ways with methyl methacrylate:

All three reactions are completed very rapidly even at temperatures as low as —33°C. The important reaction as far as polymerization is concerned is the 1,2 addition process for only the product formed thereby is capable of reacting with further monomer. Since only 2 or 3 % of the added n-butyl lithium is consumed in this process, the remainder being lost in the 1,4 and 3,4 additions, relatively few active centres are produced. As there is no termination reaction, simple kinetic behaviour would be expected since the reaction should involve no more than monomer adding to these active centres. For reasons which are not understood, these simple kinetics are not found. Another interesting but unexplained feature of the propagation reaction is the high degree of stereoregularity of the monomer placements. When the solvent used is a hydrocarbon such as toluene, a highly isotactic product is obtained; on the other hand, when a strongly solvating solvent such as tetrahydrofuran or 1,2 dimethoxyethane is used, the polymer becomes predominantly syndiotactic.

Of course, n-butyl lithium is not the only initiator of the polymerization of methyl methacrylate. Other initiators may be used such as the methoxide ion in liquid ammonia and the alkyl Grignard reagents. Apart from the knowledge that these substances act by addition to the monomer (proven by end-group studies), their precise action and the subsequent steps which follow initiation are still a matter of research. It should be noted that isotactic polymethyl methacrylate is formed under certain conditions using Grignard reagents as initiators. The electron-transfer initiators also polymerize this monomer, presumably involving similar reactions to those described under the heading of styrene polymerization.

3. *The polymerization of dienes*

The anionic polymerization of dienes has been known for quite a long time. The mechanisms postulated for the various initiators—metallic sodium, sodium naphthalide, n-butyl lithium—are closely similar to those described in the corresponding sections in the case of styrene. What is important is the nature of the products. The polybutadiene obtained using sodium metal as initiator was one of the first important synthetic rubbers (Buna rubber—the name deriving from *bu*tadiene and *na*trium). More remarkable is the polyisoprene obtained using n-butyl lithium in hydrocarbon media to initiate the polymerization. This product is similar to natural rubber,[†] in that a large number (80–85%) of the isoprene units are present as *cis* 1,4 structures, the remainder being 3,4 and *trans* 1,4. The structure is, thus, mainly

The precise control on the mode of monomer addition to the active centres is lost when ethers replace hydrocarbons as the solvent. Essentially, the same type of polymer is obtained using lithium metal as initiator. The effect is associated in some way with the use of lithium counterions for when sodium metal is used instead of lithium, 50% of the isoprene units are linked together in the *trans* 1,4 configuration, the remainder being 3,4 placed.

The control of configuration by the use of organolithium compounds is observed in other branches of organic chemistry and is of great theoretical and practical interest. It is of no less importance in this field and a detailed account of the process

† Strictly, we should say "the hydrocarbon fraction of natural rubber" since the natural product contains a small percentage of other material: fatty acids, carbohydrates and proteins.

is eminently desirable. At the present time, however, the problem cannot be solved until the precise nature of the active centres in the polymerization is known.

ANIONIC POLYMERIZATION OF OTHER MONOMER TYPES

Anionic polymerization is not confined to vinyl monomers and dienes. Particularly important are the *ring-opening* polymerizations of *heterocyclic* monomers. The anionic initiators function by cleaving the ring to form a product which behaves in exactly the same way towards another monomer molecule. A good example is the polymerization of ethylene oxide initiated by sodium methoxide in dioxane containing small amounts of methanol.[23] The product is a polyoxyethylene glycol. Three reactions take place, initiation, propagation and proton-exchange, but there is no termination process.

$$CH_3O^-Na^+ + CH_2{-}CH_2 \rightarrow CH_3OCH_2CH_2O^-Na^+$$
$$\underset{O}{\diagdown\diagup}$$

$$CH_3OCH_2CH_2O^-Na^+ + CH_2{-}CH_2 \rightarrow CH_3OCH_2CH_2OCH_2CH_2O^-Na^+$$
$$\underset{O}{\diagdown\diagup}$$

$$\vdots$$

$$CH_3O\{CH_2CH_2O\}_iCH_2CH_2O^-Na^+ + CH_2{-}CH_2$$
$$\underset{O}{\diagdown\diagup}$$
$$\rightarrow CH_3O\{CH_2CH_2O\}_{i+1}CH_2CH_2O^-Na^+$$
$$\vdots$$

$$CH_3O\{CH_2CH_2O\}_iCH_2CH_2O^-Na^+ + CH_3OH$$
$$\rightleftharpoons CH_3O^-Na^+ + CH_3O\{CH_2CH_2O\}_iCH_2CH_2OH$$
$$CH_3O\{CH_2CH_2O\}_iCH_2CH_2O^-Na^+ + CH_3O\{CH_2CH_2O\}_jCH_2CH_2OH$$
$$\Updownarrow$$
$$CH_3O\{CH_2CH_2O\}_iCH_2CH_2OH + CH_3O\{CH_2CH_2O\}_jCH_2CH_2O^-Na^+$$

The analogous compound propylene oxide (which contains incidentally an asymmetric carbon atom) is similarly attacked.

Other ring-opening polymerizations in this class include the conversion of caprolactam

to nylon 6 using a dispersion of sodium metal in xylene as initiator.

Apart from reactions involving cyclic monomers, anionic initiators also convert certain aldehydes to high molecular weight products.

ANIONIC COPOLYMERIZATION

Copolymerizations which proceed through anionic active centres show some very interesting features. In the first place the proportions of two monomers in an anionically prepared copolymer are usually quite different from those found when the copolymerization is initiated by free radicals. A particularly good example is the monomer pair, styrene — methyl methacrylate. Using an equimolar feed in the normal temperature range, the free radical initiated copolymer contains about 50 % of each monomer (see Table 4.7); the exact proportions depend on the temperature. On the other hand, a copolymer obtained under similar conditions using one of the group addition anionic initiators contains very little styrene indeed, the copolymer being 99 % methyl methacrylate. So great is the change in composition with initiator type that this result is often used to diagnose whether a given initiator is anionic or free radical in character.† The effect is due to the fact that the polymethyl methacrylate anion does not react with monomeric styrene; in other words, of the four potential propagation reactions

$$
\begin{aligned}
\text{\small\raise1pt\hbox{$\sim\!\sim\!\sim\!\sim$}}S^-\mathcal{C}^+ + S \quad &\rightarrow \quad \sim\!\sim\!\sim\!\sim S^-\mathcal{C}^+ \\
\sim\!\sim\!\sim\!\sim S^-\mathcal{C}^+ + \text{MMA} \quad &\rightarrow \quad \sim\!\sim\!\sim\!\sim\text{MMA}^-\mathcal{C}^+ \\
\sim\!\sim\!\sim\ \text{MMA}^-\mathcal{C}^+ + \text{MMA} \quad &\rightarrow \quad \sim\!\sim\!\sim\ \text{MMA}^-\mathcal{C}^+ \\
\sim\!\sim\!\sim\!\sim\text{MMA}^-\mathcal{C}^+ + S \quad &\rightarrow \quad \sim\!\sim\!\sim\!\sim S^-\mathcal{C}^+
\end{aligned}
$$

only the first three proceed with finite speed. The symbols MMA and S refer, of course, to methyl methacrylate and styrene.

There are, however, cases where the copolymerization of a mixture of monomers can be regarded in much the same terms as those discussed in Chapter 4. In these cases where there are four and four only propagation steps, we can use the general form of the copolymer composition equation and evaluate reactivity ratios and sequence lengths. These reactions are:

$$
\begin{aligned}
\sim\!\sim\!\sim\!\sim A^-\mathcal{C}^+ + A \quad &\rightarrow \quad \sim\!\sim\!\sim\!\sim A^-\mathcal{C}^+ \\
\sim\!\sim\!\sim\!\sim A^-\mathcal{C}^+ + B \quad &\rightarrow \quad \sim\!\sim\!\sim\!\sim B^-\mathcal{C}^+ \\
\sim\!\sim\!\sim\!\sim B^-\mathcal{C}^+ + B \quad &\rightarrow \quad \sim\!\sim\!\sim\!\sim B^-\mathcal{C}^+ \\
\sim\!\sim\!\sim\!\sim B^-\mathcal{C}^+ + A \quad &\rightarrow \quad \sim\!\sim\!\sim\!\sim A^-\mathcal{C}^+
\end{aligned}
$$

where, as in Chapter 4, A and B stand for the two monomers and $\sim\!\sim\!\sim A^-\mathcal{C}^+$ and $\sim\!\sim\!\sim B^-\mathcal{C}^+$ represent the two types of active centre.

The general situation is rather different from this because of the greater number of active centres which are usually involved. In fact a satisfactory treatment of many anionic copolymerizations has not yet been evolved because of the lack of precise knowledge concerning the corresponding homopolymerizations.

The anionic systems in which no termination or transfer processes occur have a special advantage in the production of

† The effect is even more useful since cationic initiators produce a copolymer which is about 99% styrene; a distinction between the three initiator types is thus conveniently made on the basis of the composition of the styrene–methyl methacrylate copolymer.

"tailor-made" block copolymers. The procedure used to prepare these substances by a free radical process (or for that matter by a condensation method) involves the synthesis of polymers $\sim\!\sim\!\sim$ AAAAA$\sim\!\sim\!\sim$ with reactive end groups which
can initiate the polymerization of the second monomer B. It is
clear that such procedures are not easy to devise or carry out.
On the other hand, by adding the monomer B to a system of
active centres of the type $\sim\!\sim\!\sim\!A^-\mathcal{C}^+$ (obtained from the monomer A and initiator), a block of the second monomer is
attached to the preformed block of the first monomer. The
sequence of operations is

$$\text{initiator} + A \rightarrow A\!\sim\!\sim\!\sim\!A^-\mathcal{C}^+$$

followed by

$$A\!\sim\!\sim\!\sim\!A^-\mathcal{C}^+ + B \rightarrow A\!\sim\!\sim\!\sim\!AB\!\sim\!\sim\!\sim\!B^-\mathcal{C}^+$$

Naturally, this scheme is only feasible if the active centres
$\sim\!\sim\!A^-\mathcal{C}^+$ react with B to form $\sim\!\sim\!B^-\mathcal{C}^+$ which is capable of
addition to further B. If the active centres $\sim\!\sim\!A^-\mathcal{C}^+$ initiate
the polymerization of B and the active centres $\sim\!\sim\!B^-\mathcal{C}^+$ initiate the original monomer A, then an *alternating block copolymer* of A and B can be produced without any difficulties
other than those associated with removing impurities. By controlling the amounts of the two monomers used at each stage,
the number of monomer units in each block is determined.
For example, an alternating block copolymer of styrene and
isoprene has been prepared in this way using sodium naphthalide initiation[24]; the following stoichiometric equations show
both the sequence of operations and the average number of
monomer units obtained in each block in a real case:

$$2(C_{10}H_8)^-Na^+ + 50\ I \rightarrow Na^+ {}^-I(I)_{48}I^-Na^+ + 2C_{10}H_8$$

$$Na^+ {}^-I(I)_{48}I^-Na^+ + 86\ S \rightarrow Na^+ {}^-S(S)_{42}(I)_{50}(S)_{42}S^-Na^+$$

$$Na^+ {}^-S(S)_{42}(I)_{50}(S)_{42}S^-Na^+ + 50\ I \rightarrow Na^+ {}^-I(I)_{24}(S)_{43}(I)_{50}(S)_{43}(I)_{24}I^-Na^+$$

$$Na^+ {}^-I(I)_{24}(S)_{43}(I)_{50}(S)_{43}(I)_{24}I^-Na^+ + 2\ H_2O \rightarrow$$

$$HI(I)_{24}(S)_{43}(I)_{50}(S)_{43}(I)_{24}IH + 2NaOH$$

(According to the type of placement of the terminal isoprene groups at stage 3, the end groups of the final block copolymer resulting from proton transfer are

$$\underset{CH_3}{\overset{CH_3}{>}}C=CH-CH_2, \quad CH_2=CH-\underset{CH_3}{\underset{|}{CH}}-CH_2 \quad \text{or} \quad CH_2=\underset{CH_3}{\underset{|}{C}}-CH_2-CH_2)$$

Before leaving the subject of anionic copolymerization, we perhaps ought to mention that the solvents employed influence the rates of monomer consumption and the structures of the products in as profound a way as is observed in the simpler homopolymerizations.

CATIONIC POLYMERIZATION OF VINYL MONOMERS AND DIENES

Table 5.2 lists a few of the monomers which undergo cationic polymerization together with the initiators and solvents which have been used.

TABLE 5.2

Monomers

Butadiene
Styrene
Isoprene
α-Methyl styrene
Cyclopropane
Propylene
Isobutene
Ethyl vinyl ether

Initiators

(a) conventional strong acids

Perchloric acid
Sulphuric acid
Phosphoric acid
Trifluoroacetic acid

(b) Friedel-Crafts catalysts + other substances called *co-catalysts* without which the former substances do not function; very often these co-catalysts need only be present in trace amounts.

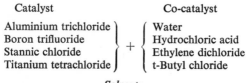

Catalyst	Co-catalyst
Aluminium trichloride	Water
Boron trifluoride	Hydrochloric acid
Stannic chloride	Ethylene dichloride
Titanium tetrachloride	t-Butyl chloride

Solvents

n-Pentane
Benzene
Carbon tetrachloride
Chloroform
Ethylene dichloride
Ethyl chloride
Nitrobenzene

Some of the monomers in the list also polymerize in the presence of typical anionic and free radical initiators, e.g. butadiene, isoprene and styrene; others only polymerize using the cationic systems exemplified in the above table. Cyclopropane, propylene and isobutene are monomers which come into this latter class. In fact the ease with which the above monomers undergo cationic polymerization increases approximately in the order butadiene < styrene < isoprene < α-methyl styrene < cyclopropane < propylene < isobutene < ethyl vinyl ether.

Although the range of phenomena encountered in cationic polymerization is large and complex, there are a number of guiding principles which are common to most systems. Some of these ideas concerning ions, ion-pairs and solvation have already been dealt with in a general way. In particular we have emphasized that the predominant ionic species in normal organic solvents are solvated ion-pairs, the extent of solvation being dependent on the chemical nature of the solvent used. In nonpolar solvents such as hydrocarbons, it must be admitted that the idea of solvation is a rather tenuous concept. However, by tacitly accepting the involvement of solvent in the elementary reactions of cationic polymerization, it is possible to rationalize the marked influence of the type of medium on polymerization rate, microstructure of the product, copolymer composition and so on. In addition, the chemical nature of the counterions must also affect these variables. Unfortunately little is known about the influence of the counterion and so, at the present time, we can do no more than draw attention to the problem.

THE INITIATION REACTION

In cationic polymerization, the polymeric partner of the ion-pair is positively charged. These organic cations are formed in the initiation reaction by addition of a positively charged group or atom to the monomer.[†] Perhaps the most common initiation process involves a proton. Thus, using perchloric acid to initiate the polymerization of styrene in ethylene dichloride solution, the reaction is

$$HClO_4 + CH_2\!=\!\underset{\underset{C_6H_5}{|}}{CH} \rightarrow CH_3\underset{\underset{C_6H_5}{|}}{CH}{}^+[ClO_4]^-$$

Organic cations of this type containing a positively charged carbon atom are termed *carbonium* ions. In the case of the Friedel-Crafts catalysts, proton transfer can obviously not occur without the presence of a source of hydrogen ions. Most co-catalysts function in this way. The most common co-catalyst is undoubtedly water which forms a compound with the catalyst which is a stronger acid than water itself. For example, in ethylene dichloride containing traces of water, stannic chloride initiates the polymerization of styrene through the formation of the intermediate

$$SnCl_4 \cdot 2\,H_2O$$

[†] This process is exactly analogous to that which we have termed "group addition" in the anionic case.

The initiation reaction is thought to be

$$SnCl_4 \cdot 2 H_2O + CH_2 = \underset{\underset{C_6H_5}{|}}{CH} \rightarrow CH_3\underset{\underset{C_6H_5}{|}}{CH} \, {}^+[SnCl_4OH]^- + H_2O$$

a water molecule being eliminated in order to preserve sixfold co-ordination of the tin atom. With boron trifluoride in carbon tetrachloride containing extremely small amounts of water (around 10^{-6} mole l.$^{-1}$), the effective initiator for the polymerization of styrene is thought to be

$$BF_3 \cdot H_2O$$

This catalyst–co-catalyst complex transfers a proton to the monomer forming the same carbonium ion as before partnered by a $[BF_3OH]^-$ counterion.

$$BF_3 \cdot H_2O + CH_2 = \underset{\underset{C_6H_5}{|}}{CH} \rightarrow CH_3\underset{\underset{C_6H_5}{|}}{CH} \, {}^+[BF_3OH]^-$$

While proton transfer processes have a special place in cationic initiation if only because trace quantities of water are so common, other sources of carbonium ions are found. For example, in certain solvents—ethylene dichloride, nitrobenzene and mixtures of the two—the combination of stannic chloride and t-butyl chloride produces a species capable of initiating styrene.

$$SnCl_4 + (CH_3)_3CCl \rightleftharpoons (CH_3)_3C\,{}^+[SnCl_5]^-$$

$$(CH_3)_3C\,{}^+[SnCl_5]^- + CH_2 = \underset{\underset{C_6H_5}{|}}{CH} \rightarrow (CH_3)_3CCH_2\underset{\underset{C_6H_5}{|}}{CH}\,{}^+[SnCl_5]^-$$

It must not be thought that the identification of the initiating species is a simple matter in the general case. For though the initiation reaction is known to involve the addition of a positively charged group (often a proton) to the monomer, the specific nature of the initiator itself depends on the solvent, monomer and temperature as well as on the added catalyst and co-catalyst. It is an unfortunate complication that, even with the same monomer, added catalyst, and co-catalyst, a change in solvent can result in a change in initiator. Perhaps one example will suffice; when instead of ethylene dichloride, carbon tetrachloride is used as the solvent for the system, styrene – stannic chloride – water, the experimental evidence suggests that the actual initiating species is the π-complex

$$SnCl_3OH \cdot H_2O \cdot C_6H_5CH=CH_2$$

formed from the dihydrate and the monomer as follows:

$$SnCl_4 \cdot 2\,H_2O \rightleftharpoons SnCl_3OH \cdot H_2O + HCl$$
$$SnCl_3OH \cdot H_2O + C_6H_5CH=CH_2 \rightleftharpoons SnCl_3OH \cdot H_2O \cdot C_6H_5CH=CH_2$$

In this case the initiation reaction is

$$SnCl_3OH \cdot H_2O \cdot C_6H_5CH=CH_2 + CH_2=CH$$
$$| \atop C_6H_5$$
$$\rightarrow CH_3CHCH_2CH\,^+[SnCl_3(OH)_2]\,^-$$
$$| \qquad\quad | \atop C_6H_5 \quad C_6H_5$$

In such circumstances it will be understood that it is not possible to specify a particular initiator corresponding to each catalyst–co-catalyst combination for all polymerization systems which might be chosen.

THE PROPAGATION AND TRANSFER REACTIONS

Each of these reactions involves the active centres without producing any net diminution in their total concentration. The propagation reaction is the simplest since it involves no more than the addition of a monomer molecule to an ion-pair to give a new ion-pair identical in type to the first but one monomer unit greater. For example,

$$\sim\sim\sim CH_2CH\,^+[ClO_4]\,^- + CH_2=CH \rightarrow \sim\sim\sim CH_2CH\,^+[ClO_4]^-$$
$$| \qquad\qquad\qquad\quad | \qquad\qquad\qquad\quad | \atop C_6H_5 \qquad\qquad\qquad C_6H_5 \qquad\qquad\qquad C_6H_5$$

The most important transfer reactions proceed via the elimination of a proton from the ion-pair. A common process is transfer with monomer. This reaction represents an alternative path to propagation as shown below for the case of isobutene

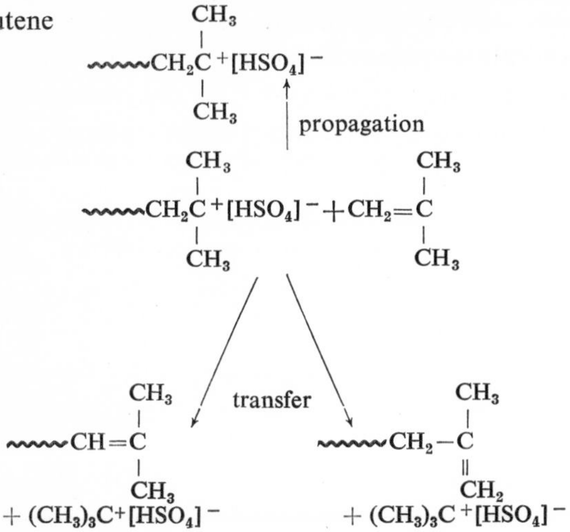

$$\text{www}CH_2\underset{\underset{CH_3}{|}}{\overset{\overset{CH_3}{|}}{C}}{}^{+}[HSO_4]^{-}$$

propagation

$$\text{www}CH_2\underset{\underset{CH_3}{|}}{\overset{\overset{CH_3}{|}}{C}}{}^{+}[HSO_4]^{-}+CH_2=\underset{\underset{CH_3}{|}}{\overset{\overset{CH_3}{|}}{C}}$$

transfer

$$\text{www}CH=\underset{\underset{CH_3}{|}}{\overset{\overset{CH_3}{|}}{C}}$$
$$+\ (CH_3)_3C^{+}[HSO_4]^{-}$$

$$\text{www}CH_2-\underset{\underset{CH_2}{\|}}{\overset{\overset{CH_3}{|}}{C}}$$
$$+\ (CH_3)_3C^{+}[HSO_4]^{-}$$

A slight variant of this reaction occurs with monomers containing an aromatic substituent: a saturated terminal ring system is formed by an internal Friedel-Crafts reaction as well as terminal unsaturation of the type illustrated above.

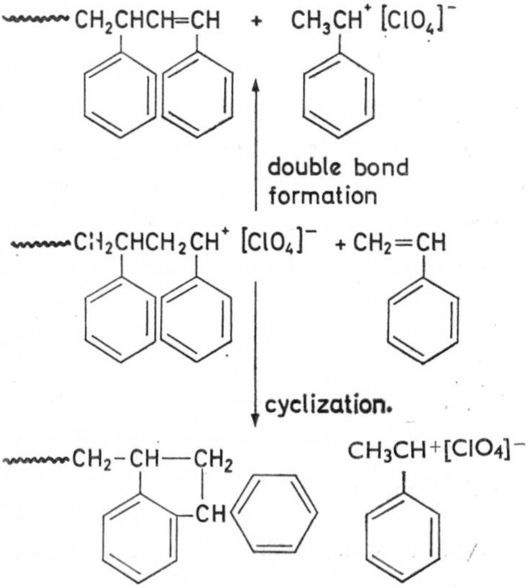

double bond formation

cyclization.

An alternative transfer process is a unimolecular reaction in which the ion-pair spontaneously decomposes by elimination of a proton. For example

$$\text{\small wwww}\ CH_2CH^+[ClO_4]^- \rightarrow \text{\small wwww}\ CH{=}CH + HClO_4 \dagger$$
$$\underset{C_6H_5}{|} \qquad\qquad\qquad \underset{C_6H_5}{|}$$

In some ways, this reaction is similar to the hydride ion elimination observed from certain carbanions—not only is a charged hydrogen ion expelled in each case but also the polymers formed possess terminal unsaturation. The major difference is that proton elimination is much more competitive with cationic propagation than hydride ion elimination is with anionic propagation. Consequently, proton elimination is an important process in cationic polymerization.

TERMINATION REACTIONS

In cationic as in free radical and anionic polymerization, there are reactions in which the active centres are irreversibly destroyed. The occurrence of these termination reactions may be an intrinsic property of the ion-pairs or may be due to substances added for the purpose. An example of the first type of termination reaction is that found in the case of the sulphuric acid initiated polymerization of styrene; the ion-pair rearranges to produce a polymer with an OSO_3H end group, thus:

$$\text{\small wwww}CH_2CH^+[HSO_4]^- \rightarrow \text{\small wwww}CH_2CH{-}OSO_3H$$
$$\underset{C_6H_5}{|} \qquad\qquad\qquad \underset{C_6H_5}{|}$$

In the second category are the termination reactions which occur between the ion-pairs and ethers, alcohols, ketones, etc. For example, benzoquinone terminates the polymerization of styrene initiated by trichloracetic acid by accepting a proton and forming a stable ion.

† In this case cyclization can also occur by attack of the carbonium ion on the benzene ring of the penultimate monomer unit.

$$\sim\!\sim\!\sim CH_2CH^+ [CCl_3COO]^- \ + \ O\!=\!\!\!\left\langle\right\rangle\!\!\!=\!O$$
$$\underset{C_6H_5}{|}$$

$$\sim\!\sim\!\sim CH\!=\!CH \ + \ [O\!=\!\!\!\left\langle\right\rangle\!\!\!=\!OH]^+ \ [CCl_3COO]^-$$
$$\underset{C_6H_5}{|}$$

Very often, the termination processes which occur with oxygen or nitrogen containing compounds are the result of several reactions which may include inactivation of the initiator through the formation of a stable complex.

The effect of temperature

One apparently curious feature often observed in cationic polymerization is that both the rate of polymerization and the molecular weight of the polymer *increase* as the temperature is *decreased*. Such temperature effects are understandable in terms of the relative magnitudes of the temperature coefficients of the various elementary reactions as we shall now show.

We can represent the general mechanism as follows:

$$I + M \ \xrightarrow{k_i} \ M_1^+ \mathcal{e}^- \qquad\qquad \text{initiation}$$

$$M_1^+ \mathcal{e}^- + M \xrightarrow{k_p} M_2^+ \mathcal{e}^-$$

$$M_2^+ \mathcal{e}^- + M \xrightarrow{k_p} M_3^+ \mathcal{e}^- \qquad\quad \text{propagation}$$

$$M_i^+ \mathcal{e}^- + M \xrightarrow{k_p} M_{i+1}^+ \mathcal{e}^-$$

$$M_i^+ \mathcal{e}^- + M \xrightarrow{k_m} M_i + M_1^+ \mathcal{e}^- \qquad \text{monomer transfer}$$

$$M_i^+ \mathcal{e}^- \ \xrightarrow{k_s} \ M_i + I \qquad \text{spontaneous decomposition}$$

$$M_i^+ \mathcal{e}^- \ \xrightarrow{k_t} \ M \qquad\qquad \text{termination}$$

The catalyst–co-catalyst complex or its effective derivative is represented by the symbol I and the monomer as usual by M; the set of symbols $M_1^+\ell^-$, $M_2^+\ell^-$, ..., $M_i^+\ell^-$, ..., represent the active centres while M_i stands for a polymer molecule containing i monomer units. It is convenient to define two other symbols to represent the total concentration of active centres and the total polymer concentration, thus:

$$[C^+] = \sum [M_i^+\ell^-]$$

and

$$[P] = \sum [M_i].$$

The rate of monomer disappearance is then

$$-\frac{d[M]}{dt} = k_i[I][M] + k_p[C^+][M] + k_m[C^+][M].$$

We shall neglect the loss of monomer in the initiation and transfer steps compared to that lost in the propagation reaction. Consequently, the above equation reduces to

$$-\frac{d[M]}{dt} = k_p[C^+][M].$$

To calculate $[C^+]$, we assume a steady state in the active centre concentration. We obtain

$$k_s[C^+]_s + k_t[C^+]_s = k_i[I][M],$$

where the symbol $[C^+]_s$ stands for the steady state concentration of active centres. In many cationic polymerizations, the loss of active centres in termination processes is unimportant compared with that in the spontaneous decomposition reaction. With this simplification, the initiator concentration remains constant as the reaction proceeds and the stationary active centre concentration is given by

$$[C^+]_s = \frac{k_i}{k_s} [I][M].$$

Our expression for the rate of monomer disappearance thus becomes

$$-\frac{d[M]}{dt} = \frac{k_i k_p}{k_s} \, [I][M]^2.$$

Provided that the only temperature dependent factors are the individual rate constants, the variation of the rate of monomer disappearance with temperature depends on the temperature coefficient of the composite quantity $k_i k_p / k_s$. In the case under discussion, k_s usually decreases more rapidly with decreasing temperature than either k_i or k_p; it follows, therefore, that the quantity $k_i k_p / k_s$ and the rate of polymerization increase as the temperature is decreased.

Although the general lines of this argument are probably correct, it is too superficial to be thoroughly satisfactory. There are two major objections. Firstly, the effective initiator concentration is seldom independent of temperature; usually it is controlled by a series of equilibria whose precise formulation is often unknown and so the influence of temperature is difficult to discuss with any exactitude. Secondly, the nature of the active centres may alter as the temperature is lowered due to the increasing dielectric constant, e.g. an increasing role may be played by free ions in the propagation step due to the enhanced dissociation of the ion-pairs.

Similar arguments with essentially the same reservations govern the increase in the number average degree of polymerization, n, found on decreasing the temperature. We know that

$$n = \frac{-d[M]/dt}{d[P]/dt}$$

and so all that we require for an explicit equation for n is an expression for $d[P]/dt$. Using the same simplifications as previously

$$\frac{d[P]}{dt} = k_m[C^+]_s[M] + k_s[C^+]_s,$$

whence

$$n = \frac{k_p[M]}{k_m[M] + k_s}.$$

With many monomers at temperatures around room temperature at the normal concentrations employed for polymerization studies, the rates of the three processes, propagation, monomer transfer and spontaneous decomposition are similar. Consequently, only low molecular weight polymers are produced. However, if the temperature is reduced, the monomer transfer and spontaneous decomposition reactions are slowed down to a much greater extent than the propagation reaction and so higher molecular weight polymer is formed.

We shall now describe some of the diverse phenomena which have been found in a small number of specific systems.

1. *The polymerization of styrene initiated by perchloric acid in ethylene dichloride and other chlorinated hydrocarbon solvents at temperatures around 0°C.*[25] When perchloric acid is added to a solution of styrene in ethylene dichloride, initiation occurs rapidly to give the ion-pairs

$$CH_3CH^+[ClO_4]^-$$
$$|$$
$$C_6H_5$$

equal in concentration to the original perchloric acid concentration. These ion-pairs react with monomer in the propagation reaction to give further ion-pairs, their growth being restricted firstly by transfer with monomer and secondly by their decomposition. There is no effective termination process and so the essential mechanism consists of four steps.[†]

[†] The rate of polymerization is unaffected by small amounts of water and consequently no co-catalytic effects need be considered.

$$HClO_4 + CH_2{=}\underset{C_6H_5}{CH} \rightarrow CH_3\underset{C_6H_5}{CH^+}[ClO_4]^-$$

$$CH_3\underset{C_6H_5}{CH^+}[ClO_4]^- + CH_2{=}\underset{C_6H_5}{CH} \rightarrow CH_3\underset{C_6H_5}{CH}CH_2\underset{C_6H_5}{CH^+}[ClO_4]^-$$

$$\cdots$$

$$H\Big\{CH_2\underset{C_6H_5}{CH}\Big\}_i CH_2\underset{C_6H_5}{CH^+}[ClO_4]^- + CH_2{=}\underset{C_6H_5}{CH} \rightarrow H\Big\{CH_2\underset{C_6H_5}{CH}\Big\}_{i+1} CH_2\underset{C_6H_5}{CH^+}[ClO_4]^-$$

$$\cdots$$

$$H\Big\{CH_2\underset{C_6H_5}{CH}\Big\}_i CH_2\underset{C_6H_5}{CH^+}[ClO_4]^- + CH_2{=}\underset{C_6H_5}{CH} \rightarrow H\Big\{CH_2\underset{C_6H_5}{CH}\Big\}_i \underset{C_6H_5}{CH}{=}CH + CH_3\underset{C_6H_5}{CH^+}[ClO_4]^-$$

$$H\Big\{CH_2\underset{C_6H_5}{CH}\Big\}_i CH_2\underset{C_6H_5}{CH^+}[ClO_4]^- \rightarrow H\Big\{CH_2\underset{C_6H_5}{CH}\Big\}_i \underset{C_6H_5}{CH}{=}CH + HClO_4$$

Instead of the terminal unsaturated group, cyclization may result as discussed earlier.

The mechanism of the polymerization does not change if mixtures of carbon tetrachloride, ethylene dichloride and nitrobenzene ($< 30\%$) are used with dielectric constants ranging from 2·3 to 16·4. Assuming that the solvation of the active centres is unaffected by variations in the proportions of the three solvents, the observed increase in the propagation rate constant by a factor of 20,000 can be attributed solely to this increase in the dielectric constant. This effect is that which would be expected for reactions of this type.

2. *The polymerization of styrene initiated by stannic chloride co-catalysed by water in carbon tetrachloride at temperatures around 25°C.*[26] Although this system has many complex features, it does illustrate the phenomenon of co-catalysis in a graphic way. If rigorously dried stannic chloride, carbon tetrachloride and styrene are mixed together in the complete absence of water or other proton-donating substances (by no means an easy matter), no polymerization takes place. As soon as traces of water are introduced, the reaction commences and monomer is converted into polymer. The monomer–time curves present a stepped appearance; immediately after mixing the reactants, the rate of monomer disappearance is very low but as time goes by it increases to a maximum value; it then decreases, *but* after a further increase in time it increases once more. This periodic change of rate with time appears to continue indicating that the reaction is highly complex.

If we concentrate our attention on the first maximum rate, we can pick out a few of the important features of this polymerization. As the concentration of water in the reaction mixture is increased, this maximum rate increases until a certain ratio of $[H_2O]/[SnCl_4]$ is reached. Thereafter, further additions of water cause the rate to drop by a small amount and produce a slight precipitate of an insoluble hydrated stannic chloride. This maximum rate of polymerization is proportional to the initial concentration of stannic chloride and to the cube of the initial concentration of styrene provided that sufficient water is added to produce the precipitate of hydrated stannic chloride. The polystyrene formed under these conditions is of low molecular weight.

These observations are explicable on the basis that the initiating species is the complex

$$SnCl_3OH.H_2O.C_6H_5CH=CH_2$$

and that the insoluble hydrated stannic chloride is the trihydrate $SnCl_4.3H_2O$. As explained previously, the addition of a monomer molecule to this complex produces the first ion-pair

$$CH_3CHCH_2CH^+[SnCl_3(OH)_2]^-$$
$$\quad |\qquad\quad |$$
$$\quad C_6H_5\quad C_6H_5$$

which propagates in the usual way. A complete explanation of the kinetic behaviour requires the formulation of termination, transfer and inhibition reactions together with the above processes. It is far too difficult for a book of this type.

3. *The polymerization of propylene initiated by aluminium tribromide co-catalysed by hydrogen bromide in n-butane solution at* $-78°C$.[27] This is another system in which no polymerization is observed in the absence of a co-catalyst; anhydrous solutions of aluminium bromide rigorously freed from adventitious hydrogen bromide do not react with propylene. Following its addition to a mixture of aluminium bromide and hydrogen bromide, the rate of disappearance of the monomer slowly increases with time until a point is reached where a precipitate is formed. This precipitate consists of the catalyst, cocatalyst and possibly some of the monomer; the concentration of the catalyst–co-catalyst complex in solution, therefore, decreases and, as a result, the rate of monomer disappearance

begins to fall. After this point, the rate of disappearance of monomer is given by

$$-\frac{d\,[M]}{dt} = \frac{k_1[M]}{1+k_2[M]},$$

where k_1 and k_2 are empirical constants. According to this equation, the rate varies from zero to first order in the monomer concentration depending on the value of the latter quantity.

The simplest explanation of these observations is as follows. At the beginning of the polymerization, the following reactions take place

1. $\qquad\qquad\qquad AlBr_3+HBr \rightleftharpoons H^+[AlBr_4]^-$

2. $\qquad CH_2=CH \;+H^+[AlBr_4]^- \rightarrow CH_3CH^+[AlBr_4]^-$
   $\qquad\qquad\; |\qquad\qquad\qquad\qquad\qquad\quad |$
   $\qquad\qquad CH_3 \qquad\qquad\qquad\qquad\qquad\; CH_3$

3. $CH_3CH^+[AlBr_4]^-+CH_2=CH \;\rightleftharpoons\; CH_3CH^+[AlBr_4]^-.\,CH_2=CH$
   $\;\;\;\; |\qquad\qquad\qquad\qquad\quad |\qquad\qquad\qquad\;\; |\qquad\qquad\qquad\qquad\quad |$
   $\;\;\; CH_3 \qquad\qquad\qquad CH_3 \qquad\qquad\quad CH_3 \qquad\qquad\qquad\quad CH_3$

4. $\;\; CH_3CH^+[AlBr_4]^-.\,CH_2=CH \;\rightarrow\; CH_3CHCH_2CH^+[AlBr_4]^-$
   $\;\;\;\;\; |\qquad\qquad\qquad\qquad\quad |\qquad\qquad\qquad\quad |\quad\;\; |$
   $\;\;\; CH_3 \qquad\qquad\qquad CH_3 \qquad\qquad\; CH_3 \;\; CH_3$

The first reaction demonstrates that the function of the co-catalyst is to produce a complex acid which can donate a proton to the monomer and form the first active centre as in reaction 2. Reactions 3 and 4 taken together are no more than the usual propagation reaction in which monomer adds on to an active centre to produce another similar active centre. The rate at which this second active centre is formed, however, depends on the rate at which the complex between the first active centre and the monomer rearranges. Repetition of reactions similar to 3 and 4 occurs with all the active centres which are produced in the polymerization—that is, every active centre complexes with the monomer before rearranging to give the next active centre one monomer unit greater:

3'. $$M_i{}^+\mathcal{e}^- + M \rightleftharpoons M_i{}^+\mathcal{e}^- . M$$

4'. $$M_i{}^+\mathcal{e}^- . M \rightarrow M_{i+1}^+\mathcal{e}^-$$

The period of accelerating rate is due to the build-up of the active centre–monomer complex concentration. At the end of this period, this quantity has reached its maximum value and no more initiating species remain. Thereafter, the rate of monomer disappearance is controlled by the rate of rearrangement of the active centre–monomer complexes.

Since the concentration of the active centre–monomer complexes is little affected by changes in the monomer concentration if this latter quantity is sufficiently high, the rate at which the monomer polymerizes is independent of its concentration—the zero order dependence already mentioned. When the monomer concentration decreases sufficiently, the concentration of these complexes becomes directly proportional to this quantity and hence the rate of monomer disappearance changes to first order in monomer.

CATIONIC POLYMERIZATION OF OTHER MONOMER TYPES

As in the case of anionic polymerization, cationic polymerization is not confined to vinyl monomers and dienes. Ethylene oxide and tetrahydrofuran, for example, can be polymerized using Friedel-Crafts catalysts such as boron trifluoride etherate or stannic chloride. Aldehydes, as for example acetaldehyde, polymerize to form linear polymers if the temperature is low enough to reduce the depropagation reaction to negligible proportions; typical of the catalysts that have been used are sulphuric acid, aluminium trichloride and boron trifluoride. Some of these reactions do not involve carbonium ions;

instead the active centres are oxonium ions where the positive charge is associated with the oxygen atom. We shall not attempt a discussion of their many complex features in this book.

CATIONIC COPOLYMERIZATION

Many of the general features of anionic copolymerization are encountered in cationic systems. In particular the copolymer compositions and the rates of copolymerization are influenced greatly by the concentration and type of the catalyst and co-catalyst employed and by the nature of the solvent. The kinetic complexities observed in the separate homopolymerizations of two monomers are equally apparent in detailed studies of their copolymerization rates and, therefore, the formulation of a reaction mechanism is rendered extremely difficult if not impossible. Even the scheme of four propagation reactions, so useful a conception in copolymerization work, is not necessarily appropriate to the discussion of the rates of disappearance of the two monomers. One reason is that the rate of disappearance of one (or both) of the monomers may be controlled by the rate of transformation of an active centre–monomer complex and not by the rate of addition of the monomer to an active centre.

For our purposes, however, it is sufficient to note that the composition of the copolymer formed from certain monomer pairs is characteristic of the type of initiating system employed. We refer, of course, to the monomer pair, styrene–methyl methacrylate, which we have already mentioned. Using cationic initiators, the copolymer contains over 90% of styrene units when equal amounts of the two monomers are taken. It will be recalled that under similar conditions free radical initiators give a copolymer containing the two monomers in almost equal proportion, while typical anionic systems yield predominantly polymethyl methacrylate.

"ZIEGLER-TYPE" POLYMERIZATION

Not all catalysts for addition polymerizations can be fitted into the previous classifications. A particularly important group are the so-called Ziegler catalysts most of which are made by mixing a metal alkyl or aryl from groups I, II and III of the periodic table with the halides of the transition metals of groups IV, V and VI. The original catalyst system discovered by Ziegler himself is typical of the combinations employed; aluminium triethyl when added to titanium tetrachloride in hexane solution produces a suspension of a brownish-black precipitate which initiates the polymerization of ethylene at low pressures, α-olefinic hydrocarbons in general, and dienes.

The important feature of these catalyst systems is the high degree of stereoregularity produced in the polymers prepared therefrom. Thus the polyethylene formed at room temperature under a pressure of 2 or 3 atmos is essentially linear

$$\sim\!\!\sim\!\!\sim CH_2-CH_2-CH_2-CH_2-CH_2 \sim\!\!\sim\!\!\sim$$

in contrast to the polyethylene formed at high pressures (1000–3000 atmos) and high temperatures (200–250°C) using oxygen as initiator. Likewise the polystyrene formed from such systems is highly isotactic, shows a high degree of crystallinity and has a higher density and melting point than its atactic counterpart. Of no less importance is the stereospecificity produced in the polymerization of the dienes, butadiene and isoprene. Taking isoprene as an example and the catalyst formed from $Al(C_2H_5)_3$ and $TiCl_4$, an essentially *cis* 1,4 product is formed at $[Al]/[Ti] > 1$; when this ratio is less than unity, the majority of the isoprene units are *trans* 1,4 situated. As would be expected, the precise degree of stereoregularity achieved is dependent on the actual catalyst combination employed; it would be out of place in a book of this kind to attempt to list the results of structure and physical property determinations which have been performed on the many polymers prepared using the large variety of catalyst systems available.

Naturally, with such interesting properties, these catalyst systems have been the subject of much research since the announcement of their discovery in 1955. Unfortunately, it is still not possible to give a completely satisfactory account of their mode of action and so we shall content ourselves here with only a few of the current ideas. In the first place it seems to be established that the exceptional degree of steric control in the propagation reaction is associated with the surface of the catalyst complex—the precipitate formed on mixing the two components to which we have already referred. In the case of the $Al(C_2H_5)_3$–$TiCl_4$ system, the precipitate contains titanium in a reduced valence state—Ti(II) and Ti(III)—and is probably a complex formed from aluminium triethyl and the lower titanium halides; the bonding probably involves bridging alkyl groups and/or halogen atoms as is found in the dimers of aluminium trimethyl and aluminium trichloride. The nature of the surface at which the actual polymer growth takes place is, however, more obscure for almost certainly adsorption of the excess of one of the reactants takes place and modifies the chemical environment presented to the incoming monomer compared with that which characterizes the bulk phase. This being the case, it is not surprising that considerable controversy exists about the precise nature of the propagation reaction. Nevertheless, one feature is common to most of the detailed mechanisms which have been proposed for this reaction: nearly all schemes suppose that the monomer forms a complex with the surface metal ions prior to its incorporation into a polymer chain. For this reason, these catalysts are sometimes referred to as *co-ordination* catalysts. It is tempting to imagine that this complex is formed as a result of the overlap of the π orbitals of the monomer with the d orbitals of the reduced transition metal ions present in the surface of the catalyst. As a result of the special geometrical requirements which must be met in forming such a complex, the monomer is "locked" in one particular configuration prior to its incorporation into a polymer chain. The idea that chain growth is preceded by the formation of a monomer–catalyst complex is, of course, not new; there is definite evidence that such a step takes place in the polymerization of propylene initiated by the aluminium bromide–hydrogen bromide system discussed earlier under cationic polymerization. What needs to be stressed is the conception that it is the complexing of the monomer with the surface ions that is the essential condition for steric control of the propagation reaction in the Ziegler catalyst systems.

REFERENCES

CHAPTER 2

1. BAWN, C. E. H., FREEMAN, R. F. J. and KAMALIDDIN, A. R., *Trans. Faraday Soc.*, **46,** 862 (1950).
2. SCHULZ, G. V. and DOLL, H., *Z. Elektrochem.*, **56,** 248 (1952).
3. SIRIANNI, A. F., WORSFOLD, D. J. and BYWATER, S., *Trans. Faraday Soc.*, **55,** 2124 (1959).
4. OUTER, P., CARR, C. I. and ZIMM, B. H., *J. Chem. Phys.*, **18,** 830 (1950).
5. DANUSSO, F. and MORAGLIO, G., *J. Polymer Sci.*, **24,** 161 (1957).
6. COUMOU, D. J., MACKOR, E. L. and HIJMANS, J., *Trans. Faraday Soc.*, **60,** 1539 (1964).
7. BUECHE, A. M., *J. Am. Chem. Soc.*, **71,** 1452 (1949).
8. Handbook of the SOFICA light scattering instrument.
9. FOX, T. G., Jr., and FLORY, P. J., *J. Am. Chem. Soc.*, **73,** 1909 (1951).
10. SCHULZ, G. V., CANTOW, H. J., and MEYERHOFF, G., *J. Polymer Sci.*, **10,** 79 (1953).

CHAPTER 3

11. BAWN, C. E. H. and HUGLIN, M. B., *Polymer*, **3,** 257 (1962).

CHAPTER 4

12. BEVINGTON, J. C., *Proc. Roy. Soc.*, A **239,** 420 (1957).
13. BEVINGTON, J. C., *Nature*, **175,** 477 (1955).
14. MATHESON, M. S., AUER, E. E., BEVILACQUA, E. B. and HART, E. J., *J. Am. Chem. Soc.*, **71,** 497 (1949); *ibid.*, **71,** 2610 (1949); *ibid.*, **73,** 1700 (1951).
15. FLORY, P. J., *Principles of Polymer Chemistry*, Cornell University Press, New York, 1953.
16. VAN HOOK, J. P. and TOBOLSKY, A. V., *J. Am. Chem. Soc.*, **80,** 779 (1958).
17. DAINTON, F. S. and IVIN, K. J., *Quarterly Reviews*, **12,** 61 (1958).

CHAPTER 5

18. HIGGINSON, W. C. E. and WOODING, N. S., *J. Chem. Soc.*, 760 (1952).
19. WORSFOLD, D. J. and BYWATER, S., *Can. J. Chem.*, **38**, 1891 (1960).
20. BYWATER, S. and WORSFOLD, D. J., *Can. J. Chem.*, **40**, 1564 (1962).
21. SZWARC, M., LEVY, M. and MILKOVICH, R., *J. Am. Chem. Soc.*, **78**, 2656 (1956).
22. BHATTACHARYYA, D. N., LEE, C. L., SMID, J. and SZWARC, M., *J. Phys. Chem.*, **69**, 608 (1965).
23. GEE, G., HIGGINSON, W. C. E. and MERRALL, G. T., *J. Chem. Soc.*, 1345 (1959).
24. SCHLICK, S. and LEVY, M., *J. Phys. Chem.*, **64**, 883 (1960).
25. PEPPER, D. C. and REILLY, P. J., *J. Polymer Sci.*, **58**, 639 (1962).
26. COLCLOUGH, R. O. and DAINTON, F. S., *Trans. Faraday Soc.*, **54**, 886 (1958).
27. FONTANA, C. M. and KIDDER, G. A., *J. Am. Chem. Soc.*, **70**, 3745 (1948).

FURTHER READING

1. *Principles of Polymer Chemistry*, Cornell University Press, New York, 1953, by P. J. FLORY.
2. *Mechanism of Polymer Reactions*, Interscience, New York, 1954, by G. M. BURNETT.
3. *The Chemistry of Cationic Polymerization*, Pergamon, Oxford, 1963, edited by P. H. PLESCH.

INDEX